Teaching Notes
and Solutions

discovering
MATHEMATICS 7A
Common Core

a Singapore Math® Program

 STAR PUBLISHING PTE LTD

 Singapore Math Inc®

STAR PUBLISHING PTE LTD

Star Publishing Pte Ltd
115A Commonwealth Drive #05-12
Singapore 149596
Tel: (65) 64796800
Website: www.starpub.com.sg
Email: contactus@starpub.com.sg

in association with

 Singapore Math Inc®

Singapore Math Inc
Website: www.SingaporeMath.com
Email: customerservice@singaporemath.com

Based on the original series entitled
Discovering Mathematics, approved by
Ministry of Education, Singapore.

© 2012 **Star Publishing Pte Ltd**

ISBN 978-981-4250-58-0

Printed in Singapore by KHL Printing Co. Pte Ltd

Contents

Notes On Teaching   **1**

Fully Worked Solutions

Acknowledgements

The publisher wishes to thank the following:

The Geometer's Sketchpad, *Key Curriculum Press, 1150 65th Street, Emeryville, CA 94608,* *www.keypress.com* for permission to use the screenshots of activities created using The Geometer's Sketchpad.

NOTES ON TEACHING

Chapter 1 Factors and Multiples

Suggested Approach

Throughout this chapter, it is advisable to use simple numbers to illustrate the concepts and reinforce them with sufficient hands-on experience.

Students are encouraged to find out more about prime numbers from the Internet.

1.1 *Factors and Multiples*

Students have learned factors and multiples in their earlier grades. It may be necessary to use two or three examples to recall these ideas before introducing prime numbers. Students should distinguish between factors and multiples of a number, and understand how they are linked.

1.2 *Prime Factorization and Exponential Notation*

It should be emphasized that 0 and 1 are neither prime numbers nor composite numbers.

Teachers may discuss the following questions with their students after defining prime numbers.
- Is there a finite number of prime numbers?
- How can we determine whether a number is a prime?

From the discussion, students will realize there is an infinite number of prime numbers.

Students should know that a factor tree may branch in different ways but it always results in giving the same prime factors. They should note that since 1 is not a prime number, we do not write the factor 1 in prime factorization. Teachers may ask students to write down the factors of a number based on its prime factorization.

1.3 *Greatest Common Factor (GCF)*

Students should understand the difference and the relationship between a common factor and the greatest common factor of two numbers. Teachers may use application problems to arouse their interest and help them relate the idea of greatest common factor to real-life situations.

1.4 *Least Common Multiple (LCM)*

Students should understand that every two numbers have an infinite number of common multiples. The least common multiple can be used to simplify the addition and subtraction of fractions.

Teachers can mention to students who are better at mathematics the relation that for any two numbers a and b, their product $a \times b$ = their HCF $\times$ their LCM.

1.5 Square Roots and Cube Roots

In this section on square roots of numbers, the coverage is limited to the positive square root of a number. Teachers may tell students that they will discuss the negative square root of a number in chapter 2 when they are introduced to negative numbers.

In this section, teachers should emphasize that besides using a calculator, the square root of a perfect square and the cube root of a perfect cube can be obtained by using prime factorization.

Chapter 2 Real Numbers

Suggested Approach

Students have learned whole numbers and fractions in their earlier grades. In this chapter, the concept of numbers is extended from whole numbers to integers through situations where the introduction of negative numbers is necessary. The number line is used as a graphical representation of numbers. Students can learn the operations of integers intuitively through some activities using the number line.

Rational numbers are introduced as a natural consequence of division of two integers. Students should recognise that a rational number can be expressed as a terminating decimal or a repeating decimal.

Teachers are not required to introduce the term irrational number. Students should be aware that some numbers cannot be represented as rational numbers and they should know that real numbers correspond to the points on the number line.

2.1 *Idea of Negative Numbers and the Number Line*

An intuitive idea of negative numbers arises from situations such as temperatures below zero, rise and fall, profit and loss, etc. Students should be able to divide integers into 3 groups, namely positive integers, zero, and negative integers.

From the number line, students can have an idea of ordering of numbers. The inequality symbols are introduced. By using physical interpretations, they have to convince themselves that $3 < 8$ but $-8 < -3$.

This section also defines the absolute value of a number and hence, students are able to understand that both 3 and -3 are the same distance from 0 (zero) on the number line but in different directions.

2.2 *Addition and Additive Inverse*

Teachers should recall the concept of addition and extend student's understandings of addition to negative numbers by illustrating it on a number line. Students should be guided to explore addition involving negative numbers and hence, obtain the rules for addition. Many students have difficulty grasping the addition and subtraction of rational numbers, and hence, the initial exploration of operations and their rules on a number line are critical.

2.3 *Subtraction and Absolute Value of the Difference*

Teachers should guide students to understand that subtraction of numbers is the same as adding the additive inverse, i.e., $p - q = p + (-q)$ and use the number line to explore the rules of subtraction. Ample practice of addition and subtraction of rational numbers should be given to students. Teachers should also give examples of the application of this principle in real-world contexts.

This section also shows that the distance between two numbers on a number line is the absolute value of the difference of the two numbers.

2.4 Multiplication, Division, and Combined Operations of Integers

Students should note that we can extend the multiplication of whole numbers to integers by pattern recognition. (Refer to Class Activity 6, page 45) Division of integers is considered as the reverse process of multiplication of integers. Students should be reminded that division by zero is undefined.

It is crucial that students know the order of operations of integers in an expression involving brackets and the four operations. Also, they should be reminded not to skip steps.

2.5 Rational Numbers

Teachers should emphasize the concept of operations of rational numbers. Tedious manipulations should be avoided. Students should learn to do the manipulations by hand at this stage.

2.6 Real Numbers and Use of Calculators

Students should understand that decimals can be classified as terminating decimals, repeating decimals, and "non-terminating and non-repeating" decimals. All decimals are real numbers with terminating decimals and repeating decimals are rational numbers.

Different calculators may use different key sequences to manipulate an expression. Students should be urged to familiarize themselves with their own calculators.

2.7 Rounding Numbers to Decimal Places

The idea of rounding a number to the nearest unit, 10, 100, and 1,000 is reviewed. Then it is extended to rounding a number to a specified decimal place. Note that a number should be rounded from its original value but not from one of its rounded values. For instance, if $x = 3.149$, then

$$x = 31.5 \quad \text{(correct to 2 d.p.)}$$
and
$$x = 3.1 \quad \text{(correct to 1 d.p.)}$$

It is wrong to round 3.149 to 3.15 and then conclude that $x = 3.2$ (correct to 1 d.p.)

Students are expected to put into practice the assessing of the reasonableness of answers using mental computation and estimation strategies in mathematics and daily life. Hence, teachers should encourage students to use rounding of numbers that they have learned in order to assess the reasonableness of answers using mental computation.

Chapter 3   Introduction to Algebra

Suggested Approach

The smooth transition from arithmetic expressions to algebraic expressions can be achieved through patterns and generalization. The basic notations in algebra should be introduced one at a time with examples. Students should compare and distinguish between arithmetic language and algebraic language.

Commonly used formulas can be used to demonstrate the idea of formulas and substitution. In order to build the confidence of students and clarify their concepts, the formulas used should not be too complicated and the values of variables should vary from positive integers to negative integers and to rational numbers gradually.

3.1   *The Use of Letters in Algebra*

By exploring some daily-life examples, students should find that the use of letters is an easy way to express a generalized arithmetic expression. Sufficient practice in translating word phrases into algebraic phrases should be given. Students should distinguish between variables and numbers and develop the habit of writing proper algebraic expressions. Some students are unable to distinguish between $2a$ and a^2, $a^2 + b^2$ and $(a + b)^2$.

3.2   *Evaluation of Algebraic Expressions and Formulas*

Students should discover that, when the values of all but one of the variables in a formula are known, the value of the remaining variable can be calculated by substitution. Some students cannot see the difference between a formula and an algebraic expression, hence, teachers may need to check student's understanding and be prepared to illustrate the difference.

3.3   *Writing Algebraic Expressions to Represent Real-world Situations*

With the skills acquired in translating word phrases into algebraic phrases learned in Section 3.1, students can extend their skill to write algebraic expressions and formulas to express the relationship between two or more quantities in our daily life. Sufficient practice from simple to more complex situations should be given.

Chapter 4 Algebraic Manipulation

Suggested Approach

Algebraic manipulation is crucial for students in learning mathematics and science. Careful elaboration of the concepts is necessary in order to build a strong foundation. Students should be encouraged not to skip steps when presenting their solutions.

An algebraic expression can be considered as a machine, with the terms as its parts. Analogously, like terms and unlike terms are like parts and unlike parts respectively of the machine. We may use an activity to ask students to identify coefficients of given terms, like terms and unlike terms. Models can be used to introduce the idea of simplification of like terms.

Numerical expressions and geometrical interpretation can be used to introduce distributive property. Teachers may present various cases and help students discuss how to handle brackets in algebraic expressions.

Teachers may draw the analogy between prime factorization of a whole number and the factorization of an algebraic expression. For factorization by grouping terms, teachers may provide some guided practice to students and let them discover the skill by themselves.

4.1 Like Terms and Unlike Terms

It should be emphasized that the sign of a term is attached to its coefficient and not the variable. Terms with the same variables may not be like terms. For instance, (x and x^3) and (a^2b and ab^2) are two pairs of unlike terms.

4.2 Distributive Law, Addition, and Subtraction of Linear Algebraic Expressions

Students should be careful when removing brackets. The vertical form of addition and subtraction will be used in long multiplication and division. Thus, it is helpful to teach this method as well.

4.3 Simplification of Linear Algebraic Expressions

This section is confined to the expansion of linear algebraic expressions. Students should learn the skill of both distribution from the left and distribution from the right.

4.4 Factorization by Extracting Common Factors

Factorization by extracting the common factor may be considered as the reverse process of expansion. After sufficient practice, students should be able to locate the appropriate factor. They should develop the habit of expanding the factorization result and see whether the original expression can be obtained. Instead of factoring $ax + ay + a$ as $a(x + y + 1)$, some students drop the 1 and get the wrong answer $a(x + y)$.

4.5 Factorization by Grouping Terms

Students should be encouraged to try different combinations of grouping terms. They should be made aware that some algebraic expressions cannot be factorized.

Chapter 5   Simple Equations in One Variable

Suggested Approach

From the mathematical sentence $\bigcirc + 3 = 8$, students can see that it is more convenient to replace the circle by letters such as x and y. Teachers can then introduce the concept of equations and solutions (roots). The process of solving a linear equation can be illustrated by using a balance. When students understand the idea, they can apply the rules of transposing terms to solve linear equations in one variable. Students should be encouraged to check the answers when solving equations. Linear equations should be introduced from simple ones (2-step solution) to more difficult ones (involving parentheses and fractions).

Some students may experience difficulty in solving word problems. The model method that students have learned in their lower grades can help bridge the gap.

5.1   *Simple Linear Equations in One Variable*

In introducing the idea of solutions of equations, teachers may encourage students to use the skill of "guess and check" to get the answers. After learning the skill of transposing terms, students should write down each working step for questions in this section. Some students may confuse algebraic expressions with equations.

5.2   *Equations Involving Parentheses*

Teachers should recall the distributive law when demonstrating the skill of solving linear equations involving parentheses. A common error of students is expanding $-3(x - 4)$ as $-3x - 12$. For linear equations with numbers for the denominators, it is advisable to multiply the whole equation by the LCM of the denominators to simplify the equation.

5.3   *Simple Fractional Equations*

Fractional equations are those equations with the variable in the denominators of the equation. The solution of a fractional equation cannot be a value that makes a denominator of the original equation zero. Students should check the solution obtained against the original equation.

5.4   *Forming Linear Equations to Solve Problems*

In solving word problems, students should be reminded of the general steps. In particular, they should define the meaning of the variable at the start of the solution. Teachers may have to provide more structured steps to help average students form an equation to solve a word problem.

Chapter 6 Ratio, Rate, and Speed

Suggested Approach

The idea of ratio, rate, and speed may be introduced using everyday examples. We may use numerical examples to illustrate the concepts. Teachers may pose more complex problems involving equations to better students. Remember to encourage students to use rounding of numbers in order to assess the reasonableness of answers using mental computation. Provide examples of estimation as you comment on students' solutions or show the working of a problem.

6.1 Ratios Involving Rational Numbers

The notation of the ratio of two terms $a : b$ is introduced. It is critical to emphasize to students that quantities involved in a ratio must be expressed in the same unit of measurement. Students should be led to discover that the value of a ratio is unaltered if both numbers in the ratio are multiplied or divided by the same quantity. After sufficient practice, the concept can be extended to three-term ratio $a : b : c$.

6.2 Average Rate

Students should note that a rate can be used to compare two similar quantities such as interest rate, exchange rate or tax rate. They should understand the concept "average rate" and its applications.

6.3 Speed

Students should differentiate the terms speed, uniform speed, and average speed through the discussion of the scenario in Class Activity 2. For the conversion of units of speed, they should adopt the general way of doing it rather than memorizing the conversion factor.

Chapter 7   Percentage

Suggested Approach

In the earlier grades, students have learned the meaning of percentage and the conversion between decimal, fraction, and percentage. In this chapter, they will learn to apply percentage to solve more daily life problems. They are also expected to use algebraic skills to present and solve percentage problems. Remember to encourage students to use rounding of numbers in order to assess the reasonableness of answers using mental computation. Provide examples of estimation as you comment on students' solutions or show the working of a problem.

7.1   Meaning of Percentage

Students should understand that percentage is a fraction with 100 as the denominator. Percentages greater than 100 and percentages less than 1 are introduced. Students are expected to be able to compare two fractions or two quantities using percentages. When one quantity is expressed as the percentage of another quantity, they need to know which quantity to use for the denominator.

7.2   Reverse Percentages

Reverse percentage problems can be considered as equations. Students must analyze the given situation and set up an appropriate equation to solve a problem.

7.3   Percentage Increase and Decrease

For percentage increase and decrease, the original quantity is taken as the denominator for comparison. Some students may mix up the increase in amount and the increased amount.

7.4   Discount and Sales Tax

Teachers may ask students to recall from their experiences the various ways where discounts are used in business and discuss the manipulation of discounts in real-life situations. It is helpful to clarify and give examples to the terms – listed price, marked price, and selling price. Teachers should also discuss the functions of taxes to the state and the country; in particular sales tax. Students can be encouraged to do a research on sales tax online.

As sales tax varies from state to state, it will be helpful for teachers to construct new examples based on their state sales tax rate.

Chapter 8 Angles, Triangles, and Quadrilaterals

Suggested Approach

This chapter is an overview of geometry learned in the earlier grades and an extension of the concept of the properties of parallel lines. Teachers can use the dynamic geometry software package, the Geometer's Sketchpad, to help students discover properties of angles and parallel lines. In general, teachers can take the intuitive approach. However, students should be encouraged to attempt some elementary reasoning. They can write down the reasons in their working steps as it will help them appreciate and remember the properties involved.

Students have learned to use protractors to measure and construct angles. They will learn basic geometrical constructions using various tools such as compasses and straight edge in this chapter. They should appreciate geometrical constructions done by ancient mathematicians using primitive tools.

8.1 Points, Lines, and Planes

The terms points, lines, and planes are undefined terms. Students should be encouraged to use their intuitive ideas to describe them. This section may be the students' first encounter with Sketchpad. Teachers may need to give some instruction on the use of the program and give students opportunity to practice using the navigation tools.

8.2 Angles

An angle can be considered as a rotation. Teachers may recall the construction and measurement of an angle using a protractor before introducing the terms acute angle, obtuse angle, etc. Students should be familiar with the different notations of angles. The properties of angles can be explored using Sketchpad. Sufficient examples and exercises can help them develop their ability to apply these properties. Some students may mix up complementary angles and supplementary angles.

8.3 Perpendicular Bisectors and Angle Bisectors

The idea of a perpendicular bisector and an angle bisector can be introduced through folding paper. Students may be challenged to devise their own method of drawing these bisectors before they are introduced to the formal ways of construction. Better students may be asked to find the incenter and the circumcenter of a triangle.

8.4 Triangles

Teachers should review the different types of triangles with their students. Students should be able to classify triangles by their sides and angles with ease. Teachers should also guide students to investigate the sufficient conditions that determine a unique triangle. In this section, students learn to draw (freehand, with ruler, compasses, and protractor, and also with technology) triangles with given conditions. They should be encouraged to draw a rough sketch of the required figure before constructing it. They should also be able to describe the construction steps in their own words.

8.5 Quadrilaterals

Special quadrilaterals such as parallelogram, rhombus, rectangle, square, and trapezoid are introduced. It will be necessary to show drawn illustrations of the different special quadrilaterals. Students can be asked to collect or name examples of such special quadrilaterals in their daily lives and surroundings. Then students are asked to draw them and explore their properties using Sketchpad.

FULLY

WORKED

SOLUTIONS

Chapter 1 Factors And Multiples

Class Activity 1

Objective: To find all the prime numbers between 0 and 99.

Consider the first 100 whole numbers.

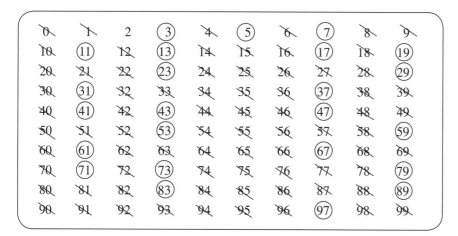

Tasks

Do the following.

(a) Cross out 0 and 1.

(b) Circle 2, and then cross out all the multiples of 2.

(c) Circle 3, the next number after 2 that is not crossed out. Then cross out all the multiples of 3.

(d) Circle 5, the next number after 3 that is not crossed out (4 has been crossed out). Then cross out all the multiples of 5.

(e) Continue doing this until you have visited all the numbers in the table.

Questions

1. What is the common property of the circled numbers?

   Each circled number has only two factors. 1 and itself.

2. Are there any patterns for the distribution of the circled numbers?

   No.

Extend Your Learning Curve

Sieve of Eratosthenes

(a) Use the Sieve of Eratosthenes to find all the prime numbers less than 200.

(b) Compare the numbers of primes in the intervals 0–99 and 100–199.

(c) Would the number of primes in the interval 200–299 be less than that in 100–199? Explain briefly.

Suggested Answer:

(a)

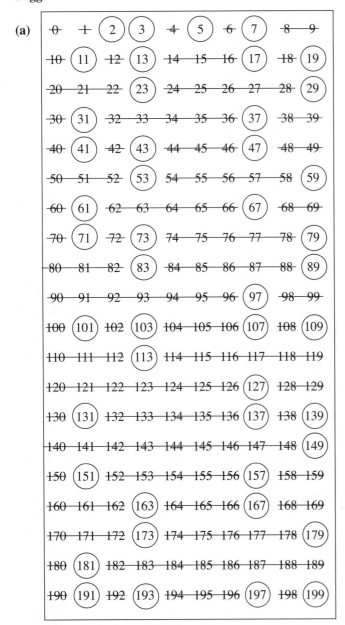

The numbers circled in the table above are all the prime numbers less than 200.

(b) The number of primes in the interval 0–99 is 25.
The number of primes in the interval 100–199 is 21.

(c) The number of prime numbers in the interval 200–299 should be less than that in 100–199. This is because more primes in the list have been introduced in the interval 100–199 and there are more "sieved-out" numbers in the interval 200–299 than in the interval 100–199.
In fact, the number of prime numbers in the interval 200–299 is 16.

Try It!

Section 1.1

1. Find the factors of 105.

Solution

$$105 = 1 \times 105$$
$$= 3 \times 35$$
$$= 5 \times 21$$
$$= 7 \times 15$$

The factors of 105 are 1, 3, 5, 7, 15, 21, 35, and 105.

2. Determine whether the following are prime numbers or composite numbers.

(a) 127   **(b)** 473

Solution

(a) 127 is not divisible by 1, 2, 3, 5, 7, 11, ...
∴ 127 is a prime number.

(b) $473 = 11 \times 43$
∴ 473 is a composite number.

3. Find the prime factorization of 585 using a factor tree and compare it with those of your classmates.

Solution

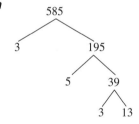

$$585 = 3 \times 3 \times 5 \times 13$$

4. Find the prime factorization of 702, giving your answer in exponential notation.

Solution

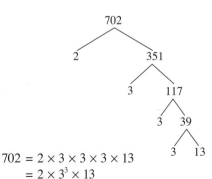

$$702 = 2 \times 3 \times 3 \times 3 \times 13$$
$$= 2 \times 3^3 \times 13$$

Section 1.2

5. Find the GCF of 252 and 360.

Solution

$$252 = 2^2 \times 3^2 \times 7$$
$$360 = 2^3 \times 3^2 \times 5$$
$$\therefore \text{ GCF} = 2^2 \times 3^2$$
$$= 36$$

6. Find the GCF of 154, 330, and 396.

Solution

$$154 = 2 \times 7 \times 11$$
$$330 = 2 \times 3 \times 5 \times 11$$
$$396 = 2^2 \times 3^2 \times 11$$
$$\therefore \text{ GCF} = 2 \times 11$$
$$= 22$$

7. A rectangular piece of paper measuring 35 cm by 28 cm is cut to obtain identical squares. Find the largest possible length of a side of each square.

Solution

$$35 = 5 \times 7$$
$$28 = 4 \times 7$$
∴ GCF of 35 and 28 is 7.
The largest possible length of a side of each square is 7 cm.

Section 1.3

8. Find the LCM of 40 and 150.

Solution

$$40 = 2^3 \times 5$$
$$150 = 2 \times 3 \times 5^2$$
$$\therefore \text{ LCM} = 2^3 \times 3 \times 5^2$$
$$= 600$$

9. Find the LCM of 34 and 57.

Solution

$$34 = 2 \times 17$$
$$57 = 3 \times 19$$
$$\therefore \text{ LCM} = 2 \times 3 \times 17 \times 19$$
$$= 1,938$$

10. Find the LCM of 54, 84, and 110.

Solution

$$54 = 2 \times 3^3$$
$$84 = 2^2 \times 3 \times 7$$
$$110 = 2 \times 5 \times 11$$
$$\therefore \text{LCM} = 2^2 \times 3^3 \times 5 \times 7 \times 11$$
$$= 41{,}580$$

11. The figure shows a gear system in which the numbers of teeth on the big and small wheels are 20 and 16 respectively. The tooth, X, on the big wheel and the tooth, Y, on the small wheel are engaged at the start.

   (a) Find the number of tooth contacts before X and Y are engaged again.

   (b) Find the number of revolutions that each wheel will have made by then.

Solution

   (a) $20 = 2^2 \times 5$
$$16 = 2^4$$
$$\therefore \text{LCM of 20 and 16} = 2^4 \times 5$$
$$= 80$$

The required number of tooth contacts is 80.

   (b) Number of revolutions the big wheel has made
$$= \frac{80}{20}$$
$$= 4$$

Number of revolutions the small wheel has made
$$= \frac{80}{16}$$
$$= 5$$

Section 1.4

12. Find the value of $\sqrt{484}$ by prime factorization.

Solution

$$484 = 2^2 \times 11^2$$
$$= (2 \times 11)^2$$
$$\therefore \sqrt{484} = 2 \times 11$$
$$= 22$$

13. The area of a square is 7,225 in². Find the length of a side of the square by prime factorization.

Solution

$$7{,}225 = 5^2 \times 17^2$$
$$\therefore \sqrt{7{,}225} = 5 \times 17$$
$$= 85$$

The length of a side of the square is 85 in.

14. Find the cube root of 1,000 by prime factorization.

Solution

$$1{,}000 = 2^3 \times 5^3$$
$$= (2 \times 5)^3$$
$$\therefore \sqrt[3]{1{,}000} = 2 \times 5$$
$$= 10$$

15. The volume of a cube is 2,744 cm³. Find the length of a side of the cube by prime factorization.

Solution

$$2{,}744 = 2^3 \times 7^3$$
$$= (2 \times 7)^3$$
$$\therefore \sqrt[3]{2{,}744} = 2 \times 7$$
$$= 14$$

The length of a side of the cube is 14 cm.

Exercise 1.1

Basic Practice

1. Write down all the factors of each of the following numbers.

   (a) 15   (b) 28

   (c) 32   (d) 43

   Solution

   (a) $15 = 1 \times 15$

   $= 3 \times 5$

   ∴ the factors of 15 are 1, 3, 5, and 15.

   (b) $28 = 1 \times 28$

   $= 2 \times 14$

   $= 4 \times 7$

   ∴ the factors of 28 are 1, 2, 4, 7, 14, and 28.

   (c) $32 = 1 \times 32$

   $= 2 \times 16$

   $= 4 \times 8$

   ∴ the factors of 32 are 1, 2, 4, 8, 16, and 32.

   (d) $43 = 1 \times 43$

   ∴ the factors of 43 are 1 and 43.

2. Write down the first four multiples of each of the following numbers.

   (a) 2   (b) 5

   (c) 11   (d) 23

   Solution

   (a) The first 4 multiples of 2: 2, 4, 6, 8.

   (b) The first 4 multiples of 5: 5, 10, 15, 20.

   (c) The first 4 multiples of 11: 11, 22, 33, 44.

   (d) The first 4 multiples of 23: 23, 46, 69, 92.

3. Determine whether 7 is a factor of 2,395.

   Solution

   $2{,}395 \div 7 = 342\frac{1}{7}$

   ∴ 7 is not a factor of 2,395.

4. Determine whether 2,816 is a multiple of 11.

   Solution

   $2{,}816 = 11 \times 256$

   ∴ 2,816 is a multiple of 11.

5. Which of the following numbers have 16 as a factor?

   96, 144, 218, 276, 304

   Solution

   $96 \div 16 = 6$

   $144 \div 16 = 9$

   $218 \div 16 = 13\frac{5}{8}$

   $276 \div 16 = 17\frac{1}{4}$

   $304 \div 16 = 19$

   ∴ 94, 144, and 304 have 16 as a factor.

6. Which of the numbers below are not factors of 108?

   1, 6, 8, 9, 12, 16, 18, 24, 27, 36, 48, 72, 108

   Solution

   $108 = 1 \times 108$

   $= 2 \times 54$

   $= 3 \times 36$

   $= 4 \times 27$

   $= 6 \times 18$

   $= 9 \times 12$

   ∴ 8, 16, 24, 48, and 72 are not factors of 108.

7. Which of the following numbers have 216 as a multiple?

   9, 12, 16, 21, 24, 27, 32, 36, 48, 54

   Solution

   $216 = 1 \times 216$

   $= 2 \times 108$

   $= 3 \times 72$

   $= 4 \times 54$

   $= 6 \times 36$

   $= 8 \times 27$

   $= 9 \times 24$

   $= 12 \times 18$

   ∴ 9, 12, 24, 27, 36, and 54 have 216 as a multiple.

8. Find the largest multiple of 17 which is less than 1,000.

   Solution

   $17 \times 58 = 986$

   $17 \times 59 = 1{,}003$

   The largest multiple of 17 which is less than 1,000 is 986.

9. Find the smallest multiple of 19 which is greater than 500.

   Solution

   $19 \times 26 = 494$

   $19 \times 27 = 513$

   The smallest multiple of 19 which is greater than 500 is 513.

Further Practice

10. **(a)** List all the factors of 56.
   (b) List all the factors of 84.
   (c) Hence find all the factors common to 56 and 84.

Solution

(a) $56 = 1 \times 56$
   $= 2 \times 28$
   $= 4 \times 14$
   $= 7 \times 8$
   The factors of 56 are 1, 2, 4, 7, 8, 14, 28, and 56.

(b) $84 = 1 \times 84$
   $= 2 \times 42$
   $= 3 \times 28$
   $= 4 \times 21$
   $= 6 \times 14$
   $= 7 \times 12$
   The factors of 84 are 1, 2, 3, 4, 6, 7, 12, 14, 21, 28, 42, and 84.

(c) The common factors of 56 and 84 are 1, 2, 4, 7, 14, and 28.

11. **(a)** Write down the first ten multiples of 2.
   (b) Write down the first ten multiples of 3.
   (c) Hence write down the first three multiples common to 2 and 3.
   (d) What can you say about the numbers in **(c)**?

Solution

(a) The first ten multiples of 2 are
   2, 4, 6, 8, 10, 12, 14, 16, 18, and 20.
(b) The first 10 multiples of 3 are
   3, 6, 9, 12, 15, 18, 21, 24, 27, and 30.
(c) The first three multiples common to 2 and 3 are 6, 12, and 18.
(d) The numbers in **(c)** are the first three multiples of 6.

12. Determine whether each statement below is true or false.
   (a) If 6 is a factor of a number, then 3 is a factor of the number.
   (b) If 2 and 7 are factors of a number, then 14 is a factor of the number.
   (c) If 2 and 8 are factors of a number, then 16 is a factor of the number.

Solution

(a) If 6 is a factor of a number n, then $n = 6t$ where t is a whole number.
   $\therefore n = 3(2t)$
   i.e., 3 is a factor of the number n.
   $\therefore$ the statement is true.

(b) If 2 and 7 are factors of a number m, then
   $m = 2 \times 7 \times s$
   where s is a whole number.
   $\therefore m = 14s$
   i.e., 14 is a factor of the number m.
   $\therefore$ the statement is true.

(c) 2 and 8 are factors of 24, but 16 is not a factor of 24.
   $\therefore$ the statement is false.
   Note: Students are not required to present the proofs in **(a)** and **(b)**.

13. Determine whether each statement below is true or false.
   (a) If two numbers are multiples of 11, then their sum is a multiple of 11.
   (b) If a number is a multiple of 2 and another number is a multiple of 3, then their sum is a multiple of 5.

Solution

(a) If a and b are multiples of 11,
   $a = 11s$
   and $b = 11t$
   for some integers s and t.
   $a + b = 11s + 11t$
   $= 11(s + t)$
   $a + b$ is a multiple of 11.
   $\therefore$ the statement is true.

(b) 4 is a multiple of 2.
   9 is a multiple of 3.
   But $4 + 9 = 13$ is not a multiple of 5.
   $\therefore$ the statement is false.

Math@Work

14. The Olympic Games are held in those years that are multiples of 4. Give the years in which the next three consecutive Olympic Games are held after the London 2012 Olympic Games.

Solution

After the year 2012, the next three consecutive Olympic Games are held in the years 2016, 2020, and 2024.

15. Square tiles are arranged to form a rectangular array. Find the number of possible designs if there are
   (a) 18 tiles,   **(b)** 41 tiles.

Solution

(a) $18 = 1 \times 18$
   $= 2 \times 9$
   $= 3 \times 6$
   $\therefore$ the number of possible designs is 6.
   Note: A design of 2 columns by 9 rows of tiles is different from a design of 9 columns by 2 rows of tiles.

(b) $41 = 1 \times 41$

$\therefore$ the number of possible designs is 2.

Brainworks

16. 35 participants from the United States, and 42 participants from other countries are attending a conference.

(a) List all the possible ways to organize the US participants into small groups of equal number.

(b) List all the possible ways to organize the overseas participants into small groups of equal number.

(c) The conference organizer decides to combine all the participants and divide them equally into small groups such that each group has an equal number of US and overseas participants. Explain how this can be done.

Solution

(a) $35 = 5 \times 7$

$\therefore$ there are 2 possible ways.

(b) $42 = 2 \times 21$

$\quad\ = 3 \times 14$

$\quad\ = 6 \times 7$

$\therefore$ there are 6 possible ways.

(c) GCF of 35 and 42 is 7.

Total number of participants $= 35 + 42$

$\qquad\qquad\qquad\qquad\qquad\ = 77$

Number of participants in each group $= 77 \div 7$

$\qquad\qquad\qquad\qquad\qquad\qquad\quad = 11$

$\therefore$ the participants can be divided into 7 groups of 11, each with 5 US participants and 6 overseas participants.

Exercise 1.2

Basic Practice

1. Determine whether the following numbers are prime numbers.

(a) 103 **(b)** 229 **(c)** 817

Solution

(a) 103 is not divisible by 2, 3, 5, 7, 11, 13, ….

$\therefore$ 103 is a prime number.

(b) 229 is not divisible by 2, 3, 5, 7, 11, 13, ….

$\therefore$ 229 is a prime number.

(c) $817 = 19 \times 43$

$\therefore$ 817 is not a prime number.

2. Find the prime factorization of the following numbers using the factor tree method. Write your answer in exponential form.

(a)

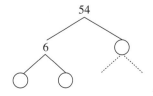

(b)

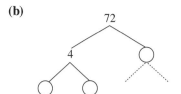

Solution

(a)

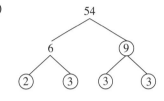

$\therefore\ 54 = 2 \times 3 \times 3 \times 3$

$\qquad\quad = 2 \times 3^3$

(b)

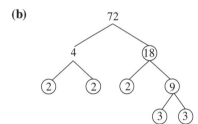

$\therefore\ 72 = 2 \times 2 \times 2 \times 3 \times 3$

$\qquad\quad = 2^3 \times 3^2$

3. Find the prime factorization of each of the following numbers, expressing your answers in exponential notation.

(a) 96 **(b)** 104

(c) 135 **(d)** 196

(e) 204 **(f)** 252

(g) 315 **(h)** 360

Solution

(a) $96 = 2 \times 2 \times 2 \times 2 \times 2 \times 3 = 2^5 \times 3$

(b) $104 = 2 \times 2 \times 2 \times 13 = 2^3 \times 13$

(c) $135 = 3 \times 3 \times 3 \times 5 = 3^3 \times 5$

(d) $196 = 2 \times 2 \times 7 \times 7 = 2^2 \times 7^2$

(e) $204 = 2 \times 2 \times 3 \times 17 = 2^2 \times 3 \times 17$

(f) $252 = 2 \times 2 \times 3 \times 3 \times 7 = 2^2 \times 3^2 \times 7$

(g) $315 = 3 \times 3 \times 5 \times 7 = 3^2 \times 5 \times 7$

(h) $360 = 2 \times 2 \times 2 \times 3 \times 3 \times 5 = 2^3 \times 3^2 \times 5$

4. Express each of the following in exponential notation.
  (a) $8 \times 8 \times 8$
  (b) $3 \times 3 \times 3 \times 3 \times 3$
  (c) $7 \times 7 \times 9$
  (d) $4 \times 4 \times 6 \times 6$
  (e) $2 \times 3 \times 11 \times 11 \times 11$
  (f) $5 \times 5 \times 13 \times 5 \times 13 \times 37$

Solution
  (a) $8 \times 8 \times 8 = 8^3$
  (b) $3 \times 3 \times 3 \times 3 \times 3 = 3^5$
  (c) $7 \times 7 \times 9 = 7^2 \times 9$
  (d) $4 \times 4 \times 6 \times 6 = 4^2 \times 6^2$
  (e) $2 \times 3 \times 11 \times 11 \times 11 = 2 \times 3 \times 11^3$
  (f) $5 \times 5 \times 13 \times 5 \times 13 \times 37 = 5^3 \times 13^2 \times 37$

5. Write each of the following in standard form.
  (a) 17^2 **(b)** 5^3
  (c) $2^2 \times 11^2$ **(d)** $3^4 \times 2^5$

Solution
  (a) $17^2 = 289$
  (b) $5^3 = 125$
  (c) $2^2 \times 11^2 = 4 \times 121 = 484$
  (d) $3^4 \times 2^5 = 81 \times 32 = 2,592$

Further Practice

6. Find the prime factorization of each of the following numbers, giving your answers in exponential notation.
  (a) 180   **(b)** 616
  (c) 735   **(d)** 1,350

Solution
(a)

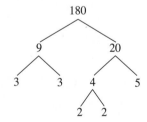

$$\therefore\ 180 = 2^2 \times 3^2 \times 5$$

(b)

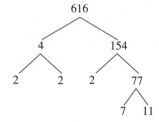

$$\therefore\ 616 = 2^3 \times 7 \times 11$$

(c)

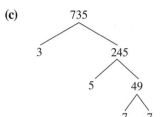

$$\therefore\ 735 = 3 \times 5 \times 7^2$$

(d)

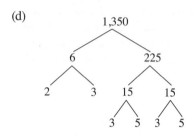

$$\therefore\ 1,350 = 2 \times 3^3 \times 5^2$$

7. (a) Find the missing numbers in the factor tree.
  (b) Can you find the number at the top of the tree without finding the other two numbers?

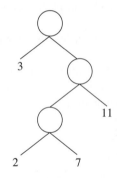

Solution
(a)

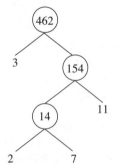

(b) Yes.
  The top number $= 2 \times 3 \times 7 \times 11$
  $$= 462$$

8. Express each of the following in exponential notation, where all the bases are prime numbers.
   (a) 12×15 (b) 54×98
   (c) $18 \times 10 \times 75$ (d) $33 \times 60 \times 125$

   Solution
   (a) $12 \times 15 = (2^2 \times 3) \times (3 \times 5)$
   $= 2^2 \times 3^2 \times 5$
   (b) $54 \times 98 = (2 \times 3^3) \times (2 \times 7^2)$
   $= 2^2 \times 3^3 \times 7^2$
   (c) $18 \times 10 \times 75 = (2 \times 3^2) \times (2 \times 5) \times (3 \times 5^2)$
   $= 2^2 \times 3^3 \times 5^3$
   (d) $33 \times 60 \times 125 = (3 \times 11) \times (2^2 \times 3 \times 5) \times 5^3$
   $= 2^2 \times 3^2 \times 5^4 \times 11$

Math@Work

9. A lock can only be opened by using a 3-digit number. Ben sets this 3-digit number to be the largest prime number under 1,000. What is this number?

   Solution
   The largest prime number under 1,000 is 997.

Brainworks

10. Express each of the following as a single number in exponential notation.
    (a) $2^3 \times 2^2$ (b) $3^4 \times 3^5$
    (c) $11^5 \div 11^2$ (d) $(5^3)^2$

    Solution
    (a) $2^3 \times 2^2 = 2^5$ (b) $3^4 \times 3^5 = 3^9$
    (c) $11^5 \div 11^2 = 11^3$ (d) $(5^3)^2 = 5^3 \times 5^3 = 5^6$

11. The prime numbers 17 and 19 are called twin primes because they differ by 2. List three other pairs of twin primes.

    Solution
    There are infinite number of pairs of twin primes. The following are some examples:
    3 and 5, 5 and 7, 11 and 13, 41 and 43, 71 and 73.

12. (a) Express each of the following even numbers as a sum of two prime numbers.
    (i) 32   (ii) 78   (iii) 116
    (b) The German mathematician, Christian Goldbach (1690–1764), proposed that "Every even number greater than 2 can be expressed as a sum of two prime numbers." Do you agree? Why?

    Solution
    (a) (i) $32 = 13 + 19$
    (ii) $78 = 11 + 67$
    (iii) $116 = 13 + 103$

(b) The statement "Every even number greater than 2 can be expressed as a sum of two prime numbers." is known as Goldbach Conjecture. No one can prove or disprove it. However, it is shown that the statement is true for very large even numbers. Therefore, we should agree with the statement.

13. The prime factorization of a number is
    $$2^4 \times 3^5 \times 7^2 \times 11.$$
    Write down three factors of the number that are greater than 100.
    [*Hint*: $16 \times 11 = 176$ which is a factor.]

    Solution
    The number $= 2^4 \times 3^5 \times 7^2 \times 11$
    A product of some of its prime factors is a factor of the number. For example,
    factor 1 $= 2^4 \times 3 \times 11$
    $= 528$,
    factor 2 $= 2^4 \times 3 \times 7$
    $= 336$,
    factor 3 $= 3^5$
    $= 243$
    are factors greater than 100.

14. The prime factorization of two numbers are
    $$2 \times 3^2 \times 7^3 \times 13 \text{ and } 3 \times 7^2 \times 13^3 \times 17.$$
    Write down three common factors of the numbers.

    Solution
    Some common factors of the two numbers are as follows:
    3, 7, 13, 3×7, 7^2, 7×13, …
    i.e., 3, 7, 13, 21, 49, 91, …

Exercise 1.3
Basic Practice

1. Find the GCF of each pair of numbers.
   (a) 8 and 12   (b) 18 and 27
   (c) 21 and 84   (d) 72 and 90
   (e) 74 and 99   (f) 120 and 225
   (g) 108 and 240   (h) 231 and 396

   Solution
   (a) $8 = 2^3$
           $12 = 2^2 \times 3$
        $\therefore$ GCF $= 2^2$
           $= 4$
   (b) $18 = 2 \times 3^2$
           $27 = 3^3$
        $\therefore$ GCF $= 3^2$
           $= 9$

(c)
$$21 = 3 \times 7$$
$$84 = 2^2 \times 3 \times 7$$
$$\therefore \text{GCF} = 3 \times 7$$
$$= 21$$

(d)
$$72 = 2^3 \times 3^2$$
$$90 = 2 \times 3^2 \times 5$$
$$\therefore \text{GCF} = 2 \times 3^2$$
$$= 18$$

(e)
$$74 = 2 \times 37$$
$$99 = 3^2 \times 11$$
$$\therefore \text{GCF} = 1$$

(f)
$$120 = 2^3 \times 3 \times 5$$
$$225 = 3^2 \times 5^2$$
$$\therefore \text{GCF} = 3 \times 5$$
$$= 15$$

(g)
$$108 = 2^2 \times 3^3$$
$$240 = 2^4 \times 3 \times 5$$
$$\therefore \text{GCF} = 2^2 \times 3$$
$$= 12$$

(h)
$$231 = 3 \times 7 \times 11$$
$$396 = 2^2 \times 3^2 \times 11$$
$$\therefore \text{GCF} = 3 \times 11$$
$$= 33$$

Further Practice

2. Find the GCF of each group of numbers.
   (a) 28, 63, and 91
   (b) 60, 75, and 300
   (c) 48, 84, and 144
   (d) 66, 154, and 484
   (e) 14, 36, and 175
   (f) 140, 210, and 350

Solution
(a)
$$28 = 2^2 \times 7$$
$$63 = 3^2 \times 7$$
$$91 = 7 \times 13$$
$$\therefore \text{GCF} = 7$$

(b)
$$60 = 2^2 \times 3 \times 5$$
$$75 = 3 \times 5^2$$
$$300 = 2^2 \times 3 \times 5^2$$
$$\therefore \text{GCF} = 3 \times 5$$
$$= 15$$

(c)
$$48 = 2^4 \times 3$$
$$84 = 2^2 \times 3 \times 7$$
$$144 = 2^4 \times 3^2$$
$$\therefore \text{GCF} = 2^2 \times 3$$
$$= 12$$

(d)
$$66 = 2 \times 3 \times 11$$
$$154 = 2^2 \times 7 \times 11$$
$$484 = 2^2 \times 11^2$$
$$\therefore \text{GCF} = 2 \times 11$$
$$= 22$$

(e)
$$14 = 2 \times 7$$
$$36 = 2^2 \times 3^2$$
$$175 = 5^2 \times 7$$
$$\therefore \text{GCF} = 1$$

(f)
$$140 = 2^2 \times 5 \times 7$$
$$210 = 2 \times 3 \times 5 \times 7$$
$$350 = 2 \times 5^2 \times 7$$
$$\therefore \text{GCF} = 2 \times 5 \times 7$$
$$= 70$$

Math@Work

3. There are two metal bars of lengths 72 cm and 96 cm. Short bars of equal length are cut from both metal bars. Find the largest possible length of each short bar.

Solution
$$72 = 2^3 \times 3^2$$
$$96 = 2^5 \times 3$$
$$\therefore \text{GCF of 72 and 96} = 2^3 \times 3$$
$$= 24$$
The largest possible length of each short bar is 24 cm.

4. A rectangular piece of metal sheet that measures 360 cm by 280 cm is cut into identical small square pieces. Find
   (a) the greatest possible length of a side of each square piece,
   (b) the number of square pieces that can be obtained.

Solution
(a)
$$360 = 2^3 \times 3^2 \times 5$$
$$280 = 2^3 \times 5 \times 7$$
$$\therefore \text{GCF of 360 and 280} = 2^3 \times 5$$
$$= 40$$
The length of a side of each square is 40 cm.

(b)
$$\frac{360}{40} \times \frac{280}{40} = 9 \times 7$$
$$= 63$$
The number of square tin plates formed is 63.

Brainworks

5. Find two different numbers such that their GCF is 18.

Solution
The two numbers can be 2×18 and 3×18,
i.e., 36 and 54.

The two numbers can also be 18 and 5×18,
i.e., 18 and 90.

6. Find three different numbers such that the GCF of each pair of these numbers is greater than 1 and the GCF of all three numbers is 1.
   [*Hint*: For instance, the numbers 6, 10 and 15 satisfy the conditions.]

Solution

Let us consider three prime numbers such as 3, 5, and 7.

We form the required three numbers by taking the pairwise products of these prime numbers:

3×5, 3×7, and 5×7,

i.e., 15, 21, and 35.

7. In a store, the price (in dollars) of a model car is a whole number greater than 1. The sales of the model cars on two days are $1,518 and $2,346. What are the possible numbers of model cars sold on each day?

Solution

$1,518 = 2 \times 3 \times 11 \times 23$

$2,346 = 2 \times 3 \times 17 \times 23$

The price (in dollars) of a model car can be any common factor of 1,518 and 2,346 that is greater than 1.

i.e., the price may be $2, $3, $6, $23, $46, $69, or $138.

The corresponding number of model cars sold on each day is shown in the following table.

Price ($)	Number of model cars sold	
	Day 1	Day 2
2	759	1,173
3	506	782
6	253	391
23	66	102
46	33	51
69	22	34
138	11	17

Exercise 1.4

Basic Practice

1. Find the LCM of each pair of numbers.
   (a) 12 and 15
   (b) 6 and 28
   (c) 25 and 40
   (d) 23 and 32
   (e) 24 and 54
   (f) 60 and 75
   (g) 59 and 118
   (h) 65 and 91

Solution

(a) $12 = 2^2 \times 3$
$15 = 3 \times 5$
$\therefore$ LCM $= 2^2 \times 3 \times 5 = 60$

(b) $6 = 2 \times 3$
$28 = 2^2 \times 7$
$\therefore$ LCM $= 2^2 \times 3 \times 7$
$= 84$

(c) $25 = 5^2$
$40 = 2^3 \times 5$
$\therefore$ LCM $= 2^3 \times 5^2$
$= 200$

(d) $23 = 1 \times 23$
$32 = 2^5$
$\therefore$ LCM $= 2^5 \times 23$
$= 736$

(e) $24 = 2^3 \times 3$
$54 = 2 \times 3^3$
$\therefore$ LCM $= 2^3 \times 3^3$
$= 216$

(f) $60 = 2^2 \times 3 \times 5$
$75 = 3 \times 5^2$
$\therefore$ LCM $= 2^2 \times 3 \times 5^2$
$= 300$

(g) $59 = 1 \times 59$
$118 = 2 \times 59$
$\therefore$ LCM $= 2 \times 59$
$= 118$

(h) $65 = 5 \times 13$
$91 = 7 \times 13$
$\therefore$ LCM $= 5 \times 7 \times 13$
$= 455$

Further Practice

2. Find the LCM of each group of numbers.
   (a) 9, 12, and 30
   (b) 13, 14, and 15
   (c) 6, 8, and 20
   (d) 28, 42, and 105
   (e) 22, 132, and 253
   (f) 63, 117, and 273

Solution

(a) $9 = 3^2$
$12 = 2^2 \times 3$
$30 = 2 \times 3 \times 5$
$\therefore$ LCM $= 2^2 \times 3^2 \times 5$
$= 180$

(b) $13 = 1 \times 13$
$14 = 2 \times 7$
$15 = 3 \times 5$
$\therefore$ LCM $= 2 \times 3 \times 5 \times 7 \times 13$
$= 2,730$

(c) $6 = 2 \times 3$
$8 = 2^3$
$20 = 2^2 \times 5$
$\therefore$ LCM $= 2^3 \times 3 \times 5$
$= 120$

(d)
$$28 = 2^2 \times 7$$
$$42 = 2 \times 3 \times 7$$
$$105 = 3 \times 5 \times 7$$
$$\therefore \text{LCM} = 2^2 \times 3 \times 5 \times 7$$
$$= 420$$

(e)
$$22 = 2 \times 11$$
$$132 = 2^2 \times 3 \times 11$$
$$253 = 11 \times 23$$
$$\therefore \text{LCM} = 2^2 \times 3 \times 11 \times 23$$
$$= 3,036$$

(f)
$$63 = 3^2 \times 7$$
$$117 = 3^2 \times 13$$
$$273 = 3 \times 7 \times 13$$
$$\therefore \text{LCM} = 3^2 \times 7 \times 13$$
$$= 819$$

3. The prime factorization of two numbers are
$$2^4 \times 3^5 \times 5^3 \times 7^2 \text{ and } 2^3 \times 3^6 \times 5 \times 7^8.$$

(a) Find the GCF of these two numbers in prime factorization form.

(b) Find the LCM of these two numbers in prime factorization form.

Solution

(a)   First number $= 2^4 \times 3^5 \times 5^3 \times 7^2$
Second number $= 2^3 \times 3^6 \times 5 \times 7^8$
$\therefore \text{ GCF} = 2^3 \times 3^5 \times 5 \times 7^2$

(b) $\text{LCM} = 2^4 \times 3^6 \times 5^3 \times 7^8$

4. (a) Find the GCF and LCM of 18 and 30.
(b) Find the GCF and LCM of 14 and 35.
(c) What can you say about the relationship between the two given numbers, and their GCF and LCM?

Solution

(a)
$$18 = 2 \times 3^2$$
$$30 = 2 \times 3 \times 5$$
$$\therefore \text{ GCF} = 2 \times 3$$
$$= 6$$
$$\therefore \text{ LCM} = 2 \times 3^2 \times 5$$
$$= 90$$

(b)
$$14 = 2 \times 7$$
$$35 = 5 \times 7$$
$$\therefore \text{ GCF} = 7$$
$$\therefore \text{ LCM} = 2 \times 5 \times 7$$
$$= 70$$

(c)   GCF $\times$ LCM = Product of the given numbers

Math@Work

5. A flashing bulb on a Christmas tree flashes once every 10 seconds. Another bulb flashes once every 15 seconds. If they are flashing together now, how long will it take for the two bulbs to next flash together?

Solution
$$10 = 2 \times 5$$
$$15 = 3 \times 5$$
$$\text{LCM of 10 and 15} = 2 \times 3 \times 5$$
$$= 30$$
$\therefore$ the bulbs will next flash together after 30 seconds.

6. John and Andrew are running along a circular track. They take 48 seconds and 56 seconds to complete a lap respectively. They begin from the same starting point at the same time and run in the same direction.

(a) How long does it take for them to next meet at the starting point?

(b) How many laps will each boy have run by then?

Solution

(a) $48 = 2^4 \times 3$
$56 = 2^3 \times 7$
LCM of 48 and 56 $= 2^4 \times 3 \times 7$
$= 336$
They will next meet at the starting point after 336 seconds.

(b)   Number of laps that John has run
$= 336 \div 48$
$= 7$
Number of laps that Andrew has run
$= 336 \div 56$
$= 6$

7. The thickness of a Science book is 20 mm and that of a Mathematics book is 28 mm. Books of each type are stacked up in two separate piles.

(a) What will be the minimum height of each pile such that both piles are of the same height?

(b) Find the number of books in each pile.

Solution

(a) $20 = 2^2 \times 5$
$28 = 2^2 \times 7$
$\therefore$ LCM of 20 and 28 $= 2^2 \times 5 \times 7$
$= 140$
The minimum height of each pile will be 140 mm.

(b)   Number of Science books in the pile
$= 140 \div 20$
$= 7$
Number of Mathematics books in the pile
$= 140 \div 28$
$= 5$

8. Each desk in a classroom has a rectangular desktop that measures 60 cm by 45 cm. Some of these desks are put together as shown in the diagram to form a large square table for a class activity. Find
   (a) the shortest length of a side of the square table,
   (b) the number of rows and columns of desks used to form the square table.

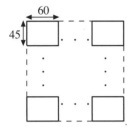

Solution
(a) $60 = 2^2 \times 3 \times 5$
$45 = 3^2 \times 5$
$\therefore$ LCM of 60 and 45 $= 2^2 \times 3^2 \times 5$
$= 180$
The shortest length of a side of the square is 180 cm.

(b) The number of rows of desks $= 180 \div 45$
$= 4$
The number of columns of desks $= 180 \div 60$
$= 3$

Brainworks

9. Find three pairs of numbers such that the LCM of each pair of numbers is 24.

Solution
$24 = 2^3 \times 3$
$\therefore$ the pairs of numbers with LCM $= 24$ can be 2^3 and 3, 2^2 and $2^3 \times 3$, 2 and $2^3 \times 3$, 2^3 and 2×3, etc.
i.e., 8 and 3, 4 and 24, 2 and 24, 8 and 6, etc.

10. Find two possible pairs of numbers such that the GCF and LCM of each pair of numbers are 21 and 630 respectively.

Solution
$21 = 3 \times 7$
$630 = 2 \times 3^2 \times 5 \times 7$

Some possible pairs of numbers are:
3×7 and $2 \times 3^2 \times 5 \times 7$,
$2 \times 3 \times 7$ and $3^2 \times 5 \times 7$,
$3 \times 5 \times 7$ and $2 \times 3^2 \times 7$.
i.e., 21 and 630, 42 and 315, 105 and 126.

Exercise 1.5
Basic Practice

1. Using prime factorization, find the value of each of the following numbers.
   (a) $\sqrt{36}$ (b) $\sqrt{121}$
   (c) $\sqrt{196}$ (d) $\sqrt{256}$
   (e) $\sqrt{441}$ (f) $\sqrt{676}$

Solution
(a) $36 = 2^2 \times 3^2$
$= (2 \times 3)^2$
$\therefore \sqrt{36} = 6$

(b) $121 = 11^2$
$\therefore \sqrt{121} = 11$

(c) $196 = 2^2 \times 7^2$
$= (2 \times 7)^2$
$\therefore \sqrt{196} = 14$

(d) $256 = 2^8$
$= 2^4 \times 2^4$
$\therefore \sqrt{256} = 2^4$
$= 16$

(e) $441 = 3^2 \times 7^2$
$= (3 \times 7)^2$
$\therefore \sqrt{441} = 21$

(f) $676 = 2^2 \times 13^2$
$= (2 \times 13)^2$
$\therefore \sqrt{676} = 26$

2. Using prime factorization, find the value of each of the following numbers.
   (a) $\sqrt[3]{343}$ (b) $\sqrt[3]{512}$
   (c) $\sqrt[3]{729}$ (d) $\sqrt[3]{1,311}$
   (e) $\sqrt[3]{4,096}$ (f) $\sqrt[3]{8,000}$

Solution
(a) $343 = 7^3$
$\therefore \sqrt[3]{343} = 7$

(b) $512 = 2^9$
$= 2^3 \times 2^3 \times 2^3$
$\therefore \sqrt[3]{512} = 2^3$
$= 8$

(c)
$$729 = 3^6$$
$$= 3^2 \times 3^2 \times 3^2$$
$$\therefore \sqrt[3]{729} = 3^2$$
$$= 9$$

(d)
$$1{,}331 = 11^3$$
$$\therefore \sqrt[3]{1{,}331} = 11$$

(e)
$$4{,}096 = 2^{12}$$
$$= 2^4 \times 2^4 \times 2^4$$
$$\therefore \sqrt[3]{4{,}096} = 2^4$$
$$= 16$$

(f)
$$8{,}000 = 2^6 \times 5^3$$
$$= (2^2 \times 5) \times (2^2 \times 5) \times (2^2 \times 5)$$
$$\therefore \sqrt[3]{8{,}000} = 2^2 \times 5$$
$$= 20$$

Further Practice

3. Find the positive square roots of the following numbers, giving your answers in prime factorization form.
(a) $5^4 \times 7^2$ **(b)** $2^6 \times 11^{10}$

Solution
(a)
$$5^4 \times 7^2 = (5^2 \times 7) \times (5^2 \times 7)$$
$$\therefore \sqrt{5^4 \times 7^2} = 5^2 \times 7$$

(b)
$$2^6 \times 11^{10} = (2^3 \times 11^5) \times (2^3 \times 11^5)$$
$$\therefore \sqrt{2^6 \times 11^{10}} = 2^3 \times 11^5$$

4. Find the cube roots of the following numbers, giving your answers in prime factorization form.
(a) $2^3 \times 19^6$ **(b)** $3^{12} \times 5^9$

Solution
(a)
$$2^3 \times 19^6 = (2 \times 19^2)^3$$
$$\therefore \sqrt[3]{2^3 \times 19^6} = 2 \times 19^2$$

(b)
$$3^{12} \times 5^9 = (3^4 \times 5^3)^3$$
$$\therefore \sqrt[3]{3^{12} \times 5^9} = 3^4 \times 5^3$$

5. (a) Find the GCF of 63 and 117.
(b) Find the positive square root of this GCF.

Solution
(a)
$$63 = 3^2 \times 7$$
$$117 = 3^2 \times 13$$
$$\therefore \text{GCF of 63 and 117} = 3^2$$
$$= 9$$

(b) The positive square root of $9 = \sqrt{9}$
$$= 3$$

6. (a) Find the LCM of 24 and 108.
(b) Find the cube root of this LCM.

Solution
(a)
$$24 = 2^3 \times 3$$
$$108 = 2^2 \times 3^3$$
$$\therefore \text{LCM of 24 and 108} = 2^3 \times 3^3$$
$$= 216$$

(b) The cube root of $216 = \sqrt[3]{216}$
$$= 6$$

7. (a) Find the cube of $2^4 \times 5^2$.
(b) Find the positive square root of the result in **(a)**.
Express your answers in prime factorization form.

Solution
(a) The required cube $= (2^4 \times 5^2)^3$
$$= 2^{12} \times 5^6$$

(b) The required square root
$$= \sqrt{2^{12} \times 5^6}$$
$$= \sqrt{(2^6 \times 5^3)^2}$$
$$= 2^6 \times 5^3$$

8. (a) Find the square of $7^6 \times 19^3$.
(b) Find the cube root of the result in **(a)**.
Express your answers in prime factorization form.

Solution
(a) The required square $= (7^6 \times 19^3)^2$
$$= 7^{12} \times 19^6$$

(b) The required cube root $= \sqrt[3]{7^{12} \times 19^6}$
$$= \sqrt[3]{(7^4 \times 19^2)^3}$$
$$= 7^4 \times 19^2$$

Math@Work

9. The area of a square tin plate is 7,056 square inches. Find the length of a side of the plate.

Solution
$$7{,}056 = 2^4 \times 3^2 \times 7^2$$
$$= (2^2 \times 3 \times 7)^2$$
$$\therefore \sqrt{7{,}056} = 2^2 \times 3 \times 7$$
$$= 84$$
The length of a side of the plate is 84 in.

10. The area of a square frame is 2,601 cm². Find the perimeter of the frame.

Solution

$$2,601 = 3^2 \times 17^2$$
$$= (3 \times 17)^2$$
$$\therefore \sqrt{2,601} = 3 \times 17 = 51$$

The length of a side of the frame is 51 cm.
The perimeter of the frame = 51×4
$$= 204 \text{ cm}$$

11. The volume of a piece of glass cube is 1,728 mm³. Find the length of a side of the cube.

Solution

$$1,728 = 2^6 \times 3^3$$
$$= (2^2 \times 3)^3$$
$$\therefore \sqrt[3]{1,728} = 2^2 \times 3$$
$$= 12$$

The length of a side of the cube is 12 mm.

12. A piece of wire is cut and soldered to form the framework of a cube. The volume of the cube is 10,648 cm³. Find
(a) the length of a side of the cube,
(b) the length of the wire used.

Solution

(a)
$$10,648 = 2^3 \times 11^3$$
$$= (2 \times 11)^3$$
$$\therefore \sqrt[3]{10,648} = 2 \times 11$$
$$= 22$$

The length of a side of the cube is 22 cm.

(b) $22 \times 12 \text{ cm} = 264 \text{ cm}$
The length of the wire used = 22×12
$$= 264 \text{ cm}$$

Brainworks

13. It is given that 6 is a factor of 5 ◆ 32 where ◆ represents a missing digit.
(a) Find all the possible values of ◆.
(b) Suppose 5 ◆ 32 is a perfect cube, find
    (i) the value represented by ◆,
    (ii) the cube root of the number.
(c) Study all the possible numbers 5 ◆ 32 formed in (a). Suggest some of their common properties.

Solution

(a) By testing the divisibility of 5 ◆ 32 by 6 for ◆ = 0, 1, 2, ... 9, we find that
$$5,232 = 6 \times 872,$$
$$5,532 = 6 \times 922,$$
$$5,832 = 6 \times 972.$$
$$\therefore \text{ the possible values of } ◆ \text{ are 2, 5, and 8.}$$

(b) (i) By testing,
$$5,832 = 18^3.$$
$$\therefore 5 ◆ 32 \text{ is a perfect cube when } ◆ = 8.$$

(ii) $\sqrt[3]{5,832} = 18$

(c) The numbers 5,232, 5,532, and 5,832 are even numbers and the sum of the digits of each number is a multiple of 3.

14. The number 600, written as the product of its prime factors, is
$$600 = 2^3 \times 3 \times 5^2.$$
Find the smallest positive whole number by which 600 should be multiplied so that
(a) the product is a perfect square,
(b) the product is a perfect cube.

Solution

(a) $600 = 2^3 \times 3 \times 5^2$
$$= (2^3 \times 3 \times 5^2) \times (2 \times 3)$$
$$= (2^2 \times 3 \times 5)^2$$
$\therefore$ the smallest positive whole number will be 6, for the product to be a perfect square.

(b) $600 = 2^3 \times 3 \times 5^2$
$$= (2^3 \times 3 \times 5^2) \times (3 \times 3 \times 5)$$
$$= (2 \times 3 \times 5)^3$$
$\therefore$ the smallest positive whole number will be 45, for the product to be a perfect cube.

Review Exercise 1

1. Find the smallest number that has 2, 5, and 7 as its prime factors.

Solution

The required number = $2 \times 5 \times 7$
$$= 70$$

2. Find the prime factorization of the greatest 3-digit number.

Solution

The greatest 3-digit number = 999
$$= 3^3 \times 37$$

3. Determine whether each number is prime or composite.
(a) 649   (b) 721

Solution

(a) $649 = 11 \times 59$
$\therefore$ 649 is a composite number.

(b) $721 = 7 \times 103$
$\therefore$ 721 is a composite number.

4. Determine whether each sentence is true or false.
    (a) If 3 and 5 are factors of a number, then 15 is a factor of the number.
    (b) If 246 is a multiple of a number, then 123 is a multiple of the number.

Solution
(a) If 3 is a factor of a number n, then
    $$n = 3 \times t$$
    where t is a whole number.
    If 5 is also a factor of n, then 5 should be a factor of t.
    $\therefore$ $t = 5 \times m$ for some integer m.
    i.e., $n = 3 \times 5 \times m = 15 \times m$
    $\therefore$ 15 is a factor of n.
    The statement is true.

(b) $246 = 3 \times 82$
    $\therefore$ 246 is a multiple of 82.
    But 123 is not a multiple of 82.
    The statement is false.

5. (a) Complete the following factor trees.
    (i)

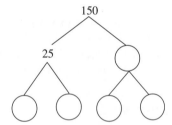

    (ii)

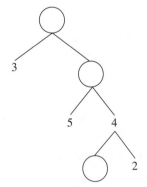

    (b) Write down the prime factorization of the number at the top of each tree.
    (c) Find the GCF and LCM of the numbers at the top of the trees.

Solution
(a) (i)

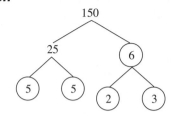

    (ii)

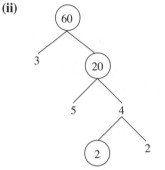

(b) $150 = 2 \times 3 \times 5^2$
    $60 = 2^2 \times 3 \times 5$

(c) GCF of 150 and 60 $= 2 \times 3 \times 5$
    $= 30$
    LCM of 150 and 60 $= 2^2 \times 3 \times 5^2$
    $= 300$

6. (a) Find the GCF of 12, 40, and 45.
    (b) Find the LCM of 12, 40, and 45.
    (c) Find the greatest 4-digit number which is a common multiple of 12, 40, and 45.

Solution
(a) $12 = 2^2 \times 3$
    $40 = 2^3 \times 5$
    $45 = 3^2 \times 5$
    $\therefore$ GCF $= 1$

(b) LCM $= 2^3 \times 3^2 \times 5$
    $= 360$

(c) $27 \times 360 = 9,720$
    $28 \times 360 = 10,080$
    The greatest 4-digit number which is a common multiple of 12, 40, and 45 is 9,720.

7. (a) Find the prime factorization of
    (i) 12,
    (ii) 144,
    (iii) 5,040.

    (b) The GCF and LCM of two numbers are 12 and 5,040 respectively. If one of the numbers is 144, find the other number.

Solution

(a) **(i)** $\quad 12 = 2^2 \times 3$

      (ii) $\quad 144 = 2^4 \times 3^2$

      (iii) $5,040 = 2^4 \times 3^2 \times 5 \times 7$

(b) The other number $= 2^2 \times 3 \times 5 \times 7$
$$= 420$$

8. The dimensions of a rectangle are $(2^5 \times 7)$ cm by $(2 \times 5^2 \times 7^3)$ cm.
   - **(a)** Find the area of the rectangle, giving your answer in prime factorization form.
   - **(b)** A square has the same area as the rectangle. Find the length of a side of the square.

Solution

(a) Area of the rectangle
$$= (2^5 \times 7) \times (2 \times 5^2 \times 7^3)$$
$$= (2^6 \times 5^2 \times 7^4) \text{ cm}^2$$

(b) Length of a side of the square
$$= \sqrt{2^6 \times 5^2 \times 7^4}$$
$$= 2^3 \times 5 \times 7^2$$
$$= 1,960 \text{ cm}$$

9. Using prime factorization, find
   - **(a)** the value of $\sqrt{1,521}$,
   - **(b)** the value of $\sqrt[3]{375 \times 243}$,
   - **(c)** the GCF of the results in **(a)** and **(b)**.

Solution

(a) $\quad 1,521 = 3^2 \times 13^2$
$$\therefore \sqrt{1,521} = 3 \times 13$$
$$= 39$$

(b) $\sqrt[3]{375 \times 243} = \sqrt[3]{(3 \times 5^3) \times 3^5}$
$$= \sqrt[3]{3^6 \times 5^3}$$
$$= 3^2 \times 5$$
$$= 45$$

(c) $\quad 39 = 3 \times 13$
$$45 = 3^2 \times 5$$
The required GCF is 3.

10. A bell rings every 25 minutes while another bell rings every 40 minutes. If the bells rang together at 6 A.M., at what time would they next ring together?

Solution

$25 = 5^2$

$40 = 2^3 \times 5$

LCM of 25 and 40 $= 2^3 \times 5^2$
$$= 200$$

200 minutes = 3 hours 20 minutes

The bells will next ring together at 9.20 A.M.

11. A box contains an assortment of three types of chocolate bars. It has 18 bars with almonds, 24 bars with hazelnuts, and 30 bars with peanuts. The chocolate bars are shared among some students. Each student gets only one type of chocolate bar and every student gets the same number of chocolate bars. If each student gets the greatest number of chocolate bars,
   - **(a)** how many chocolate bars does each student get?
   - **(b)** how many students will get chocolate bars with peanuts?

Solution

(a) $\quad 18 = 2 \times 3^2$

     $24 = 2^3 \times 3$

     $30 = 2 \times 3 \times 5$

     GCF of 18, 24, and 30 $= 2 \times 3$
$$= 6$$
Each student gets 6 chocolate bars.

(b) $30 \div 6 = 5$

Five students will get chocolate bars with peanuts.

12. A rectangular board measures 630 cm by 396 cm. It is divided into small squares of equal size.
   - **(a)** Find
      - **(i)** the largest possible length of the side of a square,
      - **(ii)** the least total number of squares.
   - **(b)** **(i)** What is the next largest possible length of the side of a square?
      - **(ii)** Find the total number of squares in this case.

Solution

(a) **(i)** $\quad 630 = 2 \times 3^2 \times 5 \times 7$

        $396 = 2^2 \times 3^2 \times 11$

        GCF of 630 and 396 $= 2 \times 3^2$
$$= 18$$
The largest possible length is 18 cm.

    (ii) $\dfrac{630}{18} \times \dfrac{396}{18} = 35 \times 22$
$$= 770$$
The least total number of squares is 770.

(b) **(i)** The next largest possible length is 9 cm.

    (ii) $\dfrac{630}{9} \times \dfrac{396}{9} = 70 \times 44$
$$= 3,080$$
The required number of squares is 3,080.

Chapter 2 Real Numbers

Class Activity 1

Objective: To recognize the use of negative numbers in the real-life situations.

Questions

1. The following are examples of how negative numbers could be used in some real-life situations.

   (a) If 20 miles denotes a distance of 20 miles due east, what denotes a distance of 6 miles due west? <u> −6 </u>

   (b) If 100 represents a gain of $100, what number represents a loss of $150? <u> −150 </u>

   (c) If 50 m denotes 50 m above sea level, what denotes a distance of 25 m below sea level? <u> −25 </u>

2. Work with your classmates to think of two other examples in your daily life where negative numbers are used.

   (i) If +12 °C means a temperature rise of 12 °C, then −8 °C means a temperature drop of 8 °C.

   (ii) If −7 means deducting 7 points, then +10 means adding 10 points.

Class Activity 2

Objective: To explore the rules of addition of integers.

Questions

Use the number line to find the answer in each case. Question **1(a)** has been partly done for you.

1. **(a)** $(-3) + 4$

   Starting from (-3), move 4 units to the right (**addition** of positive number 4). The answer is the number at the final position as shown on the number line above.

   $\therefore (-3) + 4 =$ 1

   (b) $2 + 3$

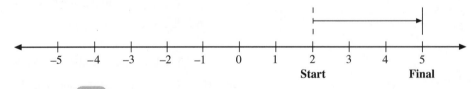

   $\therefore 2 + 3 =$ 5

2. **(a)** $(-1) + (-3)$

   $\therefore (-1) + (-3) =$ −4

(b) 2 + (–5)

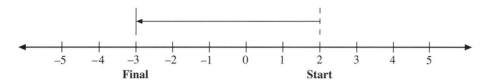

Final   Start

∴ 2 + (–5) = ⬛ **–3**

(c) 0 + (–4)

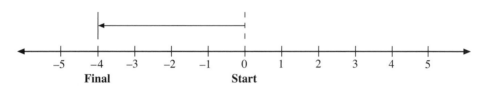

Final   Start

∴ 0 + (–4) = ⬛ **–4**

Class Activity 3

Objective: To explore the rules of addition of integers.

Tasks

(a) Copy and complete columns C and G on the spreadsheet below.

	A	B	C	D	E	F	G	H	I
	Addition of Negative Numbers								
2									
3	a	b	a + b		a	b	a + b		
4	5	-1	4		5	-5	0		
5	4	-1	3		4	-5	-1		
6	3	-1	2		3	-5	-2		
7	2	-1	1		2	-5	-3		
8	1	-1	0		1	-5	-4		
9	0	-1	-1		0	-5	-5		
10	-1	-1	-2		-1	-5	-6		
11	-2	-1	-3		-2	-5	-7		
12	-3	-1	-4		-3	-5	-8		
13	-4	-1	-5		-4	-5	-9		
14	-5	-1	-6		-5	-5	-10		
15	-6	-1	-7		-6	-5	-11		
16	-7	-1	-8		-7	-5	-12		
17	-8	-1	-9		-8	-5	-13		
18	-9	-1	-10		-9	-5	-14		
19	-10	-1	-11		-10	-5	-15		

(b) Create the spreadsheet on a computer and verify your answers in **(a)**. To do the addition in Column C in Excel, you may enter the formula "=A4 + B4" in cell C4 and then copy the formula to the cells C5 to C19.

(c) Change the entries in columns B and F to other positive and negative numbers and repeat the process.

Question

Use your results from Class Activities 2 and 3 to write down the rules for addition of integers.

In adding two integers:

- if the numbers have the same sign, the sum will have the same sign and its numerical part is the sum of the numerical parts of the given numbers.

- if the numbers have opposite signs, the sum will have the same sign as the number with a larger numerical value and its numerical part is the difference in the numerical parts of the given numbers.

Class Activity 4

Objective: To explore the rules of subtraction of integers.

Questions

Use the number line to find the answer in each case. Question **1(a)** has been partly done for you.

1. (a) $3 - 4$

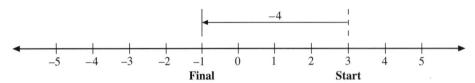

Starting from 3, move 4 units to the left (**subtraction** of positive number 4). The answer is the number on the final position as shown on the number line above.

∴ $3 - 4 =$ -1

(b) $-2 - 3$

∴ $-2 - 3 =$ -5

2. (a) $(-1) - (-3)$

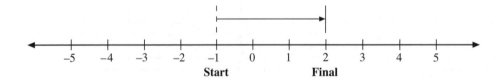

∴ $(-1) - (-3) =$ 2

(b) $2 - (-2)$

∴ $2 - (-2) =$ 4

(c) $0 - (-5)$

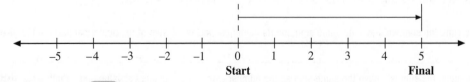

∴ $0 - (-5) =$ 5

3.

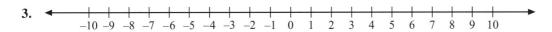

Complete the following tables.

Subtracting 4	Adding (–4)
10 – 4 = 6	10 + (–4) = 6
6 – 4 = 2	6 + (–4) = 2
0 – 4 = –4	0 + (–4) = –4
(–3) – 4 = –7	(–3) + (–4) = –7
(–5) – 4 = –9	(–5) + (–4) = –9

Subtracting (–4)	Adding 4
4 – (–4) = 8	4 + 4 = 8
2 – (–4) = 6	2 + 4 = 6
0 – (–4) = 4	0 + 4 = 4
–1 – (–4) = 5	–1 + 4 = 3
–5 – (–4) = –1	–5 + 4 = –1

4. From this activity, write down the rules of subtraction of integers.

In subtracting two integers such as *a* and *b*, write *a* – *b* as an addition, i.e., *a* + (–*b*), by changing the sign of *b* and then perform the addition.

Class Activity 5

Objective: To investigate the absolute value of the difference of two integers.

Questions

1. Simplify each of the following.

   (a) **(i)** $|6 - 2| =$ ____4____   **(ii)** $|2 - 6| =$ ____4____

   (b) **(i)** $|2 - (-2)| =$ ____4____   **(ii)** $|-2 - 2| =$ ____4____

   (c) **(i)** $|-2 - (-6)| =$ ____4____   **(ii)** $|-6 - (-2)| =$ ____4____

2. Compare the answers of **(i)** and **(ii)** for each part question. What do you observe about the order of integers in the subtraction and the absolute value of the difference?

   The absolute value of the difference remains the same regardless of the order of integers in the subtraction.

3.

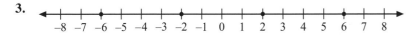

What is the distance on the number line between each pair of integers?

   (a) 2 and 6 ____4____   **(b)** –2 and 2 ____4____   **(c)** –6 and –2 ____4____

4. Draw a conclusion from your results.

   The absolute value of the difference of two integers is not affected by its order.

Class Activity 6

Objective: To explore the rules of multiplication of integers.

Tasks

By considering the given number patterns, copy and complete the multiplication table.

×	3	2	1	0	–1	–2	–3
3	9	6	3	0	–3	–6	–9
2	6	4	2	0	–2	–4	–6
1	3	2	1	0	–1	–2	–3
0	0	0	0	0	0	0	0
–1	–3	–2	–1	0	1	2	3
–2	–6	–4	–2	0	2	4	6
–3	–9	–6	–3	0	3	6	9

Questions

What is the outcome of the product of
(a) a positive number with a positive number,
(b) a positive number with a negative number,
(c) a negative number with a positive number,
(d) a negative number with a negative number?

(a) $(+)(+) =$ ___(+)___   **(b)** $(+)(-) =$ ___(−)___   **(c)** $(-)(+) =$ ___(−)___   **(d)** $(-)(-) =$ ___(+)___

Class Activity 7

Objective: To explore rational numbers.

Questions

1. Express the following numbers as decimals, using long division.

   (a) $-\dfrac{1}{2} =$ ___−0.5___   **(b)** $\dfrac{1}{3} =$ ___$0.\overline{3}$___   **(c)** $\dfrac{5}{6} =$ ___$0.8\overline{3}$___   **(d)** $-\dfrac{4}{9} =$ ___$-0.\overline{4}$___

   (e) $-\dfrac{8}{11} =$ ___$-0.\overline{72}$___   **(f)** $\dfrac{1}{7} =$ ___$0.\overline{142857}$___   **(g)** $-\dfrac{3}{14} =$ ___$0.2\overline{143857}$___   **(h)** $\dfrac{9}{25} =$ ___0.36___

2. State which numbers in Question 1 can be represented as
   (a) terminating decimal,
   (b) repeating decimal.

   These numbers can be represented as terminating decimals: $-\dfrac{1}{2}$, $\dfrac{9}{25}$

   These numbers can be represented as repeating decimals: $\dfrac{1}{3}$, $\dfrac{5}{6}$, $-\dfrac{4}{9}$, $-\dfrac{8}{11}$, $\dfrac{1}{7}$, $-\dfrac{3}{14}$

3. What can you say about the decimal representation of a rational number?

   A rational number is either a terminating decimal or a repeating decimal.

4. Write a decimal which is non-terminating and non-repeating.

   0.101001000100001 ...

Extend Your Learning Curve

Earlier you were told that $\sqrt{2}$ is an example of an irrational number and that its value truncated to 5 decimal places is 1.41421. Let us explore another irrational number $\sqrt{3}$ and find an approximation of its value.

Since $\sqrt{2.25} = 1.5$, $\sqrt{4} = 2$, and $2.25 < 3 < 4$, thus $\sqrt{3}$ will have a value somewhere between 1.5 and 2.

Try 1.7 : $1.7^2 = 2.89$
Try 1.8 : $1.8^2 = 3.24$
So, $\sqrt{3}$ is between 1.7 and 1.8.
Try 1.71, 1.72, 1.73, ..., etc.

Find the next two numbers which have the form $1.7x$ (where x is a digit) which differs by 0.01 such that between them lies the value of $\sqrt{3}$. Hence, give the approximation of $\sqrt{3}$ to two decimal places.

Solution
The two numbers used are 1.73 and 1.74, where x is 3 and 4 respectively.

$1.73^2 = 2.9929$
$1.74^2 = 3.0276$
$\sqrt{3}$ is betwes 1.73 and 1.74.

$$\therefore \quad \sqrt{3} \approx \frac{1.73 + 1.74}{2}$$
$$= 1.74 \text{ (correct to 2 d.p.)}$$

Try It!

Section 2.1

1. An airplane is 3,200 m above sea level and a submarine is 456 m below sea level. Represent these altitudes using positive and negative numbers.

   Solution
   Suppose the altitude above sea level is positive.
   Altitude of the airplane = 3,200 m
   Altitude of the submarine = −456 m

2. **(a)** Represent the numbers −1, −3.5, and $2\frac{1}{2}$ on a number line.
   (b) Hence, arrange the given numbers in descending order.

   Solution
   (a) The representation of the numbers −1, −3.5, and $2\frac{1}{2}$ is shown below.

   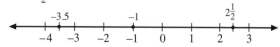

   (b) The descending order of the numbers is $2\frac{1}{2}$, −1, −3.5.

3. Simplify the following.
   (a) $\left|-5\right|$ **(b)** $-\left|24\right|$ **(c)** $-\left|-3\right|$

   Solution
   (a) $\left|-5\right| = -(-5)$
               $= 5$

   (b) $-\left|24\right| = -(24)$
               $= -24$

   (c) $-\left|-3\right| = -(3)$
               $= -3$

4. Given the numbers −218, −13.4, and 106, arrange
   (a) the numbers in descending order,
   (b) the absolute values of the numbers in ascending order.

   Solution
   (a) Since 106 > −13.4 > −218, the numbers in descending order are 106, −13.4, −218.

   (b) $\left|-218\right| = 218$

   $\left|-13.4\right| = 13.4$

   $\left|106\right| = 106$
   The numbers in ascending order are 13.4, 106, 218.
   ∴ the absolute values of the numbers in ascending order are $\left|-13.4\right|, \left|106\right|, \left|-218\right|$.

Section 2.2

5. Find the values of the following.
   (a) 9 + (−20)   **(b)** (−6) + 14
   (c) (−8) + (−13)

   Solution
   (a) $9 + (-20) = -(20 - 9)$
                    $= -11$
   (b) $(-6) + 14 = 14 - 6$
                  $= 8$
   (c) $(-8) + (-13) = -(8 + 13)$
                      $= -21$

6. Find the additive inverse of the following.
   (a) 60   **(b)** −244   **(c)** −8,921

   Solution
   (a) The additive inverse of 60 is −60.
   (b) The additive inverse of −244 is 244.
   (c) The additive inverse of −8,921 is 8,921.

Section 2.3

7. Find the values of the following.
   (a) 15 − 28   **(b)** −12 − (−4)
   (c) 3 − (−10)

   Solution
   (a) $15 - 28 = -(28 - 15) = -13$
   (b) $-12 - (-4) = -12 + 4 = -8$
   (c) $3 - (-10) = 3 + 10 = 13$

8. Evaluate the following.
   (a) $8 - \left|-28\right|$ **(b)** $-\left|-5\right| - \left|7\right|$
   (c) $10 - (-\left|-6\right|)$ **(d)** $3 - \left|-(-9)\right|$

   Solution
   (a) $8 - \left|-28\right| = 8 - 28$
                    $= 8 + (-28)$
                    $= -(28 - 8)$
                    $= -20$

   (b) $-\left|-5\right| - \left|7\right| = -5 - 7$
                     $= -5 + (-7)$
                     $= -(7 + 5)$
                     $= -12$

   (c) $10 - (-\left|-6\right|) = 10 - (-6)$
                       $= 10 + 6$
                       $= 16$

   (d) $3 - \left|-(-9)\right| = 3 - \left|9\right|$
                     $= 3 - 9$
                     $= 3 + (-9)$
                     $= -(9 - 3)$
                     $= -6$

9. A submarine is 78 m below sea level. It rises 36 m and then dives 25 m. How far is it below sea level?

Solution
Suppose the distance above sea level is positive.
Final position $= (-78) + 36 + (-25)$
$\qquad\qquad\quad = -78 + 36 - 25$
$\qquad\qquad\quad = -67$ m
It is 67 m below sea level.

10. Find -14 decreased by the distance between 25 and -17.

Solution
The required distance is $-14 - |25 - (-17)|$
$= -14 - |42|$
$= -14 - 42$
$= -56$ units

Section 2.4

11. Find the values of the following.
    (a) $8 \times (-12)$ (b) $(-3) \times (-6)$
    (c) $(-5) \times 6 \times (-4)$

Solution
(a) $8 \times (-12) = -8 \times 12$
$\qquad\qquad\quad = -96$
(b) $(-3) \times (-6) = 3 \times 6$
$\qquad\qquad\quad\;\; = 18$
(c) $(-5) \times 6 \times (-4) = -(5 \times 6) \times (-4)$
$\qquad\qquad\qquad\quad = 30 \times 4$
$\qquad\qquad\qquad\quad = 120$

12. Find the values of the following.
    (a) $54 \div (-6)$
    (b) $(-75) \div (-5)$

Solution
(a) $54 \div (-6) = -(54 \div 6) = -9$
(b) $(-75) \div (-5) = 75 \div 5 = 15$

13. Find the values of the following.
    (a) $32 \div (-4) \times (-7)$
    (b) $(-8) - (-2) + (-28) \div 4$
    (c) $(-8)^3$
    (d) -8^3

Solution
(a) $32 \div (-4) \times (-7) = (-8) \times (-7)$
$\qquad\qquad\qquad\qquad = 56$

(b) $(-8) - (-2) + (-28) \div 4$
$= (-8) - (-2) + (-7)$
$= -8 + 2 - 7$
$= -13$

(c) $(-8)^3 = (-8) \times (-8) \times (-8)$
$\qquad\quad = 64 \times (-8)$
$\qquad\quad = -512$

(d) $-8^3 = -(8^3)$
$\qquad\; = -(8 \times 8 \times 8)$
$\qquad\; = -512$

14. Evaluate $(-6)^3 \div (-12) + [(-8) - (-3)]^2 \times (-2)$.

Solution
$(-6)^3 \div (-12) + [(-8) - (-3)]^2 \times (-2)$
$= (-6)^3 \div (-12) + (-5)^2 \times (-2)$
$= (-216) \div (-12) + 25 \times (-2)$
$= 18 - 50$
$= -32$

Section 2.5

15. Find the value of $\left(-1\frac{1}{4}\right) + \left(-2\frac{1}{3}\right)$, giving your answer in its simplest form.

Solution
$$\left(-1\frac{1}{4}\right) + \left(-2\frac{1}{3}\right) = -1\frac{1}{4} - 2\frac{1}{3}$$
$$= -\frac{5}{4} - \frac{7}{3}$$
$$= \frac{-15 - 28}{12}$$
$$= -\frac{43}{12}$$
$$= -3\frac{7}{12}$$

16. Find the value of $1\frac{1}{4} + \left(-\frac{8}{3}\right) - \left(-\frac{5}{9}\right)$, giving your answer in its simplest form.

Solution
$$1\frac{1}{4} + \left(-\frac{8}{3}\right) - \left(-\frac{5}{9}\right) = 1\frac{1}{4} - \frac{8}{3} + \frac{5}{9}$$
$$= \frac{5}{4} - \frac{8}{3} + \frac{5}{9}$$
$$= \frac{45 - 96 + 20}{36}$$
$$= -\frac{31}{36}$$

17. Evaluate the following.

(a) $\dfrac{3}{-3}$

(b) $\dfrac{-7}{-\frac{1}{2}}$

(c) $\dfrac{-\frac{1}{4}}{8}$

Solution

(a) $\dfrac{3}{-3} = \dfrac{-3}{3}$

$= -1$

(b) $\dfrac{-7}{-\frac{1}{2}} = -7 \div \left(-\dfrac{1}{2}\right)$

$= -7 \times (-2)$

$= 7 \times 2$

$= 14$

(c) $\dfrac{-\frac{1}{4}}{8} = -\dfrac{1}{4} \div 8$

$= -\dfrac{1}{4} \times \dfrac{1}{8}$

$= -\dfrac{1}{32}$

18. Find the value of $\left(-6\dfrac{2}{3}\right) \times \dfrac{2}{5}$.

Solution

$\left(-6\dfrac{2}{3}\right) \times \dfrac{2}{5} = -\dfrac{20}{3} \times \dfrac{2}{5}$

$= -\dfrac{8}{3}$

19. Find the value of $\left(-\dfrac{3}{4}\right) \div \left[\left(-\dfrac{1}{5}\right) + \left(-\dfrac{1}{3}\right)\right]$, giving your answer in its simplest form.

Solution

$\left(-\dfrac{3}{4}\right) \div \left[\left(-\dfrac{1}{5}\right) + \left(-\dfrac{1}{3}\right)\right] = \left(-\dfrac{3}{4}\right) \div \left[\dfrac{-3-5}{15}\right]$

$= -\dfrac{3}{4} \times \left(-\dfrac{15}{8}\right)$

$= \dfrac{45}{32}$

$= 1\dfrac{13}{32}$

Section 2.6

20. Express $\dfrac{5}{8}$ as a decimal.

Solution

$\dfrac{5}{8} = 5 \div 8$

$= 0.625$

```
      0.6 2 5
  8 ) 5.0 0 0
      4 8
      ‾‾‾‾
        2 0
        1 6
        ‾‾‾
          4 0
          4 0
          ‾‾‾
            0
```

21. Express $\dfrac{7}{11}$ as a decimal.

Solution

$\dfrac{7}{11} = 7 \div 11$

$= 0.636363 \ldots$

$= 0.\overline{63}$

It is a repeating decimal with the repeating block 63.

```
       0.6 3 6 3
  11 ) 7.0 0 0 0
       6 6
       ‾‾‾‾
         4 0
         3 3
         ‾‾‾
           7 0
           6 6
           ‾‾‾
             4 0
             3 3
             ‾‾‾
               7
```

Section 2.7

22. Round 1,573.8 to the nearest

(a) integer,

(b) 10.

Solution

(a) $1,573.8 = 1,574$ (correct to the nearest integer)

(b) $1,573.8 = 1,570$ (correct to the nearest 10)

23. The population of California at a certain point in time is 37,253,956. State the population correct to the nearest

(a) 1,000,

(b) million.

Solution

(a) $37,253,956$

$= 37,254,000$ (correct to the nearest 1,000)

The population is 37,254,000, correct to the nearest 1,000.

(b) $37,253,956$

$= 37,000,000$ (correct to the nearest million)

The population is 37,000,000, correct to the nearest million.

24. Round 9.0476 to

    (a)   1 decimal place,

    (b)   3 decimal places.

Solution

    (a) $9.0476 = 9.0$ (correct to 1 d.p.)

    (b) $9.0476 = 9.048$ (correct to 3 d.p.)

25.   **(a)**   Evaluate $\left(3\dfrac{7}{11}\right) \times \left(-1\dfrac{9}{20}\right)$.

    (b)   Round the answer to 4 decimal places.

Solution

    (a)
$$
\begin{aligned}
\left(3\tfrac{7}{11}\right) \times \left(-1\tfrac{9}{20}\right) &= -\frac{40}{11} \times \frac{29}{20} \\
&= -\frac{58}{11} \\
&= -5\frac{3}{11}
\end{aligned}
$$

    (b)
$$
\begin{aligned}
-5\frac{3}{11} &= -5.272727\ldots \\
&= -5.2727 \quad \text{(correct to 4 d.p.)}
\end{aligned}
$$

Exercise 2.1
Basic Practice

1. Taking a gain in weight to be positive, write each change in weight using positive and negative numbers.
 (a) John is 2 lb heavier than before.
 (b) Mary is 3 lb lighter.

 Solution
 (a) Change in John's weight = 2 lb
 (b) Change in Mary's weight = −3 lb

2. If depositing money into a bank account is a positive amount, state the amount for each transaction.
 (a) A withdrawal of $2,800
 (b) A deposit of $1,650

 Solution
 (a) Amount = −$2,800
 (b) Amount = $1,650

3. If −4 mph denotes 4 mph below the speed limit, what does 12 mph mean?

 Solution
 12 mph means 12 mph above the speed limit.

4. If −7 °C denotes a temperature drop of 7 °C, what does 5 °C mean?

 Solution
 5 °C means a temperature rise of 5 °C.

5. State the numbers represented by the points A, B, and C on the number line.

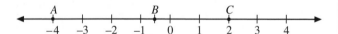

 Solution
 The numbers represented by A, B and C are -4, $-\frac{1}{2}$, and 2 respectively.

6. Represent each pair of numbers on a number line and write down their relation using the "<" sign.
 (a) 0, 4   **(b)** −2.5, 0

 Solution
 (a)

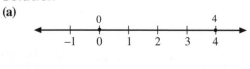

 $0 < 4$

(b)

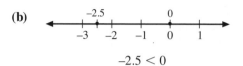

 $-2.5 < 0$

7. Represent each pair of numbers on a number line and write down their relation using the ">" sign.
 (a) −3, 1   **(b)** $-5, -1\frac{1}{2}$

 Solution
 (a)

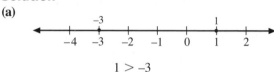

 $1 > -3$

(b)

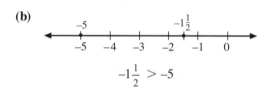

 $-1\frac{1}{2} > -5$

8. Fill in each ☐ with "<" or ">".
 (a) 2 ☐ 7   **(b)** −3 ☐ −10
 (c) 3 ☐ −2   **(d)** −14 ☐ 27
 (e) −5 ☐ 0   **(f)** −11 ☐ −6

 Solution
 (a) $2 < 7$ **(b)** $-3 > -10$
 (c) $3 > -2$ **(d)** $-14 < 27$
 (e) $-5 < 0$ **(f)** $-11 < -6$

9. Simplify the following.
 (a) $|45|$ **(b)** $|-8|$
 (c) $-|22|$ **(d)** $-|-4|$

 Solution
 (a) $|45| = 45$
 (b) $|-8| = 8$
 (c) $-|22| = -22$
 (d) $-|-4| = -4$

10. Fill in each ▢ with "<", "=", or ">".

(a) $|4|$ ▢ $|-8|$ (b) $-|7|$ ▢ 0

(c) $|-33|$ ▢ $|33|$ (d) $|-6|$ ▢ $-|6|$

(e) $|-2|$ ▢ $-|-5|$ (f) $-|-9|$ ▢ 9

Solution

(a) $|4| < |-8|$ (b) $-|7| < 0$

(c) $|-33| = |33|$ (d) $|-6| > -|6|$

(e) $|-2| > -|-5|$ (f) $-|-9| < 9$

Further Practice

11. Describe the meaning of each quantity.

(a) The adjustment of the hourly wage of a worker is $-\$5$.

(b) The movement of an elevator is positive 2 levels.

(c) The balance in a bank account is $-\$1$.

Solution

(a) The hourly wage is decreased by $5.

(b) The elevator moves up by 2 levels.

(c) The bank account is $1 in debit.

12. Given the numbers -2.7, $1\frac{1}{3}$, and -0.4,

(a) represent the numbers on a number line,

(b) arrange the numbers in ascending order.

Solution

(a) The representation is shown below.

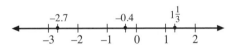

(b) The numbers in ascending order are -2.7, -0.4, $1\frac{1}{3}$.

13. Given the numbers 5, $-3\frac{1}{2}$, and 0.9,

(a) represent the numbers on a number line,

(b) arrange the numbers in descending order.

Solution

(a) The representation is shown below.

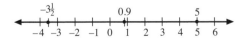

(b) The numbers in descending order are

5, 0.9, $-3\frac{1}{2}$.

14. Given the numbers -12.3, 9.5, and -46, arrange their absolute values in ascending order.

Solution

Their absolute values in ascending order are $|9.5|$, $|-12.3|$, $|-46|$.

15. Given the numbers -50, 210, 0, and -300, arrange

(a) the numbers in ascending order,

(b) the absolute values of the numbers in descending order.

Solution

(a) The numbers in ascending order are -300, -50, 0, 210.

(b) The absolute values of the numbers in descending order are $|-300|$, $|210|$, $|-50|$, $|0|$.

16. Given the numbers -42, 18, 0.7, and -4.2, arrange

(a) the numbers in descending order,

(b) the absolute values of the numbers in ascending order.

Solution

(a) The numbers in descending order are 18, 0.7, -4.2, and -42.

(b) The absolute values of the numbers in ascending order are $|0.7|$, $|-4.2|$, $|18|$, $|-42|$.

Math@Work

17. The following shows a page of a savings account summary.

Date	Deposit	Withdrawal	Balance
01/02/2012	$3,000.00		$3,000.00
01/04/2012		$200.00	$2,800.00
01/11/2012	$150.00		$2,950.00
01/23/2012		$400.00	$2,550.00

Design a page that shows the deposits and withdrawals under the same column.

Solution

Date	Deposit/With-drawal	Balance
01/02/2012	$3,000.00	$3,000.00
01/04/2012	$-200.00	$2,800.00
01/11/2012	$150.00	$2,950.00
01/23/2012	$-400.00	$2,550.00

In the table, positive value means deposit and negative value means withdrawal.

18. The table shows the minimum temperatures in four cities on a certain day.

City	Minimum temperature (°C)
Denver	–5
Churchill	–28
Singapore	27
Portland	10

Arrange these cities in ascending order of their temperatures.

Solution
The cities in ascending order of their temperatures are Churchill, Denver, Portland, Singapore.

19. The bank account balances of Rex, Sue, and Tom are –$3,250, $760, and –$2,180 respectively. Based on these figures, who is the
(a) richest?   (b) poorest?

Solution
(a) Sue is the richest.
(b) Rex is the poorest.

Brainworks

20. Discuss whether the following numbers exist. If they do, write down their values.
(a) The largest positive integer
(b) The smallest positive integer
(c) The largest negative integer
(d) The smallest negative integer

Solution
(a) The largest positive integer does not exist.
(b) The smallest positive integer exists. It is 1.
(c) The largest negative integer exists. It is –1.
(d) The smallest negative integer does not exist.

21. Which one of the following statements is false? Explain why it is false.
(a) The absolute value of every integer is a positive integer.
(b) There is at least one integer whose absolute value is zero.
(c) The absolute value of an integer is never a negative integer.

Solution
(a) The statement is false. The absolute value of the integer "0" is 0, which is neither positive nor negative.
(b) The statement is true.
(c) The statement is true.

Exercise 2.2
Basic Practice

1. Use a number line to solve each of the following.
(a) 5 + (–2)   (b) (–6) + 4
(c) 1 + (–3)   (d) (–2) + (–2)
(e) 0 + (–5)   (f) (–4) + 7

Solution
(a)
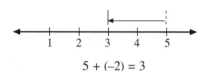
$$5 + (-2) = 3$$

(b)
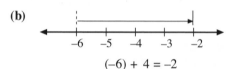
$$(-6) + 4 = -2$$

(c)
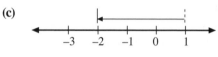
$$1 + (-3) = -2$$

(d)
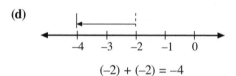
$$(-2) + (-2) = -4$$

(e)
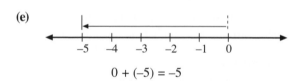
$$0 + (-5) = -5$$

(f)
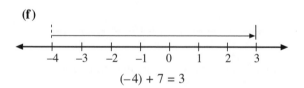
$$(-4) + 7 = 3$$

2. Evaluate the following.
(a) (–5) + 17   (b) (–12) + (–25)
(c) 24 + (–30)   (d) (–60) + 28
(e) –46 + (–54)   (f) –13 + 79

Solution
(a) $(-5) + 17 = 17 - 5$
$$= 12$$

(b) $(-12) + (-25) = -(12 + 25)$
$$= -37$$

(c) $24 + (-30) = -(30 - 24)$
$= -6$
(d) $(-60) + 28 = -(60 - 28)$
$= -32$
(e) $-46 + (-54) = -(46 + 54)$
$= -100$
(f) $-13 + 79 = 79 - 13$
$= 66$

3. Find the additive inverse of each of the following.
(a) 50   **(b)** −17
(c) 123   **(d)** −4,560

Solution
(a) The additive inverse for 50 is −50.
(b) The additive inverse for −17 is 17.
(c) The additive inverse for 123 is −123.
(d) The additive inverse for −4,560 is 4,560.

Further Practice

4. Evaluate the following.
(a) $(-2) + 5 + (-3)$
(b) $7 + (-12) + 6$
(c) $13 + (-6) + (-34)$
(d) $(-9) + (-21) + (-7)$
(e) $-25 + (-4) + 8$
(f) $-29 + 10 + 48$

Solution
(a) $(-2) + 5 + (-3) = -2 + 5 - 3$
$= 3 - 3$
$= 0$
(b) $7 + (-12) + 6 = 7 - 12 + 6$
$= -5 + 6$
$= 1$
(c) $13 + (-6) + (-34) = 13 - 6 - 34$
$= 7 - 34$
$= -27$
(d) $(-9) + (-21) + (-7) = -9 - 21 - 7$
$= -30 - 7$
$= -37$
(e) $-25 + (-4) + 8 = -25 - 4 + 8$
$= -29 + 8$
$= -21$
(f) $-29 + 10 + 48 = -19 + 48$
$= 29$

5. Find the missing number in each of the following.
(a) ▢ $+ 7 = 3$ **(b)** $11 +$ ▢ $= -5$
(c) $-8 +$ ▢ $= 6$ **(d)** ▢ $+ (-13) = -14$

Solution
(a) $(-4) + 7 = 3$
(b) $11 + (-16) = -5$
(c) $-8 + (14) = 6$
(d) $(-1) + (-13) = -14$

6. Evaluate each absolute value.
(a) $\left|41 + 14\right|$ **(b)** $\left|6 + (-8)\right|$
(c) $-\left|-5 + 17\right|$ **(d)** $\left|-12 + (-3)\right|$

Solution
(a) $\left|41 + 14\right| = \left|55\right|$
$= 55$

(b) $\left|6 + (-8)\right| = \left|6 - 8\right|$
$= \left|-2\right|$
$= 2$

(c) $-\left|-5 + 17\right| = -\left|12\right|$
$= -(12)$
$= -12$

(d) $\left|-12 + (-3)\right| = \left|-12 - 3\right|$
$= \left|-15\right|$
$= 15$

7. Find the value of each of the following.
(a) $7 + \left|-9\right|$ **(b)** $\left|-2\right| + (-13)$
(c) $-\left|25\right| + \left|-25\right|$ **(d)** $-\left|-6\right| + (-4)$
(e) $-\left|-8\right| + \left|8\right|$

Solution
(a) $7 + \left|-9\right| = 7 + 9$
$= 16$
(b) $\left|-2\right| + (-13) = 2 + (-13)$
$= -(13 - 2)$
$= -11$
(c) $-\left|25\right| + \left|-25\right| = -25 + 25$
$= 0$
(d) $-\left|-6\right| + (-4) = -6 + (-4)$
$= -(6 + 4)$
$= -10$
(e) $-\left|-8\right| + \left|8\right| = -8 + 8$
$= 0$

Math@Work

8. The bank account of a company has overdraft facility. Its balance for yesterday was –$390. The company deposits $600 into the account today and it will withdraw $450 tomorrow. Find the balance in the account
   (a) today,
   (b) tomorrow.

Solution
   (a) Today's balance = –$390 + $600 = $210
   (b) Tomorrow's balance = $210 – $450 = –$240

9. A car travels 16 mi due south, 33 mi due north, and then 12 mi due south. What is its final position from the starting point?

Solution
Suppose the movement due north is positive.
Final position = $-16 + 33 + (-12)$
$\qquad\qquad = -16 + 33 - 12$
$\qquad\qquad = 5$ mi
Its final position is 5 mi north from the starting point.

Brainworks

10. Consider the rules for addition:

For any $a > 0$ and $b > 0$,
$$a + b = a + b$$
$$-a + (-b) = -(a + b)$$
$$-a + b = -(a - b) \qquad \text{if } a > b$$
$$-a + b = b - a \qquad \text{if } b > a$$

Do these rules also hold if $a < 0$ or $b < 0$?

E.g., if $a = -4$, then
$$-a + (-b) = -(a + b)$$
$$= -(-4) + (-b)$$
$$= -(-4 + b)$$

Solution
Case 1: $a + b = a + b$
We choose $a = -4$ and $b = -5$. Obviously, LHS = RHS.

Case 2: $-a + (-b) = -(a + b)$
We choose $a = -4$ and $b = -5$.
LHS $= -(-4) + [-(-5)] = 4 + 5 = 9$
RHS $= -[(-4) + (-5)] = -[-9] = 9$
Thus, LHS = RHS.

Case 3: $-a + b = -(a - b)$ if $a > b$
We choose $a = -4$ and $b = -5$.
LHS $= -(-4) + (-5) = 4 - 5 = -1$
RHS $= -[(-4) - (-5)] = -[-4 + 5] = -1$
Thus, LHS = RHS.

Case 4: $-a + b = b - a$ if $b > a$
We choose $a = -4$ and $b = -3$.
LHS $= -(-4) + (-3) = 4 - 3 = 1$
RHS $= (-3) - (-4) = -3 + 4 = 1$
Thus, LHS = RHS.
$\therefore$ the rules hold if $a < 0$ or $b < 0$.

Exercise 2.3
Basic Practice

1. Use a number line to find the value of each of the following.
   (a) $3 - 7$ (b) $4 - (-2)$
   (c) $-5 - 3$ (d) $-6 - (-9)$

Solution
(a)
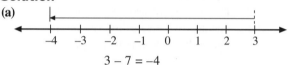
$3 - 7 = -4$

(b)

$4 - (-2) = 4 + 2$
$\qquad\qquad = 6$

(c)
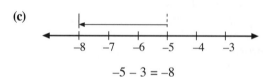
$-5 - 3 = -8$

(d)
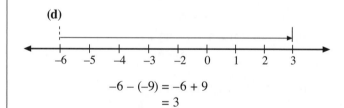
$-6 - (-9) = -6 + 9$
$\qquad\qquad = 3$

2. Evaluate the following.
   (a) $7 - 16$ (b) $0 - 20$
   (c) $3 - (-32)$ (d) $-9 - 15$
   (e) $-4 - (-18)$ (f) $-28 - (-11)$

Solution
(a) $7 - 16 = -(16 - 7)$
$\qquad\qquad = -9$

(b) $0 - 20 = -20$

(c) $3 - (-32) = 3 + 32$
$\qquad\qquad\quad = 35$

(d) $-9 - 15 = -(9 + 15)$
$\qquad\qquad\quad = -24$

(e) $-4 - (-18) = -4 + 18$
$= 14$

(f) $-28 - (-11) = -28 + 11$
$= -17$

3. Find the missing number in each ▢.

(a) $5 - \boxed{} = 12$

(b) $7 - \boxed{} = -13$

(c) $-9 - \boxed{} = -15$

(d) $-8 - \boxed{} = 10$

Solution
(a) $5 - (-7) = 12$
(b) $7 - 20 = -13$
(c) $-9 - 6 = -15$
(d) $-8 - (-18) = 10$

Further Practice

4. Evaluate the following.
(a) $2 - 4 - 11$ **(b)** $6 - (10 - 3)$
(c) $4 - (-2) - 14$ **(d)** $3 - (-8) + (-4)$
(e) $-15 - (-7) - 5$ **(f)** $-12 - (-6) + 9$

Solution
(a) $2 - 4 - 11 = -2 - 11$
$= -13$

(b) $6 - (10 - 3) = 6 - 7$
$= -1$

(c) $4 - (-2) - 14 = 4 + 2 - 14$
$= 6 - 14$
$= -8$

(d) $3 - (-8) + (-4) = 3 + 8 - 4$
$= 11 - 4$
$= 7$

(e) $-15 - (-7) - 5 = -15 + 7 - 5$
$= -8 - 5$
$= -13$

(f) $-12 - (-6) + 9 = -12 + 6 + 9$
$= -6 + 9$
$= 3$

5. Find the value for each of the following.
(a) $|4 - 19|$ **(b)** $|25 - (-2)|$
(c) $|-6 - 8|$ **(d)** $|-13 - (-7)|$

Solution
(a) $|4 - 19| = |-15|$
$= 15$

(b) $|25 - (-2)| = |25 + 2|$
$= |27|$
$= 27$

(c) $|-6 - 8| = |-14|$
$= 14$

(d) $|-13 - (-7)| = |-13 + 7|$
$= |-6|$
$= 6$

6. Evaluate the following.
(a) $|-8| - 10$ **(b)** $26 - |-5|$
(c) $-9 - |-2|$ **(d)** $-|-7| - (-3)$
(e) $|-2| - |9|$ **(f)** $-|-6| - |8|$

Solution
(a) $|-8| - 10 = 8 - 10$
$= -2$

(b) $26 - |-5| = 26 - 5$
$= 21$

(c) $-9 - |-2| = -9 - 2$
$= -11$

(d) $-|-7| - (-3) = -7 + 3$
$= -8\,4$

(e) $|-2| - |9| = 2 - 9$
$= -7$

(f) $-|-6| - |8| = -6 - 8$
$= -14$

7. Fill in ▢ with "<", ">", or "=" to make a true statement.
(a) $|3 - 6|$ ▢ $|6 - 3|$
(b) $|5 - 10|$ ▢ $5 - 10$
(c) $-(-4)$ ▢ $-|-4|$
(d) $-6 - (-2)$ ▢ $-6 - |-2|$

Solution
(a) LHS $= |3 - 6|$
$= |-3|$
$= 3$
RHS $= |6 - 3|$
$= |3|$
$= 3$
$\therefore |3 - 6| = |6 - 3|$

(b) LHS $= |5 - 10|$
$\qquad = |-5|$
$\qquad = 5$
$\quad$ RHS $= 5 - 10$
$\qquad\quad = -5$
$\quad \therefore \ |5 - 10| > 5 - 10$

(c) LHS $= -(-4)$
$\qquad = 4$
$\quad$ RHS $= -|-4|$
$\qquad\quad = -4$
$\quad \therefore \ -(-4) > -|-4|$

(d) LHS $= -6 - (-2)$
$\qquad = -6 + 2$
$\qquad = -4$
$\quad$ RHS $= -6 - |-2|$
$\qquad\quad = -6 - 2$
$\qquad\quad = -8$
$\quad \therefore \ -6 - (-2) > -6 - |-2|$

Math@Work

8. A helicopter flying at 120 m above sea level detects a submarine. If the submarine is 39 m below sea level, what is the vertical distance between the helicopter and the submarine?

Solution
The required vertical distance $= 120 - (-39)$
$\qquad\qquad\qquad\qquad\quad = 159$ m

9. The following table records the maximum and minimum daily temperatures of a city on five consecutive days.

Day	Mon	Tue	Wed	Thu	Fri
Maximum temperature (°C)	–2	6	0	–1	10
Minimum temperature (°C)	–10	–4	–3	–5	3

On which day is the temperature difference
(a) the greatest? $\qquad$ **(b)** the least?

Solution

Day	Temperature difference (°C)
Mon	$-2 - (-10) = 8$
Tue	$6 - (-4) = 10$
Wed	$0 - (-3) = 3$
Thu	$-1 - (-5) = 4$
Fri	$10 - 3 = 7$

(a) Tuesday has the greatest temperature difference.
(b) Wednesday has the least temperature difference.

10. The day temperature in the desert rose by 8°F between 6 A.M. and 7 A.M. and then rose another 43°F between 7 A.M. and 10 A.M. The temperature at 10 A.M. was 36°F. What was the initial temperature at 6 A.M.?

Solution
Initial temperature at 6 A.M. $= 36 - 43 - 8$
$\qquad\qquad\qquad\qquad\qquad = -15°F$

11. With respect to the New York local time, the local time in London is +5 hours and in Salem, Oregon, is –3 hours. Suppose it is 9 P.M., May 4, 2012, in New York, what is the local time and date in
(a) London? $\qquad$ **(b)** Salem?

Solution
(a)

By counting forward 5 hours from 9 P.M. on May 4, 2012, we see that the local time and date in London is 2 A.M., May 5, 2012.

(b)

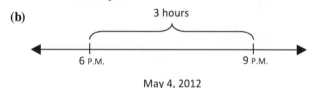

By counting backward 3 hours from 9 P.M. on May 4, 2012, we see that the local time and date in Salem is 6 P.M., May 4, 2012.

Brainworks

12. (a) Fill the same shapes with the same integers in the following table. Explore using both positive and negative integers.

Left side	Right side
□ + ◯	◯ + □
(□ + ◯) + ⬡	□ + (◯ + ⬡)
□ − ◯	◯ − □
(□ − ◯) − ⬡	□ − (◯ − ⬡)

(b) Evaluate each expression and compare the results on the left side with those on the right side. What do you notice?

(c) Check the results of your classmates. What can you conclude?

Solution

(a)

Left side	Right side
$3 + (-5)$	$(-5) + 3$
$[3 + (-5)] + 6$	$3 + [(-5) + 6]$
$3 - (-5)$	$(-5) - 3$
$[3 - (-5)] - 6$	$3 - [(-5) - 6]$

(b) The results are as follows:

Left side	Right side
-2	-2
4	4
8	-8
2	14

The values on the left side is equal to those on the right side for the first two rows.
Left side = −Right side for the third row.
Left side ≠ Right side for the fourth row.

(c) For any three different integers a, b, and c,
  (i) $a + b = b + a$
  (ii) $(a + b) + c = a + (b + c)$
  (iii) $a - b = -(b - a)$
  (iv) $(a - b) - c \neq a - (b - c)$

Exercise 2.4

Basic Practice

1. Evaluate each of the following.
  (a) $8 \times (-9)$ **(b)** $(-5) \times (-4)$
  (c) $(-6) \times 7$ **(d)** 3×17
  (e) $(-38) \div (-2)$ **(f)** $132 \div (-11)$
  (g) $65 \div 5$ **(h)** $(-57) \div 3$
  (i) $(-12)^2$ **(j)** $(-4)^3$

Solution
  (a) $8 \times (-9) = -72$ **(b)** $(-5) \times (-4) = 20$
  (c) $(-6) \times 7 = -42$ **(d)** $3 \times 17 = 51$
  (e) $(-38) \div (-2) = 19$ **(f)** $132 \div (-11) = -12$
  (g) $65 \div 5 = 13$ **(h)** $(-57) \div 3 = -19$
  (i) $(-12)^2 = 144$ **(j)** $(-4)^3 = -64$

Further Practice

2. Evaluate each of the following.
  (a) $(-6) \times 3 \times (-1)$
  (b) $(-84) \div 7 \times 5$
  (c) $(-37) \times 0 - (-8)$
  (d) $63 \div (-9) + (-2) \times (-10)$
  (e) $(-47) - 33 \div (-3) - 3 \times (-7)$
  (f) $196 \div [(-8) + (-6)] \times (-2)$
  (g) $[(-23) + 14] \times (-2)^2$

(h) $(-45) \times 6 \div (-3)^3$
(i) $(-7) \times (-8) \times 0 \times 34 - 4 \times (-5)^2$
(j) $(-6)^3 \div 3^2 \div [-9 - (-8)]^3$

Solution
(a) $(-6) \times 3 \times (-1) = (-18) \times (-1)$
$= 18$

(b) $(-84) \div 7 \times 5 = (-12) \times 5$
$= -60$

(c) $(-37) \times 0 - (-8) = 0 - (-8)$
$= 8$

(d) $63 \div (-9) + (-2) \times (-10) = (-7) + 20$
$= 13$

(e) $(-47) - 33 \div (-3) - 3 \times (-7)$
$= (-47) - (-11) + 21$
$= -47 + 11 + 21$
$= -15$

(f) $196 \div [(-8) + (-6)] \times (-2) = 196 \div (-14) \times (-2)$
$= (-14) \times (-2)$
$= 28$

(g) $[(-23) + 14] \times (-2)^2 = (-9) \times (-2)^2$
$= (-9) \times 4$
$= -36$

(h) $(-45) \times 6 \div (-3)^3 = (-45) \times 6 \div (-27)$
$= (-270) \div (-27)$
$= 10$

(i) $(-7) \times (-8) \times 0 \times 34 - 4 \times (-5)^2 = 0 - 4 \times 25$
$= -100$

(j) $(-6)^3 \div 3^2 \div [-9 - (-8)]^3 = (-6)^3 \div 3^2 \div (-1)^3$
$= (-216) \div 9 \div (-1)$
$= 24$

3. Evaluate each of the following.
  (a) $-3 \div |-3|$ **(b)** $-|-4|^2$
  (c) $(-|-5|)^2$ **(d)** $(-|-2|)^3 \div (-2)$

Solution
(a) $-3 \div |-3| = -3 \div 3$
$= -1$

(b) $-|-4|^2 = -(4)^2$
$= -16$

(c) $(-|-5|)^2 = (-5)^2$
$= 25$

(d) $(-|-2|)^3 \div (-2) = (-2)^3 \div (-2)$
$= -8 \div (-2)$
$= 4$

Math@Work

4. Tom borrowed some money from his father seven months ago. Every month, he pays back $400 to his father. Currently he owes his father $2,500.
   (a) How much will he owe his father three months from now?
   (b) How much money did he borrow from his father?

Solution
(a) Amount owed $= \$(2,500 - 400 \times 3)$
$= \$1,300$

(b) Amount borrowed $= \$[2,500 + (-400) \times (-7)]$
$= \$(2,500 + 2,800)$
$= \$5,300$

5. Mr. Ford has 400 shares of Stock A and 500 shares of Stock B. He gains $3 per share from Stock A and loses $2 per share from Stock B. How much does he gain or lose from these two stocks taken together?

Solution
The net gain $= \$[400 \times 3 + 500 \times (-2)]$
$= \$(1,200 - 1,000)$
$= \$200$

6. Jane jogs along a road. Starting from a bus station, she jogs at 4 m/s due north for 20 minutes, then at 5 m/s due south for 15 minutes and finally at 3 m/s due south for 10 minutes. Find her final position from the station.

Solution
Suppose the movement due north is positive.
Final position
$= 4 \times 20 \times 60 + (-5) \times 15 \times 60 + (-3) \times 10 \times 60$
$= 4,800 - 4,500 - 1,800$
$= -1,500$ m
Her final position is 1,500 m south from the station.

Brainworks

7. A mathematics quiz consists of five "true/false" questions. The scoring scheme for each question is as follows:

Answer	Points awarded
Correct	3
Incorrect	–2
Unanswered	0

   (a) What is the maximum score of the quiz?
   (b) What is the minimum score of the quiz?
   (c) Write about a situation where a student scores 3 points for the quiz.
   (d) Write about a situation where a student scores –3 points for the quiz.

Solution
(a) The maximum score $= 3 \times 5 = 15$ points
(b) The minimum score $= (-2) \times 5 = -10$ points
(c) The score is 3 points if there is 1 correct answer and 4 unanswered questions.
(d) The score is –3 points if there are 3 incorrect answers, 1 correct answer and 1 unanswered question.

8. (a) Fill the same shapes with the same integers in the following table.

Left side	Right side
□ × ○	○ × □
(□ × ○) × ⬡	□ × (○ × ⬡)
□ ÷ ○	○ ÷ □
(□ ÷ ○) ÷ ⬡	□ ÷ (○ ÷ ⬡)

   (b) Evaluate each expression and compare the results on the left side with those on the right side. What do you notice?
   (c) Check the results of your classmates. What can you conclude?

Solution
(a)

Left side	Right side
$4 \times (-12)$	$(-12) \times 4$
$[4 \times (-12)] \times 6$	$4 \times [(-12) \times 6]$
$4 \div (-12)$	$(-12) \div 4$
$[4 \div (-12)] \div 6$	$4 \div [(-12) \div 6]$

(b) The results are as follows.

Left side	Right side
–48	–48
–288	–288
$-\dfrac{1}{3}$	–3
$-\dfrac{1}{18}$	–2

Left side = Right side for the first two rows.

Left side $= \dfrac{1}{\text{Right side}}$ for the third row.

Left side ≠ Right side for the fourth row.

(c) For any three different integers a, b, and c,

    (i) $a \times b = b \times a$

    (ii) $(a \times b) \times c = a \times (b \times c)$

    (iii) $a \div b = \dfrac{1}{b \div a}$ provided $a \neq 0$ and $b \neq 0$.

    (iv) $(a \div b) \div c \neq a \div (b \div c)$ provided $b \neq 0$ and $c \neq 0$.

Exercise 2.5
Basic Practice

1. Fill in ▢ with a number to make a true statement.

(a) $\dfrac{48}{84} = \dfrac{▢}{7}$ **(b)** $\dfrac{-27}{-72} = \dfrac{3}{▢}$

(c) $\dfrac{4}{5} = \dfrac{-64}{▢}$ **(d)** $\dfrac{98}{-21} = \dfrac{-14}{▢}$

Solution

(a) $\dfrac{48}{84} = \dfrac{4}{7}$ **(b)** $\dfrac{-27}{-72} = \dfrac{3}{8}$

(c) $\dfrac{4}{5} = \dfrac{-64}{-80}$ **(d)** $\dfrac{98}{-21} = \dfrac{-14}{3}$

2. (a) Arrange the rational numbers $\dfrac{7}{12}$, -3, $\dfrac{2}{3}$, and $-\dfrac{13}{4}$ in ascending order.

    (b) Arrange the rational numbers $-\dfrac{3}{4}$, $\dfrac{4}{5}$, $\dfrac{7}{10}$, and $-\dfrac{11}{12}$ in descending order.

Solution

(a) The numbers in ascending order are $-\dfrac{13}{4}$, -3, $\dfrac{7}{12}$, $\dfrac{2}{3}$.

(b) The numbers in descending order are $\dfrac{4}{5}$, $\dfrac{7}{10}$, $-\dfrac{3}{4}$, $-\dfrac{11}{12}$.

3. Find the reciprocal of each of the following.

(a) $\dfrac{4}{9}$ **(b)** $\dfrac{-7}{13}$

(c) -20 **(d)** $1\dfrac{3}{5}$

Solution

(a) $1 \div \dfrac{4}{9} = \dfrac{9}{4}$

(b) $1 \div \left(-\dfrac{7}{13}\right) = -\dfrac{13}{7}$

(c) $1 \div (-20) = -\dfrac{1}{20}$

(d) $1 \div \dfrac{8}{5} = \dfrac{5}{8}$

4. Evaluate the following, giving your answers in the simplest form.

(a) $\dfrac{1}{5} + \dfrac{2}{7}$ **(b)** $\left(-\dfrac{3}{4}\right) + \left(-\dfrac{1}{2}\right)$

(c) $2\dfrac{3}{4} - 3\dfrac{11}{12}$ **(d)** $-1 - \left(-\dfrac{5}{6}\right) + \left(-\dfrac{6}{5}\right)$

(e) $\left(-\dfrac{24}{25}\right) \times \dfrac{45}{16}$ **(f)** $\left(-\dfrac{7}{11}\right)^2 - \dfrac{7}{11}$

(g) $\left(-1\dfrac{3}{5}\right) \div \left(-1\dfrac{1}{3}\right)$ **(h)** $3 + 2\dfrac{1}{2} \div \left(-1\dfrac{1}{4}\right)$

Solution

(a) $\dfrac{1}{5} + \dfrac{2}{7} = \dfrac{7 + 2 \times 5}{35} = \dfrac{17}{35}$

(b) $\left(-\dfrac{3}{4}\right) + \left(-\dfrac{1}{2}\right) = -\left(\dfrac{3}{4} + \dfrac{1}{2}\right)$

$= -\left(\dfrac{3+2}{4}\right)$

$= -\dfrac{5}{4}$

$= -1\dfrac{1}{4}$

(c) $2\dfrac{3}{4} - 3\dfrac{11}{12} = \dfrac{11}{4} - \dfrac{47}{12}$

$= \dfrac{11 \times 3 - 47}{12}$

$= \dfrac{-14}{12}$

$= -1\dfrac{1}{6}$

(d) $-1 - \left(-\dfrac{5}{6}\right) + \left(-\dfrac{6}{5}\right) = -1 + \dfrac{5}{6} - \dfrac{6}{5}$

$= \dfrac{-30 + 25 - 36}{30}$

$= \dfrac{-41}{30}$

$= -1\dfrac{11}{30}$

(e) $\left(-\dfrac{24}{25}\right) \times \dfrac{45}{16} = -\dfrac{24}{25} \times \dfrac{45}{16}$

$= -\dfrac{27}{10}$

$= -2\dfrac{7}{10}$

(f) $\left(-\dfrac{7}{11}\right)^2 - \dfrac{7}{11} = \dfrac{49}{121} - \dfrac{7}{11}$

$= \dfrac{49 - 77}{121}$

$= -\dfrac{28}{121}$

(g) $\left(-1\dfrac{3}{5}\right) \div \left(-1\dfrac{1}{3}\right) = \dfrac{8}{5} \div \dfrac{4}{3}$

$$= \dfrac{8}{5} \times \dfrac{3}{4}$$

$$= \dfrac{6}{5}$$

$$= 1\dfrac{1}{5}$$

(h) $3 + 2\dfrac{1}{2} \div \left(-1\dfrac{1}{4}\right) = 3 + \dfrac{5}{2} \div \left(-\dfrac{5}{4}\right)$

$$= 3 - \dfrac{5}{2} \times \dfrac{4}{5}$$

$$= 3 - 2$$

$$= 1$$

Further Practice

5. Evaluate the following, giving your answers in the simplest form.

(a) $\left(-\dfrac{2}{5}\right)^3 \times \dfrac{9}{16} \div (-4)$

(b) $\left(-\dfrac{1}{5}\right)^2 \div \dfrac{1}{50} \times (-5)^3$

(c) $\dfrac{3 \div \dfrac{1}{2}}{-\dfrac{3}{5} + \dfrac{1}{2}}$

(d) $\dfrac{\dfrac{7}{8} \div \left(-2\dfrac{3}{4}\right)}{\dfrac{1}{11} - \dfrac{5}{22}}$

Solution

(a) $\left(-\dfrac{2}{5}\right)^3 \times \dfrac{9}{16} \div (-4) = -\dfrac{8}{27} \times \dfrac{9}{16} \times \left(-\dfrac{1}{4}\right)$

$$= \dfrac{1}{24}$$

(b) $\left(-\dfrac{1}{5}\right)^2 \div \dfrac{1}{50} \times (-5)^3 = \dfrac{1}{25} \times 50 \times (-125)$

$$= -250$$

(c) $\dfrac{3 \div \dfrac{1}{2}}{-\dfrac{3}{5} + \dfrac{1}{2}} = \dfrac{3 \times 2}{-\dfrac{6}{10} + \dfrac{5}{10}}$

$$= \dfrac{6}{-\dfrac{1}{10}}$$

$$= 6 \times (-10)$$

$$= -60$$

(d) $\dfrac{\dfrac{7}{8} \div \left(-2\dfrac{3}{4}\right)}{\dfrac{1}{11} - \dfrac{5}{22}} = \dfrac{\dfrac{7}{8} \times \left(-\dfrac{4}{11}\right)}{\dfrac{2}{22} - \dfrac{5}{22}}$

$$= \left(-\dfrac{7}{22}\right) \div \left(-\dfrac{3}{22}\right)$$

$$= \dfrac{7}{22} \times \dfrac{22}{3}$$

$$= \dfrac{7}{3}$$

$$= 2\dfrac{1}{3}$$

6. Evaluate the following, giving your answers in the simplest form.

(a) $\left(-\dfrac{1}{2} + \dfrac{1}{3} + \dfrac{1}{6}\right) \times \left(-\dfrac{2}{5}\right)$

(b) $1\dfrac{5}{7} \times \left(\dfrac{1}{4} - \dfrac{1}{9}\right) \div \left(-1\dfrac{1}{4}\right)$

(c) $\left(-\dfrac{2}{3}\right) \times \left(-\dfrac{9}{8}\right) + \left(-\dfrac{7}{4}\right) \times \dfrac{2}{21}$

(d) $\left[-\dfrac{1}{4} - \left(-\dfrac{1}{6}\right)\right] \div \left[\dfrac{1}{3} + \left(-\dfrac{1}{2}\right)\right]$

Solution

(a) $\left(-\dfrac{1}{2} + \dfrac{1}{3} + \dfrac{1}{6}\right) \times \left(-\dfrac{2}{5}\right) = \left(\dfrac{-3 + 2 + 1}{6}\right) \times \left(-\dfrac{2}{5}\right)$

$$= 0 \times \left(-\dfrac{2}{5}\right)$$

$$= 0$$

(b) $1\dfrac{5}{7} \times \left(\dfrac{1}{4} - \dfrac{1}{9}\right) \div \left(-1\dfrac{1}{4}\right) = \dfrac{12}{7} \times \dfrac{9-4}{36} \div \left(-\dfrac{5}{4}\right)$

$$= -\dfrac{12}{7} \times \dfrac{5}{36} \times \dfrac{4}{5}$$

$$= -\dfrac{4}{21}$$

(c) $\left(-\dfrac{2}{3}\right) \times \left(-\dfrac{9}{8}\right) + \left(-\dfrac{7}{4}\right) \times \dfrac{2}{21}$

$$= \dfrac{2}{3} \times \dfrac{9}{8} - \dfrac{7}{4} \times \dfrac{2}{21}$$

$$= \dfrac{3}{4} - \dfrac{1}{6}$$

$$= \dfrac{9-2}{12}$$

$$= \dfrac{7}{12}$$

(d) $\left[-\dfrac{1}{4} - \left(-\dfrac{1}{6}\right)\right] \div \left[\dfrac{1}{3} + \left(-\dfrac{1}{2}\right)\right]$

$= \left(-\dfrac{1}{4} + \dfrac{1}{6}\right) \div \left(\dfrac{2-3}{6}\right)$

$= \left(\dfrac{-3+2}{12}\right) \div \left(\dfrac{2-3}{6}\right)$

$= \left(\dfrac{-1}{12}\right) \div \left(-\dfrac{1}{6}\right)$

$= \dfrac{1}{12} \times 6$

$= \dfrac{1}{2}$

Math@Work

7. If a fraction is equal to $\dfrac{3}{5}$, and the sum of its numerator and denominator is 16, what is the fraction?

Solution

$\dfrac{3 \times 2}{5 \times 2} = \dfrac{6}{10}$

Sum of numerator and denominator of $\dfrac{6}{10} = 6 + 10$
$\phantom{Sum of numerator and denominator of \dfrac{6}{10}} = 16$

$\therefore$ the required fraction is $\dfrac{6}{10}$.

8. For each of the following, find two rational numbers between the given fractions.

(a) $\dfrac{4}{7}$ and $\dfrac{5}{7}$ **(b)** $-\dfrac{8}{11}$ and $-\dfrac{9}{11}$

Solution

(a) Any two rational numbers in the range of
$$\dfrac{4}{7} < a < \dfrac{5}{7},$$
where a is a rational number.
Suggested answers: $\dfrac{7}{28}, \dfrac{9}{14}$

(b) Any two rational numbers in the range of
$$-\dfrac{8}{11} < b < -\dfrac{9}{11},$$
where b is a rational number.
Suggested answers: $-\dfrac{3}{4}, -\dfrac{17}{22}$

9. Julia, Katie, and Lisa walk around a circular track. They take $\dfrac{1}{3}$ hr, $\dfrac{2}{5}$ hr, and $\dfrac{5}{12}$ hr to complete a loop respectively.

(a) Find the sum of the time taken by each girl to complete a loop.

(b) Express the time taken in minutes by each of them to complete a loop.

(c) Suppose they start to walk at the same time, location and direction. How many loops will each person have completed before all three of them next meet at the starting point?

Solution

(a) Total time taken $= \dfrac{1}{3} + \dfrac{2}{5} + \dfrac{5}{12}$

$ = \dfrac{20 + 24 + 25}{60}$

$ = \dfrac{69}{60}$

$ = 1\dfrac{3}{20}$ hr

(b) Time taken by Julia $= \dfrac{1}{3} \times 60$ min $= 20$ min

Time taken by Katie $= \dfrac{2}{5} \times 60$ min $= 24$ min

Time taken by Lisa $= \dfrac{5}{12} \times 60$ min $= 25$ min

(c) LCM of 20, 24, and 25 $= 600$
They all meet again at the starting point after 600 minutes.

Number of loops Julia completed $= \dfrac{600}{20}$
$ = 30$

Number of loops Katie completed $= \dfrac{600}{24}$
$ = 25$

Number of loops Lisa completed $= \dfrac{600}{25}$
$ = 24$

Brainworks

10. Consider the rational numbers $\dfrac{3}{4}$ and $\dfrac{9}{11}$.

(a) Which number is larger?

(b) Find two rational numbers between them.

(c) Compare your answers in **(b)** with those of your classmates.

(d) Are you able to suggest the number of rational numbers between $\dfrac{3}{4}$ and $\dfrac{9}{11}$? Give a reason for your answer.

Solution

(a) $\dfrac{3}{4} = \dfrac{3 \times 11}{4 \times 11} = \dfrac{33}{44}$

$\dfrac{9}{11} = \dfrac{9 \times 4}{11 \times 4} = \dfrac{36}{44}$

$\therefore \dfrac{9}{11}$ is larger.

(b) $\dfrac{17}{22}\left(= \dfrac{34}{44}\right)$ and $\dfrac{35}{44}$ are two numbers between $\dfrac{3}{4}$ and $\dfrac{9}{11}$.

In fact, $\dfrac{a+c}{b+d}$ is a rational number between $\dfrac{a}{b}$ and $\dfrac{c}{d}$.

i.e., $\dfrac{3+9}{4+11} = \dfrac{12}{15} = \dfrac{4}{5}$ is also a rational number between $\dfrac{3}{4}$ and $\dfrac{9}{11}$.

(c) The answers from different students may be different.

(d) There are an infinite number of rational numbers between $\dfrac{3}{4}$ and $\dfrac{9}{11}$.

This is because, as illustrated in **(b)**, there is a rational number between any two rational numbers.

Exercise 2.6
Basic Practice

1. Express the following rational numbers as decimals.

    (a) $\dfrac{3}{4}$ **(b)** $-1\dfrac{2}{5}$

    (c) $\dfrac{2}{9}$ **(d)** $-\dfrac{13}{11}$

    (e) $-\dfrac{7}{12}$ **(f)** $-\dfrac{17}{20}$

Solution

    (a) $\dfrac{3}{4} = 0.75$ **(b)** $-1\dfrac{2}{5} = -1.4$

    (c) $\dfrac{2}{9} = 0.\overline{2}$ **(d)** $-\dfrac{13}{11} = -1.\overline{18}$

    (e) $-\dfrac{7}{12} = -0.58\overline{3}$ **(f)** $-\dfrac{17}{20} = -0.85$

2. Evaluate the following using a calculator.

    (a) 29^2 **(b)** 15^3

    (c) 6^5 **(d)** $\sqrt{15{,}129}$

    (e) $\sqrt[3]{22 + 8}$ **(f)** $-11 \times [-5 + (-4)]$

    (g) $(-7) \times (-8) \div (-5)^2$

(h) $[1 + 2 \times (-3)] \div [1 - 2 \times (-3)]$

(i) $\dfrac{3}{4} + \dfrac{1}{6}$

(j) $-4 + \left(-\dfrac{2}{3}\right) \times 1\dfrac{1}{8}$

Solution

(a) $29^2 = 841$

(b) $15^3 = 3{,}375$

(c) $6^5 = 7{,}776$

(d) $\sqrt{15{,}129} = 123$

(e) $\sqrt[3]{22 + 8} = 3.107232506$

(f) $-11 \times [-5 + (-4)] = 99$

(g) $(-7) \times (-8) \div (-5)^2 = 56 \div 25$

$= 2\dfrac{6}{25}$

(h) $[1 + 2 \times (-3)] \div [1 - 2 \times (-3)] = (-5) \div 7$

$= -\dfrac{5}{7}$

$= -0.\overline{714285}$

(i) $\dfrac{3}{4} + \dfrac{1}{6} = \dfrac{11}{12} = 0.91\overline{6}$

(j) $-4 + \left(-\dfrac{2}{3}\right) \times 1\dfrac{1}{8} = -4 + \left(-\dfrac{2}{3} \times \dfrac{9}{8}\right)$

$= -4 - \dfrac{3}{4}$

$= -4\dfrac{3}{4}$

$= -4.75$

Further Practice

3. Evaluate the following, expressing the answers in decimals.

    (a) $\dfrac{2}{5} + \left(-\dfrac{1}{3}\right)$ **(b)** $-4\dfrac{3}{4} - \left(-5\dfrac{1}{2}\right)$

Solution

(a) $\dfrac{2}{5} + \left(-\dfrac{1}{3}\right) = \dfrac{2}{5} - \dfrac{1}{3}$

$= \dfrac{6 - 5}{15}$

$= \dfrac{1}{15}$

$= 0.0\overline{6}$

(b) $-4\frac{3}{4} - \left(-5\frac{1}{2}\right) = -4\frac{3}{4} + 5\frac{1}{2}$

$$= -\frac{19}{4} + \frac{11}{2}$$

$$= \frac{-19 + 22}{4}$$

$$= 0.75$$

4. Evaluate the following using a calculator.

(a) $\sqrt{37^2 - 35^2}$ **(b)** $\sqrt[3]{2,005} - \left(-3\frac{1}{7}\right)^2$

(c) $\left[-5\frac{3}{4} - \left(-6\frac{1}{2}\right)\right]^3$ **(d)** $\dfrac{\sqrt{3.21 + \frac{2}{5}}}{4.7 - 2.2}$

(e) $-1\frac{1}{9} \times \left(0.5 - \frac{2}{3}\right)^2 \div 2\frac{1}{4}$

(f) $\left[-3\frac{1}{8} + 1\frac{1}{6} + \left(-2\frac{1}{12}\right)\right] \times \left(-\frac{3}{2}\right)^2$

Solution

(a) $\sqrt{37^2 - 35^2} = 12$

(b) $\sqrt[3]{2,005} - \left(-3\frac{1}{7}\right)^2 = 2.73215008$

(c) $\left[-5\frac{3}{4} - \left(-6\frac{1}{2}\right)\right]^3 = 0.421875$ or $\frac{27}{64}$

(d) $\dfrac{\sqrt{3.21 + \frac{2}{5}}}{4.7 - 2.2} = 0.76$ or $\frac{19}{25}$

(e) $-1\frac{1}{9} \times \left(0.5 - \frac{2}{3}\right)^2 \div 2\frac{1}{4} = -0.0137$

(f) $\left[-3\frac{1}{8} + 1\frac{1}{6} + \left(-2\frac{1}{12}\right)\right] \times \left(-\frac{3}{2}\right)^2 = -9.09375$

$$= -9\frac{3}{32}$$

Brainworks

5. Jack thinks that $0.\overline{9} = 1$. Do you agree or disagree with him. Why?

Solution

$\frac{1}{3} = 0.\overline{3}$

$\frac{2}{3} = 0.\overline{6}$

$\therefore \frac{1}{3} + \frac{2}{3} = 0.\overline{9}$

Based on the above working, Jack is correct.

6. (a) Use a calculator to evaluate the following exponents of 3.
    (i) 3^{19} **(ii)** 3^{20}
    (iii) 3^{21} **(iv)** 3^{100}
    (v) 3^{200} **(vi)** 3^{300}

(b) What do you observe about the display format?
(c) Find the highest exponent of 3 that can be displayed on your calculator.

Solution

(a) (i) $3^{19} = 1,162,261,467$
    (ii) $3^{20} = 3,486,784,401$
    (iii) $3^{21} = 1.046\ 03532 \times 10^{10}$
    (iv) $3^{100} = 5.153775207 \times 10^{47}$
    (v) $3^{200} = 2.656139889 \times 10^{95}$
    (vi) 3^{300} cannot be evaluated using a calculator.
(b) When the integral answer is greater than 10 digits, the answer in display is a decimal together with an exponent of 10.
(c) Some calculators can calculate up to 3^{209}.

Exercise 2.7
Basic Practice

1. Round the following numbers to the nearest integer.
    (a) 13.4   **(b)** 321.8

Solution
(a) $13.4 = 13$ (correct to the nearest integer)
(b) $321.8 = 322$ (correct to the nearest integer)

2. Round the following numbers to the nearest 100.
    (a) 7,289   **(b)** 13,562

Solution
(a) $7,289 = 7,300$ (correct to the nearest 100)
(b) $13,562 = 13,600$ (correct to the nearest 100)

3. Round the following numbers to 1 decimal place.
    (a) 23.69   **(b)** 0.72

Solution
(a) $23.69 = 23.7$ (correct to 1 d.p.)
(b) $0.72 = 0.7$ (correct to 1 d.p.)

4. Round the following numbers to 2 decimal places.
    (a) 10.7543   **(b)** 2.9968

Solution
(a) $10.7543 = 10.75$ (correct to 2 d.p.)
(b) $2.9968 = 3.00$ (correct to 2 d.p.)

5. Round the following numbers to 3 decimal places.
    (a) 0.04025   **(b)** 17.92653

    Solution
    (a) 0.04025 = 0.040   (correct to 3 d.p.)
    (b) 17.92653 = 17.927   (correct to 3 d.p.)

6. Round the following numbers to 4 decimal places.
    (a) 3.004056   **(b)** 8.471345

    Solution
    (a) 3.004056 = 3.0041   (correct to 4 d.p.)
    (b) 8.471345 = 8.4713   (correct to 4 d.p.)

Further Practice

7. **(a)** Evaluate $(-13) \times [(-17) + (-12)]$.
    (b) Round the answer to the nearest 10.

    Solution
    (a) $(-13) \times [(-17) + (-12)] = (-13) \times (-29)$
    $= 377$
    (b) $377 = 380$ (correct to the nearest 10)

8. **(a)** Evaluate 3^{15} using a calculator.
    (b) Round the answer to the nearest million.

    Solution
    (a) $3^{15} = 14{,}348{,}907$
    (b) $14{,}000{,}000$ (correct to the nearest million)

9. Express each fraction correct to 4 decimal places.
    (a) $\dfrac{5}{9}$ **(b)** $\dfrac{10}{11}$

    Solution
    (a) $\dfrac{5}{9} = 0.55555 \ldots = 0.5556$ (correct to 4 d.p.)
    (b) $\dfrac{10}{11} = 0.909090 \ldots = 0.9091$ (correct to 4 d.p.)

10. Evaluate the following, giving the answers correct to 3 decimal places.
    (a) $\dfrac{2}{3} \times (-8 + 12)$ **(b)** $4\dfrac{1}{7} - 5\dfrac{1}{8}$
    (c) $\left(-4\dfrac{2}{9}\right) \div 1\dfrac{7}{12}$ **(d)** $\dfrac{\sqrt{17^2 - 8^2}}{13}$

    Solution
    (a) $\dfrac{2}{3} \times (-8 + 12) = \dfrac{2}{3} \times 4$
    $= \dfrac{8}{3}$
    $= 2.667$ (correct to 3 d.p.)

(b) $4\dfrac{1}{7} - 5\dfrac{1}{8} = \dfrac{29}{7} - \dfrac{41}{8}$
$= \dfrac{232 - 287}{56}$
$= -\dfrac{55}{56}$
$= -0.982$ (correct to 3 d.p.)

(c) $\left(-4\dfrac{2}{9}\right) \div 1\dfrac{7}{12} = -\dfrac{38}{9} \times \dfrac{12}{19}$
$= -\dfrac{8}{3}$
$= -2.667$ (correct to 3 d.p.)

(d) $\dfrac{\sqrt{17^2 - 8^2}}{13} = \dfrac{\sqrt{289 - 64}}{13}$
$= \dfrac{\sqrt{225}}{13}$
$= \dfrac{15}{13}$
$= 1.154$ (correct to 3 d.p.)

Math@Work

11. The number of people attending a community event is 12,756. Round this number to the nearest
    (a) hundred,   **(b)** thousand.

    Solution
    (a) $12{,}756 = 12{,}800$ (correct to the nearest 100)
    The required number of people is 12,800, correct to the nearest 100.
    (b) $12{,}756 = 13{,}000$ (correct to the nearest 1,000)
    The required number of people is 13,000, correct to the nearest 1,000.

12. The area of a room is 219.3 ft^2. Round off this area to the nearest
    (a) ft^2,   **(b)** 10 ft^2.

    Solution
    (a) $219.3 = 219$ (correct to the nearest whole number)
    The required area is 219 ft^2, correct to the nearest ft^2.
    (b) $219.3 = 220$ (correct to the nearest 10)
    The required area is 220 ft^2, correct to the nearest 10 ft^2.

13. The height of a basketball player is 2.1036 m when measured with a precise instrument.
    Express his height correct to
    (a) 2 decimal places,
    (b) 3 decimal places.

Solution

(a) His height = 2.1036 m

= 2.10 m   (correct to 2 d.p.)

(b) His height = 2.1036 m

= 2.104 m   (correct to 3 d.p.)

14. The length of a piece of paper is 29.7302 cm. Express the length correct to the nearest
(a) cm,   (b) 0.1 cm,
(c) 0.001 cm.

Solution

(a) The length = 29.7302 cm

= 30 cm   (correct to the nearest cm)

(b) The length = 29.7302 cm

= 29.7 cm

(correct to the nearest 0.1 cm)

(c) The length = 29.7302 cm

= 29.730 cm

(correct to the nearest 0.001 cm)

15. Susan wants to estimate the thickness of a quarter-dollar coin using a ruler with millimeter scale. The height of a stack of 29 quarter-dollar coins is 51 mm.
(a) Find the thickness of a quarter-dollar coin based on Susan's method of measurement, correct to 0.1 mm.
(b) Is Susan's method better than measuring the height of one coin?

Solution

(a) Thickness of a coin

= 51 ÷ 29

= 1.76

= 1.8 mm (correct to the nearest 0.1 mm)

(b) Yes, the rounding error due to the precision of the measuring instrument is smaller.

Brainworks

16. A number is rounded off to 38,000.
(a) What are the possible degrees of accuracy of the approximation?
(b) Suggest a value of the actual number corresponding to your answer in (a).

Solution

(a) 38,000 can be correct to the nearest thousand, hundred, ten or whole number.
(b) Some possible values are:
(i) 38,125

= 38,000   (correct to the nearest 1,000)

(ii) 38,047

= 38,000   (correct to the nearest 100)

(iii) 38,003

= 38,000   (correct to the nearest 10)

(iv) 38,000.49

= 38,000   (correct to the nearest whole number)

17. Michael's time for the 100-meter sprint is recorded as 9.96 seconds. State two possible values of his actual time for the 100-meter sprint.

Solution

Two possible values of his actual time for the 100-meter sprint are 9.957 seconds and 9.962 seconds.

18. Find some examples of the use of decimals in the media. Are the numbers exact or estimated? If they are estimated, what are their degrees of accuracy?

Solution

Some examples of the use of decimals are:

stock price index (correct to 2 d.p.),

maximum daily temperature

(correct to the nearest 0.1°C),

unemployment rate (correct to the nearest 0.1%).

Review Exercise 2

1. Complete the following addition table.

+	8	1	☐
2	☐	☐	☐
☐	3	–4	–7
–3	☐	☐	–5

Solution

Let $a, b, c, d, e, f,$ and $g,$ and represent the missing values in the table.

+	8	1	a
2	b	c	d
e	3	–4	–7
–3	f	g	–5

$$-3 + a = -5$$
$$a = -2$$

$$e + a = -7$$
$$e + (-2) = -7$$
$$e = -5$$

$$b = 2 + 8$$
$$= 10$$

$$c = 2 + 1$$
$$= 3$$

$$d = 2 + a$$
$$= 2 + (-2)$$
$$= 0$$

$$f = -3 + 8$$
$$= 5$$

$$g = -3 + 1$$
$$= -2$$

The values in the table are as follows:

+	8	1	-2
2	10	3	0
-5	3	-4	-7
-3	5	-2	-5

2. Complete the following multiplication table.

Solution

Let $a, b, c, d, e, f, g, h,$ and i represent the missing values in the table.

×	-3	a	b
c	15	d	e
-2	f	8	g
7	h	i	-42

$$(-2) \times a = 8$$
$$a = -4$$

$$7 \times b = -42$$
$$b = -6$$

$$c \times (-3) = 15$$
$$c = -5$$

$$d = c \times a$$
$$= (-5) \times (-4)$$
$$= 20$$

$$e = c \times b$$
$$= (-5) \times (-6)$$
$$= 30$$

$$f = (-2) \times (-3)$$
$$= 6$$

$$g = (-2) \times b$$
$$= (-2) \times (-6)$$
$$= 12$$

$$h = 7 \times (-3)$$
$$= -21$$

$$i = 7 \times a$$
$$= 7 \times (-4)$$
$$= -28$$

The values in the table are as follows:

×	-3	-4	-6
-5	15	20	30
-2	6	8	12
7	-21	-28	-42

3. (a) The night temperature in the Gobi Desert was −22°F after it has dropped 14°F. What was the initial temperature before the decrease?

(b) On another day, the temperature in the desert at 12 midnight was 14.6°F. The temperature decreased constantly during that day at 2°F every hour. What was the temperature in the desert at 6 A.M. on that day?

Solution

(a) Initial temperature before the decrease
$$= -22 + 14$$
$$= -8°F$$

(b) Time difference from 12 midnight to 6 A.M.
$$= 6 \text{ hours}$$
∴ temperature in the desert at 6 A.M. on that day
$$= 14.6 - (2)(6)$$
$$= 2.6°F$$

4.

Location	Altitude
Death Valley, The United States	86 m below sea level
Turfan Depression, China	154 m below sea level
Mount Everest, Nepal	8,848 m above sea level

Using the information in the table above, find the difference in altitude between

(a) Death Valley and Turfan Depression,

(b) Turfan Depression and Mount Everest.

Solution

(a) Difference in altitude between Death Valley and Turfan Depression = 154 − 86
$$= 68 \text{ m}$$

(b) Difference in altitude between Turfan Depression and Mount Everest = 8,848 + 154
$$= 9,002 \text{ m}$$

5. (a) Find the value of $(-2)^2$ and $\left(\dfrac{7}{6}\right)^2$.

(b) Represent the numbers -2, $\dfrac{7}{6}$, $(-2)^2$, and $\left(\dfrac{7}{6}\right)^2$ on a number line.

(c) Fill in ▢ with "<", ">", or "=" to make a true statement.

(i) -2 ▢ $\dfrac{7}{6}$ **(ii)** $(-2)^2$ ▢ $\left(\dfrac{7}{6}\right)^2$

Solution

(a) $(-2)^2 = 4$

$\left(\dfrac{7}{6}\right)^2 = \dfrac{49}{36}$

(b)

(c) (i) $-2 < \dfrac{7}{6}$

(ii) $(-2)^2 > \left(\dfrac{7}{6}\right)^2$

---

6. A quality control supervisor measures the actual volumes of six packets of fruit juice. Each packet of fruit juice is supposed to contain 375 mL of juice. The table shows the inspection results.

Packet	1	2	3	4	5	6
Amount below or above the required volume (mL)	−5	+12	−6	−9	+7	−2

(a) Find the actual volumes of juice in packet 1 and packet 2.

(b) Find the total volume of juice in the six packets.

Solution

(a) Volume of juice in Packet 1 = (375 − 5)
$$= 370 \text{ mL}$$
Volume of juice in Packet 2 = (375 + 12)
$$= 387 \text{ mL}$$

(b) $(-5) + (+12) + (-6) + (-9) + (+7) + (-2)$
$$= -5 + 12 - 6 - 9 + 7 - 2$$
$$= -3$$
Total volume of juice = $375 \times 6 + (-3)$
$$= 2,247 \text{ mL}$$

7. There are four participants in a golf tournament. Their scores (which are the numbers of strokes below or above a standard value) in three rounds are shown in the following table.

	Alex	Ben	Charles	Dave
Round 1	−5	+3	+10	−3
Round 2	−1	−2	+2	−4
Round 3	−2	−1	−3	+5

(a) Who had the lowest score in Round 1?

(b) Find the total score of each person at the end of three rounds.

(c) The winner in the tournament was the person with the lowest total score. Who was the winner?

Solution

(a) $-5 < -3 < 3 < 10$
$\therefore$ Alex had the lowest score in Round 1.

(b) Alex's total score = $(-5) + (-1) + (-2)$
$$= -8$$
Ben's total score = $(+3) + (-2) + (-1)$
$$= 0$$
Charles' total score = $(+10) + (+2) + (-3)$
$$= 9$$
Dave's total score = $(-3) + (-4) + (+5)$
$$= -2$$

(c) The winner was Alex.

8. Evaluate the following.

(a) $(-16) \times (-3) - (-8) \times 5$

(b) $[-2 + (-7)]^3$

(c) $3\dfrac{1}{2} \times \left(-5\dfrac{1}{7}\right) \div \left(1\dfrac{4}{5}\right)$

(d) $\dfrac{2}{3} \times \left(\dfrac{1}{4} - \dfrac{1}{8}\right)^2$

Solution

(a) $(-16) \times (-3) - (-8) \times 5 = 48 + 40$
$$= 88$$

(b) $[-2 + (-7)]^3 = (-9)^3$
$$= -729$$

(c) $3\dfrac{1}{2} \times \left(-5\dfrac{1}{7}\right) \div \left(1\dfrac{4}{5}\right) = -\dfrac{7}{2} \times \dfrac{36}{7} \div \dfrac{9}{5}$
$$= -18 \times \dfrac{5}{9}$$
$$= -10$$

(d) $\dfrac{2}{3} \times \left(\dfrac{1}{4} - \dfrac{1}{8} \right)^2 = \dfrac{2}{3} \times \left(\dfrac{1}{8} \right)^2$

$$= \dfrac{2}{3} \times \dfrac{1}{64}$$

$$= \dfrac{1}{96}$$

9. Evaluate the following.

(a) $\left| 4 \times \left(-2\dfrac{3}{8} \right) \right|$

(b) $-\left| (-2)^2 \right|$

(c) $\dfrac{-3}{|-15|} \times \left| (-5)^3 \right|$

Solution

(a) $\left| 4 \times \left(-2\dfrac{3}{8} \right) \right| = \left| 4 \times \left(-\dfrac{19}{8} \right) \right|$

$$= \left| -\dfrac{19}{2} \right|$$

$$= \dfrac{19}{2}$$

$$= 9\dfrac{1}{2}$$

(b) $-\left| (-2)^2 \right| = -\left| 4 \right|$

$$= -4$$

(c) $\dfrac{-3}{|-15|} \times \left| (-5)^3 \right| = \dfrac{-3}{15} \times \left| -125 \right|$

$$= -\dfrac{1}{5} \times 125$$

$$= -25$$

10. New York City, the most populous city in the United States, has a population of 8,263,710 and a land area of 304.71 square miles. What is the average number of people per square mile of the city? Give your answer correct to
(a) the nearest integer,
(b) the nearest hundred.

Solution
(a) Average number of people per square mile
$= 8,263,710 \div 304.71$
$= 27,119.9173$
$= 27,120$ (correct to nearest integer)

(b) $27,119.9173 = 27,100$ (correct to nearest hundred)

11. In year 2011, the population of Singapore was 5,183,700 and the total number of mobile phone subscribers was 7,443,800. Find the average number of mobile phone subscribed per person in Singapore, giving your answer correct to
(a) 2 decimal places,
(b) 1 decimal place.

Solution
(a) Average number of mobile phones subscribed per person $= 7,443,800 \div 5,183,700$
$= 1.436$
$= 1.44$ (correct to 2 d.p.)

(b) $1.436 = 1.4$ (correct to 1 d.p)

12. The world is divided into 24 one-hour time zones. The table below shows the time difference between the local times of London and some cities. A difference of "+10" means the time is 10 hours ahead of the London time while "−10" means 10 hours behind the London time.

City	Time difference (hours) from London
Auckland	+13
Los Angeles	−8
New York	−5
Singapore	+8

(a) Which two cities in the table have the greatest time difference? What is the difference?

(b) What is the time difference between each of the following pairs of cities?
(i) Los Angeles and Singapore,
(ii) New York and Los Angeles.

(c) For each pair of cities in part **(b)**, state if the time of the first city is ahead of or behind that of the second city.

(d) When Auckland ushered in New Year at 12:00 A.M. on January 1, 2012, what is the date and local time in New York?

Solution
(a) Auckland and Los Angeles have the greatest time difference.
The difference is $\left| 13 - (-8) \right| = 21$ hours.

(b) **(i)** Time difference between Los Angeles and Singapore is $\left| -8 - (8) \right| = 16$ hours.
(ii) Time difference between New York and Los Angeles is $\left| -8 - (-5) \right| = 3$ hours.

(c) **(i)** Since −8 < 8,

∴ the time of Los Angeles is behind the time of Singapore.

(ii) Since −5 > −8,

∴ the time of New York is ahead of the time of Los Angeles.

(d) Time difference between Auckland and New York
$$= \left| 13 - (-5) \right|$$
= 18 hours
Since 13 > −5, the time of Auckland is ahead of the time of New York.

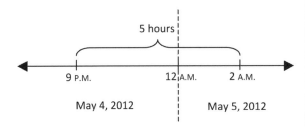

By counting backward 18 hours from 12 A.M. on January 1, 2012, we see that the local time and date in New York is 6 A.M., December 31, 2011.

Chapter 3   Introduction To Algebra

Extend Your Learning Curve

Hand-Shaking Problem

There are n persons attending a party. Each person shakes hands with every other person just once. Let T be the total number of handshakes.

(a)   Complete the following table.

n	2	3	4	5	6
T					

(b)   Establish a formula connecting n and T.

Solution

(a)

n	2	3	4	5	6
T	1	3	6	10	15

(b)   Suppose the n persons in the party are arranged in order.

The 1st person will shake hands with $n - 1$ persons.
The 2nd person will shake hands with the remaining $n - 2$ persons, without repeating.
The 3rd person will shake hands with the remaining $n - 3$ persons, without repeating.

The $(n - 1)$th person will just shake hands with the nth person, without repeating.
$\therefore$ the total number of handshakes is given by
$$T = (n - 1) + (n - 2) + (n - 3) + \ldots + 3 + 2 + 1 \ldots\ldots\ldots\ldots\ldots\ldots(1)$$

By reversing the above expression, we have

$$T = 1 + 2 + 3 + \ldots + (n - 3) + (n - 2) + (n - 1)\ldots\ldots\ldots\ldots\ldots(2)$$

$(1) + (2)$, $2T = n + n + n + \ldots$ for $(n - 1)$ terms
$$2T = n(n - 1)$$
$$\therefore\ T = \frac{1}{2}n(n - 1)$$

Try It!

Section 3.1

1. Mary is 9 years old. Find her age after
   (a) 3 years, (b) 10 years,
   (c) t years.

   Solution

   Mary's present age = 9 years
   (a) Age after 3 years = (9 + 3)
   = 12 years
   (b) Age after 10 years = (9 + 10)
   = 19 years
   (c) Age after t years = (9 + t) years

2. A worker's salary is $200 less than one-third of a manager's salary. Find the worker's salary when the manager's salary is
   (a) $7,200, (b) $9,000,
   (c) m.

   Solution

   Worker's salary = $\frac{1}{3}$ × Manager's salary – $200
   (a) When the manager's salary is $7200,

   worker's salary = $\left(\frac{1}{3} \times 7{,}200 - 200 \right)$
   = $2,200
   (b) When the manager's salary is $9,000,

   worker's salary = $\left(\frac{1}{3} \times 9{,}000 - 200 \right)$
   = $2,800
   (c) When the manager's salary is m,

   worker's salary = $\left(\frac{1}{3} \times m - 200 \right)$
   = $\left(\frac{m}{3} - 200 \right)$

3. The price of a cup is $5 and the price of a plate is $12. Find the total price of
   (a) 3 cups and 2 plates,
   (b) n cups and m plates.

   Solution

   (a) Total price of 3 cups and 2 plates
   = $(5 × 3 + 12 × 2)
   = $39
   (b) Total price of n cups and m plates
   = $(5 × n + 12 × m)
   = $(5$n$ + 12m)

4. Simplify the following.
   (a) $d \times e \times 1 \times e$
   (b) $4m \times 5n \times m \times m$
   (c) $7t \div y \times 2$

   Solution

   (a) $d \times e \times 1 \times e = 1 \times d \times e \times e$
   $= de^2$

   (b) $4m \times 5n \times m \times m = 4 \times m \times 5 \times n \times m \times m$
   $= 20m^3 n$

   (c) $7t \div y \times 2 = \dfrac{14t}{y}$

5. Distinguish between $3z^2$ and $(3z)^2$.

   Solution

   $3z^2 = 3 \times z \times z$
   $(3z)^2 = 3z \times 3z$
   $= 3 \times 3 \times z \times z$
   $\therefore \ (3z)^2$ is 3 times $3z^2$.

6. Express the following statements algebraically.
   (a) Multiply the sum of c and d by u.
   (b) Subtract the quotient of a divided by b from the cube of v.

   Solution

   (a) Sum of c and $d = c + d$
   Multiply $c + d$ by $u = (c + d)u$
   The required expression is $(c + d)u$.

   (b) Quotient of a divided by $b = \dfrac{a}{b}$
   Cube of $v = v^3$
   Subtract $\dfrac{a}{b}$ from $v^3 = v^3 - \dfrac{a}{b}$
   The required expression is $v^3 - \dfrac{a}{b}$.

Section 3.2

7. When $x = 5$ and $y = 2$, find the value of
   (a) $2x - 7y$,
   (b) $xy^2 - 3xy + 10$.

   Solution

   (a) When $x = 5$ and $y = 2$,
   $2x - 7y = 2(5) - 7(2)$
   $= -4$

   (b) When $x = 5$ and $y = 2$,
   $xy^2 - 3xy + 10 = (5)(2)^2 - 3(5)(2) + 10$
   $= 0$

8. When $x = \dfrac{3}{4}$, $y = 4$, and $z = -1$, find the values of the following expressions.

   (a) $z(8x + yz)$

   (b) $\dfrac{10xy - z + 2}{xy^2 - 3}$

Solution

(a) When $x = \dfrac{3}{4}$, $y = 4$, and $z = -1$,

$$z(8x + yz) = (-1)\left[8\left(\dfrac{3}{4}\right) + 4 \times (-1)\right]$$
$$= (-1) \times 2$$
$$= -2$$

(b) When $x = \dfrac{3}{4}$, $y = 4$, and $z = -1$,

$$\dfrac{10xy - z + 2}{xy^2 - 3} = \dfrac{10\left(\dfrac{3}{4}\right)(4) - (-1) + 2}{\dfrac{3}{4}(4)^2 - 3}$$
$$= \dfrac{33}{9}$$
$$= 3\dfrac{2}{3}$$

9. The perimeter, P meters, of a rectangular field with dimension l meters by w meters is given by the formula $P = 2(l + w)$. Find the perimeter of a rectangular field whose dimension is 60 meters by 45 meters.

Solution

$$P = 2(l + w)$$
When $l = 60$ and $w = 45$,
$$P = 2(60 + 45)$$
$$= 210$$

∴ The perimeter of the rectangular field is 210 m.

10. Given the formula $D = \dfrac{1}{2}n(n - 3)$, find the value of D when

   (a) $n = 5$,

   (b) $n = 12$.

Solution

(a) When $n = 5$,
$$D = \dfrac{1}{2}n(n - 3)$$
$$= \dfrac{1}{2} \times 5 \times (5 - 3)$$
$$= 5$$

(b) When $n = 12$,
$$D = \dfrac{1}{2} \times 12 \times (12 - 3)$$
$$= 54$$

11. If $s = \dfrac{v^2 - u^2}{2a}$, find the value of s when $u = 3$, $v = 12$ and $a = 6$.

Solution

When $u = 3$, $v = 12$ and $a = 6$,
$$s = \dfrac{v^2 - u^2}{2a}$$
$$= \dfrac{12^2 - 3^2}{2 \times 6}$$
$$= \dfrac{135}{12}$$
$$= 11\dfrac{1}{4}$$

12. Peter is 3 inches taller than Sue.

   (a) Suppose the height of Sue is s feet. What is the height of Peter in terms of s feet?

   (b) Given that Peter's height is p feet, write a formula connecting s and p.

Solution

(a) Peter's height = s ft + 3 in.
$$= s \text{ ft} + \dfrac{1}{4}\text{ft}$$
$$= \left(s + \dfrac{1}{4}\right) \text{ ft}$$

(b) $p = s + \dfrac{1}{4}$

13. In a summer camp, the number of girls is 7 less than two-thirds of the number of boys.

   (a) Suppose the number of boys in the camp is b. Express the number of girls in terms of b.

   (b) If g is the number of girls in the camp, write a formula connecting b and g.

Solution

(a) number of girls $= \dfrac{2}{3} \times b - 7$
$$= \dfrac{2}{3}b - 7$$

(b) $g = \dfrac{2}{3}b - 7$

14. Victor's age is 7 years more than one-sixth of his father's age this year and Victor's mother is 4 years less than 3 times as old as Victor. Let v, f, and m years be the present ages of Victor, his father, and his mother respectively.

   (a) Express v and m each in terms of f.

   (b) If Victor's father is 48 years old now, how old are Victor and his mother?

Solution

(a)
$$v = \frac{1}{6} \times f + 7$$
$$= \frac{1}{6}f + 7$$
$$m = 3 \times \left(\frac{1}{6}f + 7\right) - 4$$
$$= 3\left(\frac{1}{6}f + 7\right) - 4$$

(b) when $f = 48$,
$$v = \frac{1}{6}f + 7 = \frac{1}{6}(48) + 7$$
$$= 15$$
$$m = 3\left(\frac{1}{6}f + 7\right) - 4$$
$$= 3\left(\frac{1}{6}(48) + 7\right) - 4$$
$$= 41$$

$\therefore$ Victor is 15 years old.

Victor's mother is 41 years old.

Exercise 3.1

Basic Practice

1. A man's monthly income is $3,600. Find his savings when his expenditure is
   (a) $2,500,   (b) $3,400,
   (c) x.

   Solution
   (a) His savings = $(3,600 − 2,500) = $1,100
   (b) His savings = $(3,600 − 3,400) = $200
   (c) His savings = $(3,600 − x)

2. Mr. White is 5 centimeters taller than his wife. Find Mr. White's height if the height of his wife is
   (a) 160 cm,   (b) 168 cm,
   (c) h cm.

   Solution
   (a) Mr. White's height = (160 + 5)
       = 165 cm
   (b) Mr. White's height = (168 + 5)
       = 173 cm
   (c) Mr. White's height = $(h + 5)$ cm

3. Find the number of days in
   (a) 5 weeks,   (b) 12 weeks,
   (c) n weeks.

   Solution
   (a) Number of days in 5 weeks = 7×5
       = 35
   (b) Number of days in 12 weeks = 7×12
       = 84
   (c) Number of days in n weeks = $7 \times n$
       = $7n$

4. The test score of John is three quarters that of Mary. Find John's score if Mary's score is
   (a) 76,   (b) 92,   (c) s.

   Solution
   (a) John's score = $\dfrac{3}{4} \times 76$
       = 57
   (b) John's score = $\dfrac{3}{4} \times 92$
       = 69
   (c) John's score = $\dfrac{3}{4} \times s$
       = $\dfrac{3s}{4}$

5. The number of U.S. stamps in a stamp album is 23 more than twice the number of British stamps. Find the number of U.S. stamps in the album when there are
   (a) 10 British stamps,
   (b) p British stamps.

   Solution
   (a) Number of U.S. stamps = $2 \times 10 + 23$
       = 43
   (b) Number of U.S. stamps = $2 \times p + 23$
       = $2p + 23$

6. The time taken by an airplane to travel from one city to another is 20 minutes more than one-eighth of the time taken by a train. Find the time taken by the airplane if the time taken by the train is
   (a) 12 hours,   (b) t hours.

   Solution
   (a) Time taken by the airplane
       $$= \left(\frac{1}{8} \times 12 + \frac{20}{60} \right)$$
       $$= \left(\frac{3}{2} + \frac{1}{3} \right)$$
       $$= 1\frac{5}{6} \text{ hours}$$
   (b) Time taken by the airplane
       $$= \left(\frac{1}{8} \times t + \frac{20}{60} \right)$$
       $$= \left(\frac{1}{t} + \frac{1}{3} \right) \text{ hours}$$

7. Simplify the following.
   (a) $a \times 5$ (b) $b \times b \times 4$
   (c) $2c \div d$ (d) $e \div f \times g$
   (e) $6h \times 3k$ (f) $9m \div 27$
   (g) $3p \times p \times 5p$ (h) $4q \times 5r \times q$
   (i) $s \div 6 + 1 \times t$ (j) $u + 6v \div 9w$

   Solution
   (a) $a \times 5 = 5a$ (b) $b \times b \times 4 = 4b^2$
   (c) $2c \div d = \dfrac{2c}{d}$ (d) $e \div f \times g = \dfrac{eg}{f}$
   (e) $6h \times 3k = 18hk$ (f) $9m \div 27 = \dfrac{9m}{27} = \dfrac{m}{3}$
   (g) $3p \times p \times 5p = 15p^3$ (h) $4q \times 5r \times q = 20q^2r$
   (i) $s \div 6 + 1 \times t = \dfrac{s}{6} + t$
   (j) $u + 6v \div 9w = u + \dfrac{6v}{9w} = u + \dfrac{2v}{3w}$

8. Express the following word statements algebraically.
   (a) Add 5 to the product of h and k.
   (b) Subtract $3m$ from the quotient of n divided by p.
   (c) Divide the sum of $2t$ and $3u$ by v.
   (d) Multiply the product of y and z by $7y$.

Solution
   (a) Expression $= hk + 5$

   (b) Expression $= \dfrac{n}{p} - 3m$

   (c) Expression $= (2t + 3u) \div v = \dfrac{2t + 3u}{v}$

   (d) Expression $= (yz) \times 7y = 7y^2z$

Further Practice

9. The price of a pineapple is $2 and the price of a watermelon is $5. Find the total price of
   (a) 5 pineapples and 1 watermelon,
   (b) x pineapples and y watermelons.

Solution
   (a) Total price $= \$(2 \times 5 + 5 \times 1)$
       $= \$15$
   (b) Total price $= \$(2 \times x + 5 \times y)$
       $= \$(2x + 5y)$

10. The weight of a mathematics book is 759 grams and the weight of a cookbook is 400 grams. Find the total mass of
   (a) 4 copies of the mathematics books and 3 copies of the cookbook,
   (b) p copies of the mathematics books and q copies of the cookbook.

Solution
   (a) Total mass $= (759 \times 4 + 400 \times 3)$
       $= 4236$ g
   (b) Total mass $= (759 \times p + 400 \times q)$
       $= (759p + 400q)$ g

11. A woman has $500. Find the amount left if she spends
   (a) $120 on a skirt and $30 on her dinner,
   (b) k on a skirt and d on her dinner.

Solution
   (a) Amount left $= \$(500 - 120 - 30)$
       $= \$350$
   (b) Amount left $= \$(500 - k - d)$

12. Mr. Jones goes to a movie with his family. He has 2 free tickets. Find the amount he has to pay for the tickets if
   (a) there are 5 family members and each ticket costs $11,
   (b) there are n family members and each ticket costs p.

Solution
   (a) Amount Mr. Jones has to pay $= \$11 \times (5 - 2)$
       $= \$33$
   (b) Amount Mr. Jones has to pay $= \$p \times (n - 2)$
       $= \$(n - 2)p$

13. There are 4 rotten grapefruits in a crate. The good grapefruits in the crate are shared among some households. Find the number of grapefruits that each household gets if there are
   (a) 100 grapefruits in the crate and 12 households,
   (b) n grapefruits in the crate and m households.

Solution
   (a) Number of eggs per household $= (100 - 4) \div 12$
       $= 8$
   (b) Number of eggs per household $= (n - 4) \div m$
       $= \dfrac{n - 4}{m}$

Math@Work

14. A car salesman has a basic salary of $2,000 a month. For every car sold, he gets a commission of $800. Let n be the number of cars that he sells in a month.
   (a) Find his monthly salary when $n = 18$.
   (b) Express his monthly salary in terms of n.

Solution
   (a) When $n = 18$,
       his monthly salary $= \$(2,000 + 800 \times 18)$
       $= \$16,400$
   (b) His monthly salary $= \$(2,000 + 800 \times n)$
       $= \$(2,000 + 800n)$

15. A grocer has p crates of oranges. Each crate contains q oranges and r of them are rotten. Express, in terms of p, q, and r,
   (a) the total number of oranges in all the crates,
   (b) the total number of good oranges.

Solution
   (a) Total number of oranges $= q \times p = pq$
   (b) Total number of good oranges $= (q - r) \times p$
       $= p(q - r)$

16. The length of a metal bar is L feet. It is melted and recast into a thin bar whose length is k feet longer than n times its original length. The thin bar is then cut into m equal sticks. Express, in terms of k, L, m, and n, the length of
(a) the thin bar, (b) each stick.

Solution
(a) Length of the thin bar $= (L \times n + k)$
$= (nL + k)$ ft
(b) Length of each stick $= (nL + k) \div m$
$= \dfrac{nL + k}{m}$ ft

17. Jane is x years old now. Peter, her brother, is 5 years older than she. Their mother is 3 times as old as Jane. Their father is twice as old as Peter. Write an expression, in terms of x, for each of the following
(a) Peter's current age,
(b) their father's age,
(c) their mother's age in 4 years' time,
(d) the sum of Jane's and Peter's age 3 years ago.

Solution
(a) Peter's current age $= (x + 5)$ years
(b) Their father's age $= 2(x + 5)$ years
(c) Their mother's age in 4 years's time
$= (3x + 4)$ years
(d) Sum of their age 3 years ago $= (x - 3) + (x + 5 - 3)$
$= (2x - 1)$ years

18. A test paper consists of Section A and Section B with a number of questions in each section. Find the total score of the paper in each case.

(a)

Section A	8 questions with each question carrying 5 points	
Section B	4 questions with each question carrying 15 points	
		Total score

(b)

Section A	n questions with each question carrying a points	
Section B	m questions with each question carrying b points	
		Total score

(c)

Section A	m questions with each question carrying a points. Students are required to answer all the questions in this section	
Section B	m questions with each question carrying b points. Students are required to answer $(m - 1)$ questions in this section	
		Total score

Solution
(a) Total score $= (5 \times 8 + 15 \times 4)$
$= 100$ points
(b) Total score $= (a \times n + b \times m)$
$= (an + bm)$ points
(c) Total score $= a \times m + b \times (m - 1)]$
$= [am + b(m - 1)]$ points

Brainworks

19. Describe a real-life situation that could be represented by the expression $2n + 4m$.

Solution
The number of legs of n chickens and m rabbits is $2n + 4m$.
The number of wheels of n bicycles and m cars is $2n + 4m$.

20. (a) How many breaths do you take in a minute?
(b) Suppose you take n breaths in a minute, how many breaths do you take in
(i) an hour, (ii) a day?
(c) Work out the approximate number of breaths you take per day, correct to the nearest thousand.

Solution
(a) The number of breaths in a minute may be 15, 16, 17, 18, 19, or 20.

(b) (i) Number of breaths in an hour $= n \times 60$
$= 60n$
(ii) Number of breaths in a day $= 60n \times 24$
$= 1{,}440n$

(c) The approximate number of breaths taken per day varies.
For example, when $n = 16$,
$1{,}440n = 1{,}440 \times 16$
$= 23{,}040$
$= 23{,}000$ (correct to the nearest 1,000)

Exercise 3.2
Basic Practice

1. Find the value of $3x - 1$ when
   (a) $x = 1$,
   (b) $x = \dfrac{4}{5}$.

   Solution
   (a) When $x = 1$,
   $$3x - 1 = 3(1) - 1$$
   $$= 2$$

   (b) When $x = \dfrac{4}{5}$,
   $$3x - 1 = 3\left(\dfrac{4}{5}\right) - 1$$
   $$= \dfrac{7}{5}$$

2. Find the value of $25 - 4y$ when
   (a) $y = 0$,
   (b) $y = \dfrac{5}{2}$.

   Solution
   (a) When $y = 0$,
   $$25 - 4y = 25 - 4(0)$$
   $$= 25 - 0$$
   $$= 25$$

   (b) When $y = \dfrac{5}{2}$,
   $$25 - 4y = 25 - 4\left(\dfrac{5}{2}\right)$$
   $$= 25 - 10$$
   $$= 15$$

3. Find the value of $3a + 4b$ when
   (a) $a = 7$ and $b = -5$,
   (b) $a = \dfrac{-1}{3}$ and $b = \dfrac{-1}{2}$.

   Solution
   (a) When $a = 7$ and $b = -5$,
   $$3a + 4b = 3(7) + 4(-5)$$
   $$= 21 - 20$$
   $$= 1$$

   (b) When $a = \dfrac{-1}{3}$ and $b = \dfrac{-1}{2}$,
   $$3a + 4b = 3\left(\dfrac{-1}{3}\right) + 4\left(\dfrac{-1}{2}\right)$$
   $$= -1 - 2$$
   $$= -3$$

4. Find the value of $(2m + n)(m - n + 1)$ when
   (a) $m = 5$ and $n = 3$,
   (b) $m = 11$ and $n = -6$.

Solution
(a) When $m = 5$ and $n = 3$,
$$(2m + n)(m - n + 1) = [2(5) + 3](5 - 3 + 1)$$
$$= 13 \times 3$$
$$= 39$$

(b) When $m = 11$ and $n = -6$,
$$(2m + n)(m - n + 1)$$
$$= [2(11) + -(6)][(11 - (-6) + 1)]$$
$$= 16 \times 18$$
$$= 288$$

5. Find the value of x in the following formulas.
   (a) $x = 2a + 1$; given $a = 3$
   (b) $x = 32 - 5b$; given $b = 4$
   (c) $x = c^2 - 2c$; given $c = 5$
   (d) $x = 4d(d + 5)$; given $d = -8$
   (e) $x = \dfrac{1}{e^3 - 1}$; given $e = 2$
   (f) $x = \dfrac{3f + 4}{5f - 2}$; given $f = -1$

Solution
(a) When $a = 3$,
$$x = 2a + 1$$
$$= 2(3) + 1$$
$$= 7$$

(b) When $b = 4$,
$$x = 32 - 5b$$
$$= 32 - 5(4)$$
$$= 12$$

(c) When $c = 5$,
$$x = c^2 - 2c$$
$$= 5^2 - 2(5)$$
$$= 15$$

(d) When $d = -8$,
$$x = 4d(d + 5)$$
$$= 4(-8)(-8 + 5)$$
$$= 96$$

(e) When $e = 2$,
$$x = \dfrac{1}{e^3 - 1}$$
$$= \dfrac{1}{2^3 - 1}$$
$$= \dfrac{1}{7}$$

(f) When $f = 1$,
$$x = \dfrac{3f + 4}{5f - 2}$$
$$= \dfrac{3(-1) + 4}{5(-1) - 2}$$
$$= -\dfrac{1}{7}$$

6. Find the value of y in the following formulas.

(a) $y = 3g + 4h$; given $g = 1$ and $h = 5$

(b) $y = m(3 + 2n)$; given $m = 4$ and $n = 6$

(c) $y = \dfrac{p^2 - q^2}{2}$; given $p = -7$ and $q = 3$

(d) $y = \dfrac{r}{s} + \dfrac{s}{r}$; given $r = 6$ and $s = -3$

(e) $y = uv^2$; given $u = -2$ and $v = -9$

(f) $y = \dfrac{(tx)^2}{3t - 5x}$; given $t = 4$ and $x = 2$

Solution

(a) When $g = 1$, $h = 5$,
$$y = 3g + 4h$$
$$= 3(1) + 4(5)$$
$$= 23$$

(b) When $m = 4$, $n = 6$,
$$y = m(3 + 2n)$$
$$= 4[3 + 2(6)]$$
$$= 60$$

(c) When $p = -7$, $q = 3$,
$$y = \frac{p^2 - q^2}{2}$$
$$= \frac{(-7)^2 - 3^2}{2}$$
$$= \frac{40}{2}$$
$$= 20$$

(d) When $r = 6$, $s = -3$,
$$y = \frac{r}{s} + \frac{s}{r}$$
$$= \frac{6}{(-3)} + \frac{(-3)}{6}$$
$$= -2\frac{1}{2}$$

(e) When $u = -2$, $v = -9$,
$$y = uv^2$$
$$= -2 \times (-9)^2$$
$$= -162$$

(f) When $t = 4$, $x = 2$,
$$y = \frac{(tx)^2}{3t - 5x}$$
$$= \frac{(4 \times 2)^2}{3(4) - 5(2)}$$
$$= \frac{64}{2}$$
$$= 32$$

Further Practice

7. Find the value of $b^2 - 4ac$ when

(a) $a = 1$, $b = 5$, and $c = 3$,

(b) $a = 2$, $b = 7$, and $c = \dfrac{-3}{4}$.

Solution

(a) When $a = 1$, $b = 5$, and $c = 3$,
$$b^2 - 4ac = 5^2 - 4(1)(3)$$
$$= 13$$

(b) When $a = 2$, $b = 7$, and $c = \dfrac{-3}{4}$,
$$b^2 - 4ac = 7^2 - 4(2)$$
$$= 55$$

8. Find the value of $p^2q - (2q)^2$ when

(a) $p = 8$ and $q = 3$, **(b)** $p = \dfrac{-9}{2}$ and $q = 4$.

Solution

(a) When $p = 8$ and $q = 3$,
$$p^2q - (2q)^2 = 8^2(3) - (2 \times 3)^2$$
$$= 156$$

(b) When $p = \dfrac{-9}{2}$ and $q = 4$,
$$p^2q - (2q)^2 = \left(\frac{9}{2}\right)^2(4) - (2 \times 4)^2$$
$$= 17$$

9. Find the value of $a^2 + 3b^2 - c^2$ when

(a) $a = 1$, $b = 2$, and $c = 3$,

(b) $a = 5$, $b = 4$, and $c = 6$.

Solution

(a) When $a = 1$, $b = 2$, and $c = 3$,
$$a^2 + 3b^2 - c^2 = 1^2 + 3 \times 2^2 - 3^2$$
$$= 4$$

(b) When $a = 5$, $b = 4$, and $c = 6$,
$$a^2 + 3b^2 - c^2 = 5^2 + 3 \times (-4)^2 - 6^2$$
$$= 37$$

10. Find the value of $\dfrac{x^2 - 2xy}{z^3 - 4y^2}$ when

(a) $x = 9$, $y = 3$, and $z = 6$,

(b) $x = 8$, $y = -1$, and $z = 2$.

Solution

(a) When $x = 9$, $y = 3$, and $z = 6$,
$$\frac{x^2 - 2xy}{z^3 - 4y^2} = \frac{9^2 - 2(9)(3)}{6^3 - 4(3)^2}$$
$$= \frac{27}{180}$$
$$= \frac{3}{20}$$

(b) When $x = 8$, $y = -1$, and $z = 2$,

$$\frac{x^2 - 2xy}{z^3 - 4y^2} = \frac{8^2 - 2(8)(-1)}{2^3 - 4(-1)^2}$$
$$= \frac{80}{4}$$
$$= 20$$

11. If $T = \dfrac{v^2 - u^2}{2w}$, find the value of T when $u = 0$, $v = 5$, and $w = 4$.

Solution

When $u = 0$, $v = 5$, and $w = 4$,

$$T = \frac{v^2 - u^2}{2a}$$
$$= \frac{5^2 - 0^2}{2 \times 4}$$
$$= \frac{25}{8}$$
$$= 3\frac{1}{8}$$

12. If $z = kt^{n-1}$, find the value of z when $k = 2$, $t = 5$, and $n = 4$.

Solution

When $k = 2$, $t = 5$, and $n = 4$,

$$z = kt^{n-1}$$
$$= 2 \times 5^{4-1}$$
$$= 2 \times 125$$
$$= 250$$

Math@Work

13. The daily wage of a worker is given by the expression $\$15t$, where t is the number of working hours.
  (a) Find the daily wage of the worker when $t = 8$.
  (b) What do you think the number 15 in the expression represents?

Solution

(a) When $t = 8$,
  daily wage of worker $= \$15t$
  $$= \$(15 \times 8)$$
  $$= \$120$$

(b) The number 15 represents the hourly wage in dollars.

14. The price of a square frame of side x centimeter is $\$\left(\dfrac{1}{4}x^2 + 5x\right)$.
  Find the price of a square frame of side
  (a) 10 cm, **(b)** 20 cm.

Solution

(a) When $x = 10$,
  price of the frame $= \$\left(\dfrac{1}{4}x^2 + 5x\right)$
  $$= \$\left[\frac{1}{4}(10)^2 + 5(10)\right]$$
  $$= \$75$$

(b) When $x = 20$,
  price of the frame $= \$\left(\dfrac{1}{4}x^2 + 5x\right)$
  $$= \$\left[\frac{1}{4}(20)^2 + 5(20)\right]$$
  $$= \$200$$

15. The admission fee, $\$F$, to a theme park for a family of x adults and y children is given by
  $$F = 80x + 50y.$$
  (a) Find the total admission fee to the park for a family of 2 adults and 3 children.
  (b) What do you think the numbers 80 and 50 in the formula represents?

Solution

(a) When $x = 2$ and $y = 3$,
  $$F = 80x + 50y$$
  $$= 80(2) + 50(3)$$
  $$= 310$$
  The admission fee is $310.
(b) 80 is the price of an adult ticket in dollars.
  50 is the price of a child ticket in dollars.

16. The formula to convert a temperature of $H\,°F$ (Fahrenheit) to $S\,°C$ (Celsius) is given by
  $$S = \frac{5}{9}(H - 32).$$
  (a) The boiling point of water is 212 °F. Express this in °C.
  (b) The temperature in New York at a certain moment was 77 °F. Express this temperature in °C.

Solution

(a) When $H = 212$,
  $$S = \frac{5}{9}(H - 32)$$
  $$= \frac{5}{9}(212 - 32)$$
  $$= 100$$
  The boiling point is 100 °C.

(b) When $H = 77$,
  $$S = \frac{5}{9}(77 - 32)$$
  $$= 25$$
  The temperature in New York at a certain moment was 25 °C.

17. The price $P for a birthday cake of radius r centimeters and height h centimeters is given by the formula
$$P = \frac{1}{25}r^2h.$$
(a) Find the price for a cake of radius 10 cm and height 8 cm.
(b) If the height of the cake in **(a)** is increased to 10 cm, what is the increase in price?

Solution
(a) When $r = 10$ and $h = 8$,
$$P = \frac{1}{25}r^2h$$
$$= \frac{1}{25} \times 10^2 \times 8$$
$$= 32$$
The price of the cake is $32.

(b) When $r = 10$ and $h = 10$,
$$P = \frac{1}{25}r^2h$$
$$= \frac{1}{25} \times 10^2 \times 10$$
$$= 40$$
Increase of price = $(40 – 32)$
= $8
The increase in price is $8.

Brainworks

18. **(a)** When two resistors of resistance a ohms and b ohms are connected to two points, X and Y, by using different wires in a circuit as shown in Diagram 1, the equivalent resistance R ohms is given by the formula
$$R = \frac{ab}{a+b}.$$
Find the value of R when $a = 20$ and $b = 30$.

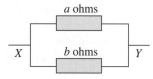

Diagram 1

(b) Suppose 3 resistors of 20 ohms, 30 ohms, and 15 ohms are connected to the points X and Y in the circuit as shown in Diagram 2. Using the formula in **(a)**, find their equivalent resistance.

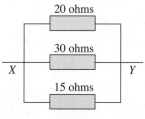

Diagram 2

Solution
(a) When $a = 20$ and $b = 30$,
$$R = \frac{ab}{a+b}$$
$$= \frac{20 \times 30}{20 + 30}$$
$$= 12$$
The value of R is 12.

(b) Combining the 20 ohms and 30 ohms resistors first, we have an equivalent circuit as shown. Take $a = 12$ and $b = 15$,

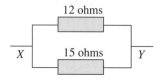

$$R = \frac{ab}{a+b}$$
$$= \frac{12 \times 15}{12 + 15}$$
$$= \frac{180}{27}$$
$$= \frac{20}{3}$$
$$= 6\frac{2}{3}$$

The equivalent resistance is $6\frac{2}{3}$ ohms.

Exercise 3.3
Basic Practice

1. The length of a rectangular room is 10 feet more than its width. Suppose the width of the room is w feet, what is the length of the room in terms of w?

Solution
Length of the room = $(w + 10)$ ft

2. The price of a burger is $6 less than that of a pizza. Given that the price of the pizza is $p, express the price of the burger in terms of p.

Solution
Price of burger = $(p – 6)$

3. Keith is 15 centimeters taller than Jack. If Keith's height is k meters, express Jack's height, in meters, in terms of k.

Solution

Jack's height = k m – 15 cm

$$= k \text{ m} - \frac{3}{20} \text{ m}$$

$$= \left(k - \frac{3}{20} \right) \text{ m}$$

4. Daisy's mother is 4 times as old as she is. Suppose the ages of Daisy and her mother are d years and m years respectively. Express m in terms of d.

Solution

$m = 4 \times d = 4d$

5. The length of Avery Avenue is 3 times that of Scott Street. If the lengths of Avery Avenue and Scott Street are x miles and y miles respectively, write a formula connecting x and y.

Solution

$x = 3 \times y = 3y$

6. The weight of a strawberry is $\frac{1}{10}$ that of an apple. Suppose the weight of the strawberry is s grams and the weight of the apple is a grams. Write a formula relating a and s.

Solution

$s = \dfrac{1}{10} \times a = \dfrac{1}{10} a$

Further Practice

7. There are 7 more apples than pears in the refrigerator. Suppose there are a apples in the refrigerator.
   (a) How many pears are there in terms of a?
   (b) If the number of apples is 16, what is the total number of apples and pears in the refrigerator?

Solution

(a) Number of pears = $a - 7$

(b) When $a = 16$,
   Total number of apples and pears
   $= a + (a - 7)$
   $= 16 + (16 - 7)$
   $= 25$

8. Wesley buys three movie tickets which cost $\$p$ each.
   (a) How much did he pay in total in terms of p?
   (b) Suppose Wesley pays $50 and gets a change of $\$q$. Express q in terms of p.
   (c) If the price of each ticket is $9, what is the amount of change Wesley receive?

Solution

(a) Total amount paid = $3 \times \$p$
   $= \$3p$

(b) Change = $50 – total amount paid
   $q = 50 - 3p$

(c) When $p = 9$,
   $q = 50 - 3(p)$
   $= 50 - 3(9)$
   $= 23$
   ∴ Wesley receives $23

9. Mrs. Foster takes 30 minutes less than twice as long as Mrs. Taylor to prepare a dinner for their family. Let t minutes be the time Mrs. Taylor takes to prepare a dinner.
   (a) Express the time Mrs. Foster takes to prepare a dinner in terms of t.
   (b) If Mrs. Taylor takes 55 minutes, find the time Mrs. Foster takes to prepare a dinner.

Solutions

(a) Time Mrs. Foster takes = $2 \times t - 30$
   $= (2t - 30)$ minutes

(b) When $t = 55$,
   Time Mrs. Foster takes = $2(55) - 30$
   $= 80$ minutes

10. On a particular day in the library, the number of adults was 51 more than one-quarter of the number of children. Let x and y be the numbers of children and adults in the library respectively.
    (a) Express y in terms of x.
    (b) If 168 children went to the library that day, what was the total number of adults and children in the library?

Solution

(a) $y = \dfrac{1}{4} \times x + 51$

   $= \dfrac{1}{4} x + 51$

(b) When $x = 168$,
   Total number of adults and children
   $= x + \dfrac{1}{4} x + 51$
   $= 168 + \dfrac{168}{4} + 51$
   $= 261$

11. The daily wage of a restaurant supervisor is $12 less than one and a half times that of a waitress. Let $v and $w be the daily wages of the supervisor and the waitress respectively.

    (a) Write a formula connecting v and w.

    (b) If the daily wage of the waitress is $58, what is the daily wage of the supervisor?

Solution

    (a) $v = \dfrac{3}{2} \times w - 12$

           $= \dfrac{3}{2}w - 12$

    (b) When $w = 58$,

        Daily wage of supervisor $= \dfrac{3}{2}w - 12$

                                 $= \dfrac{3}{2}(58) - 12$

                                 $= \$75$

12. Three numbers are such that the second number is three times of the first number and the third number is 6 less than four times of the first number. Let x be the first number.

    (a) What is the second number in terms of x?

    (b) What is the third number in terms of x?

    (c) If the first number is 9, what are the second and third numbers?

Solution

    (a) Second number $= 3 \times x = 3x$

    (b) Third number $= 4 \times x - 6 = 4x - 6$

    (c) When $x = 9$,
        Second number $= 3(9) = 27$
        Third number $= 4(9) - 6 = 30$

13. Mariah's age is 2 years more than twice that of Prince's age this year and Queen's age is 2 years less than three times that of Prince's age. Let $m, p,$ and q years be the current ages of Mariah, Prince, and Queen respectively.

    (a) Express m and q each in terms of p.

    (b) If Prince is 13 years old now, how old are Mariah and Queen?

Solution

    (a) $m = 2 \times p + 2 = 2p + 2$
           $q = 3 \times p - 2 = 3p - 2$

    (b) When $p = 13$,
         $m = 2p + 2$
             $= 2(13) + 2$
             $= 28$

         $q = 3p - 2$
            $= 3(13) - 2$
            $= 37$

    $\therefore$ Mariah is 28 years old and Queen is 37 years old..

14. Daisy, Emily, and Fred went jogging in the morning. Emily jogged 0.5 miles more than Daisy and Fred jogged one and a half times as far as Emily. Let d miles be the distance Daisy jogged.

    (a) Express the distance Emily jogged in terms of d.

    (b) Express the distance Fred jogged in terms of d.

    (c) If Daisy jogged 1.7 miles, find the distance Emily and Fred each jogged.

Solution

    (a) Distance Emily jogged $= (d + 0.5)$ miles

    (b) Distance Fred jogged $= \dfrac{3}{2} \times (d + 0.5)$

                               $= \dfrac{3}{2}(d + 0.5)$ miles

    (c) When $d = 1.7$,
        Distance Emily jogged $= d + 0.5$
                              $= 1.7 + 0.5$
                              $= 2.2$ miles

        Distance Fred jogged $= \dfrac{3}{2}(d + 0.5)$

                            $= \dfrac{3}{2}(1.7 + 0.5)$

                            $= 3.3$ miles

15. Anne, Bella, and Chris share to buy a birthday gift for their grandmother. Anne's share is three-quarters of Bella's share and Chris's share is twice that of Anne's share. Let $a, $b,$ and c be the amount of Anne's, Bella's, and Chris's share respectively.

    (a) Express a and c each in terms of b.

    (b) If Bella's share is $48, what is the price of the gift?

Solution

    (a) $a = \dfrac{3}{4} \times b = \dfrac{3}{4}b$

           $c = 2 \times \left(\dfrac{3}{4}b\right) = \dfrac{3}{2}b$

    (b) When $b = 48$,
        Price of gift $= a + b + c$

                     $= \dfrac{3}{4}b + b + \dfrac{3}{2}b$

                     $= \dfrac{3}{4}(48) + 48 + \dfrac{3}{2}(48)$

                     $= \$156$

16. Richard works one and a half times as many hours as Thomas and Simon works one hour more than three-quarters as many hours as Richard. Let r, s, and t hours be the number of hours Richard, Simon, and Thomas work in a week.

(a) Express r and s each in terms of t.

(b) If Thomas works 32 hours in a week, find the number of hours Richard and Simon each work.

(c) What is the total number of hours the three men work in a week?

Solution

(a) $r = \dfrac{3}{2} \times t = \dfrac{3}{2}t$

$s = \dfrac{9}{8} \times t + 1 = \dfrac{9}{8}t + 1$

(b) When $t = 32$,

$r = \dfrac{3}{2}t = \dfrac{3}{2}(32) = 48$

$s = \dfrac{9}{8}t + 1 = \dfrac{9}{8}(32) + 1 = 37$

∴ Richard works for 48 hours and Simon works for 37 hours.

(c) Total number of hours the three men work
$= 32 + 48 + 37$
$= 117$ hours

Math@Work

17. In a mathematics examination, Yan scores 18 points more than three-fifths as much as Xavier and Zoe scores 45 points less than twice as much as Yan. Let x points be the score of Xavier.

(a) What are the scores of Yan and Zoe in terms of x?

(b) Express the sum of the three students' scores in terms of x.

(c) If the score of Xavier is 75, what is the sum of the three students' scores?

Solution

(a) Yan's score $= \dfrac{3}{5} \times x + 18 = \dfrac{3}{5}x + 18$

Zoe's score $= 2 \times \left(\dfrac{3}{5}x + 18\right) - 45$

$= 2\left(\dfrac{3}{5}x + 18\right) - 45$

(b) Sum of the three students' scores

$= x + \left(\dfrac{3}{5}x + 18\right) + \left[2\left(\dfrac{3}{5}x + 18\right) - 45\right]$

$= \dfrac{8}{5}x + 2\left(\dfrac{3}{5}x + 18\right) - 27$

(c) When $x = 75$,
Sum of the three students' scores

$= \dfrac{8}{5}x + 2\left(\dfrac{3}{5}x + 18\right) - 27$

$= \dfrac{8}{5}(75) + 2\left(\dfrac{3}{5}(75) + 18\right) - 27$

$= 219$

18. For a fund-raiser last week, the seventh-graders sold candy bars, hot dogs, and cupcakes. They made a profit of $0.50 per candy bar, $1.20 per hot dog, and $2 per cupcake. The number of hot dogs the students sold is 35 more than the number of cupcakes, and the number of candy bars sold is 4 times the number of hot dogs. Let p, q, and c be the numbers of candy bars, hot dogs, and cupcakes the students sold respectively.

(a) Express p and q each in terms of c.

(b) If the students sold 29 cupcakes, find the numbers of candy bars and hot dogs they sold.

(c) How much profit did the students make in total?

Solution

(a) $q = c + 35$
$p = 4 \times (c + 35) = 4(c + 35)$

(b) When $c = 29$,
$p = 4(c + 35)$
$\quad = 4(29 + 35)$
$\quad = 256$
$q = c + 35$
$\quad = 29 + 35$
$\quad = 64$

∴ Number of candy bars sold = 256
Number of hot dogs sold = 64

(c) Profit from candy bars = 0.50 × 256 = $128
Profit from hot dogs = 1.20 × 64 = $76.8
Profit from cupcakes = 2.00 × 29 = $58
Total profit = $128 + $76.8 + $58
$\qquad\qquad = 262.80

19. In an NBA basketball game, the number of 2-point scores that a team made is 5 more than 3 times its 1-point scores. The number of 3-point scores is four-fifth of the number of 1-point scores. Let x be the number of 1-point scores that the team made.

(a) Express in terms of x,
  (i) the number of 2-point scores made,
  (ii) the number of 3-point scores made,
  (iii) the total score in the game.

(b) If the team had ten 1-point scores in the game, find its total score in the game.

Solution

(a) **(i)** Number of 2-point scores made
$$= 3 \times x + 5$$
$$= 3x + 5$$

(ii) Number of 3-point scores made
$$= \frac{4}{5} \times x$$
$$= \frac{4}{5}x$$

(iii) Total score in the game
$$= x + (3x + 5) + \left(\frac{4}{5}x\right)$$
$$= 4\frac{4}{5}x + 5$$

(b) When $x = 10$,

Total score in the game $= 4\frac{4}{5}(10) + 5$
$$= 53$$

20. A concert has two types of tickets. Adult tickets are sold at $75 each and student tickets are sold at $40 each. The total number of tickets sold is 1,200. Define a variable and express the total ticket sales using an algebraic expression.

Solution

Let x be the number of adults.
Sales from adult tickets $= 75 \times x$
$$= \$(75x)$$
Number of students $= 1,200 - x$
Sales from student tickets $= 40 \times (1,200 - x)$
$$= \$[(40(1,200 - x)]$$
Total ticket sales $= \$[(75x + 40(1,200 - x)]$

Review Exercise 3

1. Simplify the following.
   (a) $5s \times 3t + 1 \times u$
   (b) $m - 4n \times 6m \times m$
   (c) $(a \times 4 - b \times b) \div 2c$
   (d) $3x - b \div c - 5 \times y$

Solution

(a) $5s \times 3t + 1 \times u = 15st + u$
(b) $m - 4n \times 6m \times m = m - 24m^2n$
(c) $(a \times 4 - b \times b) \div 2c = \dfrac{4a - b^2}{2c}$
(d) $3x - b \div c - 5 \times y = 3x - \dfrac{b}{c} - 5y$

2. Express the following word statements algebraically.
   (a) Subtract $c \times c$ from $d \times 5$.
   (b) Divide x cubed by y squared.
   (c) Divide the product of $6a$ and 4 by $8b$.

Solution

(a) Expression $= d \times 5 - c \times c$
$$= 5d - c^2$$

(b) Expression $= x^3 \div y^2 = \dfrac{x^3}{y^2}$

(c) Expression $= (6a \times 4) \div 8b$
$$= \frac{24a}{8b}$$
$$= \frac{3a}{b}$$

3. Given the formula $E = \frac{1}{2}m(v^2 - u^2)$, find the value of E when $m = 5$, $v = 11$, and $u = 7$.

Solution

When $m = 5$, $v = 11$, and $u = 7$,
$$E = \frac{1}{2}m(v^2 - u^2)$$
$$= \frac{1}{2} \times 5 \times (11^2 - 7^2)$$
$$= 180$$

4. Given the formula $y = \dfrac{a - 3b^2}{(a - 3b)^2}$, find the value of y when $a = 10$ and $b = 2$.

Solution

When $a = 10$ and $b = 2$,
$$y = \frac{a - 3b^2}{(a - 3b)^2}$$
$$= \frac{10 - 3 \times 2^2}{(10 - 3 \times 2)^2}$$
$$= \frac{-2}{16}$$
$$= -\frac{1}{8}$$

5. The capacity of a car is 5 passengers and that of a van is 8 passengers. Find the total capacity for m cars and n vans.

Solution

Total capacity $= (5 \times m + 8 \times n)$
$$= (5m + 8n) \text{ passengers}$$

6. Find the value of the expression $(2a + 3b)^2$ when $a = 1$ and $b = -2$.

Solution

When $a = 1$ and $b = -2$,
$$(2a + 3b)^2 = [2 \times 1 + 3 \times (-2)^2]$$
$$= 16$$

7. A piece of wire is 100 centimeters long. One piece of a centimeters and two pieces of b centimeters each are cut from it.
   (a) Express the length of the remaining part in terms of a and b.
   (b) **(i)** If the remaining part is bent into a square, express the length of one side of the square in terms of a and b.
      (ii) When $a = 24$ and $b = 16$, find the length of one side of the square.

Solution
(a) Length of remaining part of wire
$$= (100 - a - b \times 2)$$
$$= (100 - a - 2b) \text{ cm}$$
(b) **(i)** Length of one side of the square
$$= \frac{100 - a - 2b}{4} \text{ cm}$$
   (ii) When $a = 24$ and $b = 16$,
length of one side of the square
$$= \frac{100 - 24 - 2 \times 16}{4}$$
$$= 11 \text{ cm}$$

8. There are x boys and y girls in a class. Half of the boys and $\frac{1}{3}$ of the girls join a math club.
   (a) Express, in terms of x and y,
      (i) the total number of students in the class,
      (ii) the total number of students joining the math club.
   (b) When $x = 18$ and $y = 24$, find the number of students joining the math club.

Solution
(a) **(i)** Total number of students in the class
$$= x + y$$
   (ii) Total number of students joining the math club $= \frac{1}{2}x + \frac{1}{3}y$
(b) When $x = 18$ and $y = 24$,
number of students joining the math club
$$= \frac{1}{2} \times 18 + \frac{1}{3} \times 24$$
$$= 17$$

9. John's savings after n months is $\$(2,500 + 300n)$.
   (a) Find the amount of savings he has after
      (i) 5 months,   **(ii)** 1 year.
   (b) After n months, John uses all his savings to buy gold coins costing $\$g$ each.
      (i) Express the number of gold coins he buys in terms of g and n.
      (ii) When $g = 100$ and $n = 6$, find the number of gold coins John buys.

Solution
(a) **(i)** When $n = 5$,
amount of savings John has
$$= \$(2,500 + 300 \times 5)$$
$$= \$4,000$$
   (ii) 1 year = 12 months
When $n = 12$,
amount of savings John has
$$= \$(2,500 + 300 \times 12)$$
$$= \$6,100$$
(b) **(i)** Number of gold coins he buys
$$= \frac{2,500 + 300n}{g}$$
   (ii) When $g = 100$ and $n = 6$,
number of gold coins he buys
$$= \frac{2,500 + 300 \times 6}{100}$$
$$= 43$$

10. Helen is h years old now.
   (a) Find, in terms of h, Helen's age
      (i) 3 years ago,
      (ii) in 3 years time.
Helen's mother is now 4 times as old as Helen 3 years ago. Her sister's present age is 2 years more than one-third of Helen's age in 3 years' time.
   (b) How old is Helen's mother now in terms of h?
   (c) What is the present age of Helen's sister in terms of h?
   (d) If Helen is 12 years old, how old are her mother and her sister?

Solutions
(a) **(i)** $(h - 3)$ years old
      (ii) $(h + 3)$ years old
(b) $4 \times (h - 3) = 4(h - 3)$
Helen's mother is $4(h - 3)$ years old now.
(c) $\frac{1}{3} \times (h + 3) + 2 = \frac{1}{3}(h + 3) + 2$
Helen's sister is $\left(\frac{1}{3}(h + 3) + 2\right)$ years old now.
(d) When $h = 12$,
$$4(h - 3) = 4(12 - 3) = 36$$
$$\frac{1}{3}(h + 3) + 2 = \frac{1}{3}(12 + 3) + 2 = 7$$
∴ Helen's mother is 36 years old and Helen's sister is 7 years old.

11. Mrs. Jones went shopping, and bought a dress, a skirt, and a diamond ring. The price of the dress is $80 more than the price of the skirt, and the price of the ring is 25 times as much as that of the dress. Let k be the price of the skirt.

(a) Express the price of the dress in terms of k.

(b) Express the price of the ring in terms of k.

(c) Given that the total sum of money Mrs. Jones spent in this shopping spree is T, write a formula connecting T and k.

(d) If the skirt costs $49, find the total sum Mrs. Jones spent.

Solution

(a) Price of dress = $(k + 80)$

(b) Price of ring = $25 \times (k + 80)$
$$= \$[(25(k + 80)]$$

(c) $T = k + (k + 80) + [(25(k + 80)]$
$$= 2k + 80 + 25(k + 80)$$

(d) When $k = 49$,
$$T = 2k + 80 + 25(k + 80)$$
$$= 2(49) + 80 + 25(49 + 80)$$
$$= 3,403$$
∴ Mrs. Jones spent $3,403.

12. Yvonne saves her nickels, dimes, and quarters in a box. The number of dimes in the box is 30 more than the number of nickels, and the number of quarters is 15 less than twice the number of dimes. Let x, y, and z be the number of nickels, dimes, and quarters Yvonne saves respectively.

(a) Express y and z each in terms of x.

(b) How many dimes and quarters are there in the box if there are 18 nickels?

(c) What is the total sum of money Yvonne saves?

Solution

(a) $y = x + 30$
$z = 2 \times (x + 30) - 15$
$$= 2(x + 30) - 15$$

(b) When $x = 18$,
$y = x + 30$
$$= 18 + 30$$
$$= 48$$
$z = 2(x + 30) - 15$
$$= 2(18 + 30) - 15$$
$$= 81$$
∴ There are 48 dimes and 81 quarters.

(c) Total sum of money Yvonne saves
$$= 18(0.05) + 48(0.1) + 81(0.25)$$
$$= \$25.95$$

Chapter 4 Algebraic Manipulation

Class Activity 1

Questions

1. Classify the following expressions into different groups based on their variable parts.

4x and –5x, 3y and 7y, x^2 and $3x^2$, –6xy and 3xy.

2. There are some pink sticks of length 2 units each and some green sticks of length y units each.

Using the given models, express the results of the following as simply as possible.

(a)

$$A \quad\quad\quad B \quad + \quad C \quad\quad\quad D$$

(i) *AB* is formed by 2 pink sticks. Find the length of *AB*.   2x units

(ii) *CD* is formed by 3 pink sticks. Find the length of *CD*.   3x units

(iii) If *AB* and *CD* are joined together, what is the total length?   5x units

(iv) Find 2x + 3x.   5x

(b)

$$E \quad\quad\quad\quad\quad F \quad G \quad\quad H$$

(i) *EF* is formed by 5 green sticks. Find the length of *EF*.   5y units

(ii) *GH* is formed by 2 green sticks. Find the length of *GH*.   2y units

(iii) If a part of length *GH* is cut off from *EF*, find the length of the remaining part.   3y units

(iv) Find 5y – 2y.   3y

(c) If *AB* and *EF* are joined together, what is the total length?   (2x + 5y) cm

Note: The expression in *x* and *y* obtained in **(c)** cannot be further simplified.

Class Activity 2

Questions

1. Evaluate the following.

    (i) $4 \times (2 + 7)$ = ____36____

    (ii) $4 \times 2 + 4 \times 7$ = ____8____ + ____28____ = ____36____

2. Cut the rectangle A into two parts, B and C, as shown below.

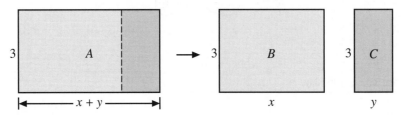

    (a) Find the area of
        (i) rectangle A,

        Area of rectangle $A = 3(x + y)$

        (ii) rectangle B,

        Area of rectangle $B = 3x$

        (iii) rectangle C.

        Area of rectangle $C = 3y$

    (b) Use the areas to write the relationship:
        the area of rectangle A = the sum of rectangle B and rectangle C.

        $3(x + y) = 3x + 3y$

3. Write a relationship between $a(x + y)$, ax, and ay.

    $a(x + y) = ax + ay$

4. Evaluate the following.
    (i) $4 \times (8 - 3)$ **(ii)** $(4 \times 8) - (4 \times 3)$

5. Consider the following diagram.

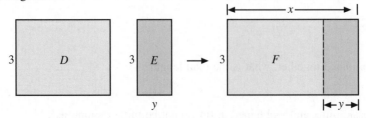

    (a) Find the length of rectangle D in terms of x and y.

        $x - y$

(b) Find the area of

   (i)   rectangle D,

   Area of rectangle $D = 3(x - y)$

   (ii) rectangle E,

   Area of rectangle $E = 3y$

   (iii) rectangle F.

   Area of rectangle $F = 3x$

(c) Use the areas in question **5(b)** to write the relationship:
the area of rectangle D = the difference between the areas of rectangle F and rectangle E.

   $3(x - y) = 3x - 3y$

6. Write the relationship between $a(x - y)$, ax, and ay.

   $a(x - y) = ax - ay$

Class Activity 3

Tasks

1. Remove the parentheses of each of the following expressions.

   (a) $-(x + y)$ $-x - y$ **(b)** $-(x - y)$ $-x + y$

   (c) $x + (y - z)$ $x + y - z$ **(d)** $x + (-y + z)$ $x - y + z$

   (e) $x - (y + z)$ $x - y - z$ **(f)** $x - (y - z)$ $x - y + z$

   (h) $x - (-y + z)$ $x + y - z$ **(i)** $x - (-y - z)$ $x + y + z$

2. Check and discuss your results in Question 1 with your classmate.

Class Activity 4

Questions

1. Four rectangles I, II, III, and IV are combined together to form the rectangle $ABCD$ as shown below.

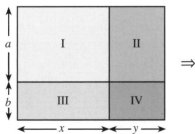

(a) Find in terms of $a, b, x,$ and y, the area of rectangle

    (i) I,   **(ii)** II,

    (iii) III,   **(iv)** IV.

Area of rectangle I   = _____ ax _____

Area of rectangle II   = _____ ay _____

Area of rectangle III = _____ bx _____

Area of rectangle IV = _____ by _____

(b) Express in terms of $a, b, x,$ and y,

    (i)   the length of AD,   _____ $a+b$ _____

    (ii)   the length of AB,   _____ $x+y$ _____

    (iii) the area of $ABCD$.   _____ $(a+b)(x+y)$ _____

(c) What is the relationship between the areas of rectangles I, II, III, IV, and the area of rectangle $ABCD$?

Area of I + Area of II + Area of III + Area of IV = Area of $ABCD$.

(d) Hence write $ax + ay + bc + by$ as a product of two simple expressions.

$ax + ay + bx + by = (a+b)(x+y)$

2. **(a)** Factor $ax + ay$.   _____ $a(x+y)$ _____

    (b) Factor $bx + by$.   _____ $b(x+y)$ _____

    (c) Hence, factor $ax + ay + bx + by$.

$ax + ay + bx + by = a(x+y) + b(x+y) = (a+b)(x+y)$

Extend Your Learning Curve

Month of Birth and Family Size

Step 1: Multiply your month of birth by 2.

Step 2: Add 200 to the result.

Step 3: Multiply the sum by 5.

Step 4: Add your family size to the product in Step 3.

If you follow the above steps in order, you can find your month of birth and your family size (assume the family size is less than 10) from the result obtained after Step 4. Do you know the trick? Try to create some other mathematics tricks and share them with your classmates.

Suggested Answer

Let m be the month of birth and f be the family size. The resulting expression E in each step is as follows:

Step 1: $E = 2m$

Step 2: $E = 2m + 200$

Step 3: $E = 5(2m + 200)$

Step 4: $E = 5(2m + 200) + f$

$\qquad = 10m + 1{,}000 + f$

When $m = 3$ and $f = 4$,

$\qquad E = 10 \times 3 + 1{,}000 + 4$

$\qquad\quad = 1{,}034.$

Hence m = tens digit and f = units digit.

When $m = 11$ and $f = 6$,

$\qquad E = 10 \times 11 + 1{,}000 + 6$

$\qquad\quad = 1{,}116.$

Hence m = the two-digit number formed by the hundreds digit and the tens digit and f = units digit.

Try It!

Section 4.1

1. Simplify the following.
   (a) $5t + 6t - 7t$
   (b) $-4bz - 3bz + \dfrac{5}{2}bz$

   (c) $3n - 8n + 5n$

   ### Solution

   (a) $\begin{aligned} 5t + 6t - 7t &= (5+6)t - 7t \\ &= 11t - 7t \\ &= (11-7)t \\ &= 4t \end{aligned}$

   (b) $-4bz - 3bz + \dfrac{5}{2}bz = (-4-3)bz + \dfrac{5}{2}bz$

   $$= -7bz + \dfrac{5}{2}bz$$

   $$= \left(-7 + \dfrac{5}{2}\right)bz$$

   $$= -\dfrac{9}{2}bz$$

   (c) $\begin{aligned} 3n - 8n + 5n &= (3-8)n + 5n \\ &= -5n + 5n \\ &= (-5+5)n \\ &= 0 \end{aligned}$

2. Simplify the following.
   (a) $5c - 4d - 3c - d$

   (b) $2ax - 7x + \dfrac{3}{2} + ax - 2x - \dfrac{1}{5}$

   ### Solution

   (a) $\begin{aligned} 5c - 4d - 3c - d &= 5c - 3c - 4d - d \\ &= (5-3)c + (-4-1)d \\ &= 2c - 5d \end{aligned}$

   (b) $2ax - 7x + \dfrac{3}{2} + ax - 2x - \dfrac{1}{5}$

   $$= 2ax + ax - 7x - 2x + \dfrac{3}{2} - \dfrac{1}{5}$$

   $$= (2+1)ax - (7+2)x + \dfrac{15}{10} - \dfrac{2}{10}$$

   $$= 3ax - 9x + \dfrac{13}{10}$$

Section 4.2

3. Expand each expression by removing the parentheses.
   (a) $a(2b - 3c)$
   (b) $-x(-5y + z)$

   ### Solution

   (a) $a(2b - 3c) = 2ab - 3ac$
   (b) $\begin{aligned} -x(-5y + z) &= -x(-5y) + (-x)(z) \\ &= 5xy - xz \end{aligned}$

4. Simplify $(4a + b) + (3a - 6b)$.

   ### Solution
   $\begin{aligned} (4a + b) + (3a - 6b) &= 4a + b + 3a - 6b \\ &= 4a + 3a + b - 6b \\ &= 7a - 5b \end{aligned}$

5. Find the sum of $5p - 4q + 7$ and $-3p - q + 2$.

   ### Solution
   $\begin{aligned} &(5p - 4q + 7) + (-3p - q + 2) \\ &= 5p - 4q + 7 - 3p - q + 2 \\ &= 5p - 3p - 4q - q + 7 + 2 \\ &= 2p - 5q + 9 \end{aligned}$

6. Simplify $(3y - 2) - (4y - 9)$.

   ### Solution
   $\begin{aligned} (3y - 2) - (4y - 9) &= 3y - 2 - 4y + 9 \\ &= -y + 7 \end{aligned}$

Section 4.3

7. Expand the following.
   (a) $5(2x + 7y)$
   (b) $-3(-4a + 8b) + 10b$

   ### Solution
   (a) $\begin{aligned} 5(2x + 7y) &= 5(2x) + 5(7y) \\ &= 10x + 35y \end{aligned}$

   (b) $\begin{aligned} -3(-4a + 8b) + 10b &= (-3)(-4a) - 3(8b) + 10b \\ &= 12a - 24b + 10b \\ &= 12a - 14b \end{aligned}$

8. Expand the following.
   (a) $c(4x + 6y + 9z)$
   (b) $(3m - 6n + p)(-4d)$

   ### Solution
   (a) $\begin{aligned} c(4x + 6y + 9z) &= c(4x) + c(6y) + c(9z) \\ &= 4cx + 6cy + 9cz \end{aligned}$

   (b) $\begin{aligned} &(3m - 6n + p)(-4d) \\ &= 3m(-4d) - 6n(-4d) + p(-4d) \\ &= -12dm + 24dn - 4dp \end{aligned}$

9. Simplify $7y - 3[4 - 5(1 - y)]$.

   ### Solution
   $\begin{aligned} 7y - 3[4 - 5(1 - y)] &= 7y - 3[4 - 5 + 5y] \\ &= 7y - 3(-1 + 5y) \\ &= 7y + 3 - 15y \\ &= 7y - 15y + 3 \\ &= 3 - 8y \end{aligned}$

10. Express each of the following as a single fraction in its simplest form.

(a) $\dfrac{8p}{9} + \dfrac{p}{3} - 2p$ (b) $\dfrac{p+9}{2} - 3p$

Solution

(a) $\dfrac{8p}{9} + \dfrac{p}{3} - 2p = \dfrac{8p}{9} + \dfrac{3p}{9} - \dfrac{18p}{9}$

$= -\dfrac{7p}{9}$

(b) $\dfrac{p+9}{2} - 3p = \dfrac{p+9-6p}{2}$

$= \dfrac{-5p+9}{2}$

11. Express each of the following as a simple fraction in its simplest form.

(a) $\dfrac{2x+1}{2} + \dfrac{x+4}{3}$

(b) $\dfrac{x-1}{7} - \dfrac{6-2x}{5} + \dfrac{3x+1}{2}$

Solution

(a) $\dfrac{2x+1}{2} + \dfrac{x+4}{3} = \dfrac{3(2x+1)+2(x+4)}{6}$

$= \dfrac{6x+3+2x+8}{6}$

$= \dfrac{8x+11}{6}$

(b) $\dfrac{x-1}{7} - \dfrac{6-2x}{5} + \dfrac{3x+1}{2}$

$= \dfrac{10x-10-84+28x+105x+35}{70}$

$= \dfrac{10x-10-84+28x+105x+35}{70}$

$= \dfrac{143x-59}{70}$

Section 4.4

12. Factor $21a + 18b$.

Solution

$21a + 18b = 3(7a) + 3(6b)$

$= 3(7a + 6b)$

13. Factor $14by - 35bz + 7b$

Solution

$14by - 35bz + 7b = 7b(2y - 5z + 1)$

Section 4.5

14. Factor the following expressions completely.

(a) $6ax + 10ay + 3bx + 5by$

(b) $18az - 30cz - 15a + 25c$

Solution

(a) $6ax + 10ay + 3bx + 5by$

$= (6ax + 10ay) + (3bx + 5by)$

$= 2a(3x + 5y) + b(3x + 5y)$

$= (2a + b)(3x + 5y)$

(b) $18az - 30cz - 15a + 25c$

$= 6z(3a - 5c) - 5(3a - 5c)$

$= (6z - 5)(3a - 5c)$

15. Factor $7ax - 21x + 12 - 4a$.

Solution

$7ax - 21x + 12 - 4a = 7x(a - 3) + (12 - 4a)$

$= 7x(a - 3) - 4(a - 3)$

$= (7x - 4)(a - 3)$

Exercise 4.1

Basic Practice

1. State the number of terms and the constant term in each of the following expressions.
   - (a) $2a - 3b - 1$
   - (b) $3x + 5 - 4x^2 + x^3$

   Solution
   - (a) $2a - 3b - 1$
     There are 3 terms and the constant term is −1.
   - (b) $3x + 5 - 4x^2 + x^3$
     There are 4 terms and the constant term is 5.

2. State the coefficients of x and y in each of the following expressions.
   - (a) $5x - 2y + 3$
   - (b) $x^2 - x + y - y^2$

   Solution
   - (a) $5x - 2y + 3$
     The coefficient for x and y is 5 and −2 respectively.
   - (b) $x^2 - x + y - y^2$
     The coefficient for x and y is −1 and 1 respectively.

3. Simplify the following.
   - (a) $7a + 2a$
   - (b) $5b - 8b$
   - (c) $-c + 6c$
   - (d) $-3d - 4d$
   - (e) $p + p + p$
   - (f) $q + 2q - 10q$
   - (g) $4by - 9by + 5by$
   - (h) $-4m - 2m + 5m - m$

   Solution
   - (a) $7a + 2a = 9b$
   - (b) $5b - 8b = -3b$
   - (c) $-c + 6c = 5c$
   - (d) $-3d - 4d = -7d$
   - (e) $p + p + p = 3p$
   - (f) $q + 2q - 10q = 3q - 10q = -7q$
   - (g) $4by - 9by + 5by = 5by - 9by = 0$
   - (h) $-4m - 2m + 5m - m = -6m + 5m - m$
     $= -m - m$
     $= -2m$

Further Practice

4. Simplify the following.
   - (a) $3n + 10 - 4n - 11$
   - (b) $-6 + 3k - 4k + 7$
   - (c) $2x - y + 3y - 5x$
   - (d) $-4w - 2v + 9w + 2v$
   - (e) $\frac{2}{3}p - \frac{1}{4}q + \frac{1}{6}p - \frac{1}{2}q$
   - (f) $7t + 4av - \frac{5}{3}t + \frac{1}{2}av$

Solution
- (a) $3n + 10 - 4n - 11 = 3n - 4n + 10 - 11$
  $= -n - 1$
- (b) $-6 + 3k - 4k + 7 = -6 + 7 + 3k - 4k$
  $= 1 - k$
- (c) $2x - y + 3y - 5x = 2x - 5x - y + 3y$
  $= -3x + 2y$
- (d) $-4w - 2v + 9w + 2v = -4w + 9w - 2v + 2v$
  $= 5w$
- (e) $\frac{2}{3}p - \frac{1}{4}q + \frac{1}{6}p - \frac{1}{2}q$
  $= \frac{2}{3}p + \frac{1}{6}p - \frac{1}{4}q - \frac{1}{2}q$
  $= \frac{5}{6}p - \frac{3}{4}q$
- (f) $7t + 4av - \frac{5}{3}t + \frac{1}{2}av$
  $= 7t - \frac{5}{3}t + 4av + \frac{1}{2}av$
  $= \frac{16}{3}t + \frac{9}{2}av$

5. (a) Simplify the expression $-4 - 2x + 5 + x$.
   (b) Find the value of the expression when $x = 2$.

   Solution
   - (a) $-4 - 2x + 5 + x = -4 + 5 - 2x + x$
     $= 1 - x$
   - (b) When $x = 2$,
     $-4 - 2x + 5 + x = 1 - x$
     $= 1 - 2$
     $= -1$

6. (a) Simplify the expression $7a - 2b + 5b - a - 3$.
   (b) Find the value of the expression when $a = -1$ and $b = 2$.

   Solution
   - (a) $7a - 2b + 5b - a - 3 = 7a - a - 2b + 5b - 3$
     $= 6a + 3b - 3$
   - (b) When $a = -1$ and $b = 2$,
     $6a + 3b - 3 = 6(-1) + 3(2) - 3$
     $= -6 + 6 - 3$
     $= -3$

7. (a) Simplify the expression
   $\frac{3}{4}x - \frac{2}{5}ax - y + \frac{1}{3}ax - \frac{1}{8}x$.
   (b) Find the value of the expression when $a = 3$, $x = -2$, and $y = -6$.

Solution

(a) $\frac{3}{4}x - \frac{2}{5}ax - y + \frac{1}{3}ax - \frac{1}{8}x$

$= \frac{3}{4}x - \frac{1}{8}x - \frac{2}{5}ax + \frac{1}{3}ax - y$

$= \frac{5}{8}x - \frac{1}{15}ax - y$

(b) When $a = 3$, $x = -2$, and $y = -6$,

$\frac{5}{8}x - \frac{1}{15}ax - y = \frac{5}{8}(-2) - \frac{1}{15}(3)(-2) - (-6)$

$= -\frac{5}{4} + \frac{2}{5} + 6$

$= \frac{-25 + 8 + 120}{20}$

$= \frac{103}{20}$

$= 5\frac{3}{20}$

Math@Work

8. The lengths of the sides of a triangle are $2x$ units, $4y$ units and $3x$ units. Express the perimeter of the triangle in terms of x and y.

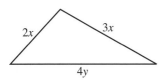

Solution
Perimeter of the triangle
$= (2x + 4y + 3x)$
$= (5x + 4y)$ units

9. A rectangle is $3p$ units long and $2p$ units wide.
  (a) Express the perimeter of the rectangle in terms of p.
  (b) When $p = 12$, find the perimeter of the rectangle.

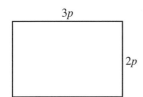

Solution
(a) Perimeter of the rectangle $= 2(3p + 2p)$
$\qquad\qquad\qquad\qquad\quad = 10p$ units

(b) When $p = 12$,
perimeter of the rectangle $= 10(12)$
$\qquad\qquad\qquad\qquad\quad = 120$ units

10. A woman works $2t$ hours each day from Monday to Friday. She works $(2t - y)$ hours on Saturdays. She does not work on Sundays.
  (a) Express her total working hours in a week in terms of t and y.
  (b) How many hours does she work each week when $t = 4\frac{1}{2}$ and $y = 3$?

Solution
(a) Working hours in a week $= [2t \times 5 + (2t - y)]$
$\qquad\qquad\qquad\qquad\qquad = (10t + 2t - y)$
$\qquad\qquad\qquad\qquad\qquad = (12t - y)$ hours

(b) When $t = 4\frac{1}{2}$ and $y = 3$,
working hours in a week $= \left[12\left(4\frac{1}{2}\right) - 3\right]$
$\qquad\qquad\qquad\qquad\qquad = 51$ hours
She works 51 hours each week when $t = 4\frac{1}{2}$ and $y = 3$.

11. A man walks $(5d + 1)$ kilometers due east, then $\frac{3}{2}d$ kilometers due west and finally $\left(2d - \frac{1}{4}\right)$ kilometers due east. How far east is he from the starting point?

Solution
The required distance

$= \left[(5d + 1) - \frac{3}{2}d + \left(2d - \frac{1}{4}\right)\right]$

$= \left[5d - \frac{3}{2}d + 2d + 1 - \frac{1}{4}\right]$

$= \left(\frac{11}{2}d + \frac{3}{4}\right)$ km

He is $\left(\frac{11}{2}d + \frac{3}{4}\right)$ km east from the starting point.

Brainworks

12. Write an algebraic expression that has three terms involving the variables p and q.

Solution
Some possible expressions are:
$\qquad 2p + q - 6,$
$\qquad p^2 + 2pq - 3q^2.$

13. Create an application problem whose answer can be simplified to $7x$.

Solution
Find the number of days in x weeks.
There are 7 days in a week.
$\therefore$ there are $7x$ days in x weeks.

14. The total length of four roads is $(3x - 1)$ kilometers. Suggest a set of possible lengths of the four roads in kilometers?

Solution

The possible lengths of the four roads in kilometers are

$\frac{x}{2}$ km, $\left(\frac{x}{2} - 4\right)$ km, x km and $(x - 3)$ km.

i.e. $\left(\frac{x}{2} + \frac{x}{2} - 4 + x + x + 3\right)$ km $= (3x - 1)$ km

Exercise 4.2

Basic Practice

1. Simplify the following expressions.
  (a) $-(-2a + 7)$ **(b)** $-(4b - c - 5d)$
  (c) $-5 + (7k + 3)$ **(d)** $m - (8m - 9)$

Solution
  (a) $-(-2a + 7) = 2a - 7$
  (b) $-(4b - c - 5d) = -4b + c + 5d$
  (c) $-5 + (7k + 3) = -5 + 7k + 3$
  $\qquad = 7k - 2$
  (d) $m - (8m - 9) = m - 8m + 9$
  $\qquad = -7m + 9$

2. Evaluate the following.

  (a)
$$\begin{array}{r} 3a + 2 \\ +\quad 5a + 7 \\ \hline 8a + 9 \\ \hline \end{array}$$
  (b)
$$\begin{array}{r} 2b + 3c \\ +\quad 4b - 2c \\ \hline 6b + c \\ \hline \end{array}$$

  (c)
$$\begin{array}{r} -4d - 7e \\ +\quad -6d + e \\ \hline -10d - 6e \\ \hline \end{array}$$
  (d)
$$\begin{array}{r} 4f - 5 \\ -\quad 3f + 6 \\ \hline f - 11 \\ \hline \end{array}$$

  (e)
$$\begin{array}{r} -7x + 6y \\ -\quad 2x - 3y \\ \hline -9x + 9y \\ \hline \end{array}$$
  (f)
$$\begin{array}{r} 5t + 9z \\ -\quad -6t - 7z \\ \hline 11t + 16z \\ \hline \end{array}$$

3. Simplify the following expressions.
  (a) $(2p + 3) + (p - 4)$
  (b) $(q + 2r) + (q - 2r)$
  (c) $(-4x - 5y) + (-2x + 7y)$
  (d) $(3t + 2u) - (t - 3u)$
  (e) $-1 - (6w - 1)$
  (f) $(-4n + 3s) - (4n + 8s)$

Solution
  (a) $(2p + 3) + (p - 4) = 2p + 3 + p - 4$
  $\qquad = 3p - 1$

(b) $(q + 2r) + (q - 2r) = q + 2r + q - 2r$
  $\qquad = 2q$
(c) $(-4x - 5y) + (-2x + 7y) = -4x - 5y - 2x + 7y$
  $\qquad = -6x + 2y$
(d) $(3t + 2u) - (t - 3u) = 3t + 2u - t + 3u$
  $\qquad = 2t + 5u$
(e) $-1 - (6w - 1) = -1 - 6w + 1$
  $\qquad = -6w$
(f) $(-4n + 3s) - (4n + 8s) = -4n + 3s - 4n - 8s$
  $\qquad = -8n - 5s$

Further Practice

4. Simplify the following expressions.
  (a) $(2h - 3k + 6) + (8h - 5k - 2)$
  (b) $\left(-m - 8n + \frac{1}{2}\right) + \left(-7m + 6n + \frac{3}{2}\right)$
  (c) $(7x + 2y) + (4x - 6) - (-3 + 2y)$

Solution
  (a) $(2h - 3k + 6) + (8h - 5k - 2)$
  $\qquad = 2h - 3k + 6 + 8h - 5k - 2$
  $\qquad = 10h - 8k + 4$

  (b) $\left(-m - 8n + \frac{1}{2}\right) + \left(-7m + 6n + \frac{3}{2}\right)$
  $\qquad = -m - 8n + \frac{1}{2} - 7m + 6n + \frac{3}{2}$
  $\qquad = -8m - 2n + 2$

  (c) $(7x + 2y) + (4x - 6) - (-3 + 2y)$
  $\qquad = 7x + 2y + 4x - 6 + 3 - 2y$
  $\qquad = 11x - 3$

5. Add $7x - 2y - 4z$ to $-2x + 3y - 5z$.

Solution
$(-2x + 3y - 5z) + (7x - 2y - 4z)$
$= -2x + 3y - 5z + 7x - 2y - 4z$
$= 5x + y - 9z$

6. Find the sum of $5a - 3b$, $7b - 3c$ and $9c - a$.

Solution
$(5a - 3b) + (7b - 3c) + (9c - a)$
$= 5a - 3b + 7b - 3c + 9c - a$
$= 4a + 4b + 6c$

7. Subtract $a - 4b - 3c$ from $a + 2b - 6c$.

Solution
$(a + 2b - 6c) - (a - 4b - 3c)$
$= a + 2b - 6c - a + 4b + 3c$
$= 6b - 3c$

8. Subtract $t - 3v$ from the sum of $7t - 2u - 3v$ and $3t + 5u - 8v$.

Solution

$(7t - 2u - 3v + 3t + 5u - 8v) - (t - 3v)$
$= 7t - 2u - 3v + 3t + 5u - 8v - t + 3v$
$= 9t + 3u - 8v$

Math@Work

9. There are three consecutive integers. If the smallest one is n, find the sum of the three integers.

Solution

The three integers are n, $n + 1$ and $n + 2$.
Their sum $= n + (n + 1) + (n + 2)$
$\qquad\qquad = n + n + 1 + n + 2$
$\qquad\qquad = 3n + 3$

10. The masses of 3 boxes of chocolates are $(3p + 4q + 2)$ grams, $(4p + 6q + 5)$ grams, and $(p + 7q + 9)$ grams. Find their total mass.

Solution

Total mass
$= [(3p + 4q + 2) + (4p + 6q + 5) + (p + 7q + 9)]$
$= (3p + 4q + 2 + 4p + 6q + 5 + p + 7q + 9)$
$= (8p + 17q + 16)$ g

11. The perimeter of a triangle is $(7x - 3y + 6)$ feet. The lengths of two sides of the triangle are $(2x + y - 1)$ feet and $(x - 2y + 10)$ feet.
    (a) Find the length of the third side in terms of x and y.
    (b) If $x = 5$ and $y = -1$, find the length of the third side.

Solution

(a) Length of the third side
$\quad = (7x - 3y + 6) - (2x + y - 1) - (x - 2y + 10)$
$\quad = 7x - 3y + 6 - 2x - y + 1 - x + 2y - 10$
$\quad = (4x - 2y - 3)$ feet

(b) Length of the third side $= 4x - 2y - 3$
$\qquad\qquad\qquad\qquad\quad = 4(5) - 2(-1) - 3$
$\qquad\qquad\qquad\qquad\quad = 20 + 2 - 3$
$\qquad\qquad\qquad\qquad\quad = 19$ feet

Brainworks

12. The perimeter of a rectangle is $(6x + 5y)$ centimeters. Suggest two possible dimensions of the rectangle.

Solution

Perimeter $= (6x + 5y)$ cm
Sum of the length and the breadth
$= \frac{1}{2}(6x + 5y)$
$= \left(3x + \frac{5}{2}y\right)$ cm

Two possible dimensions of the rectangle are

$3x$ cm by $\frac{5}{2}y$ cm and $2x$ cm by $\left(x + \frac{5}{2}y\right)$ cm.

13.

Sun	Mon	Tue	Wed	Thu	Fri	Sat
		1	2	3	4	5
6	7	8	9	10	11	12
13	14	15	16	17	18	19
20	21	22	23	24	25	26
27	28	29	30	31		

Suppose nine dates in a certain month are enclosed by a rectangle as shown above.

(a) Explain a quick way to calculate the sum of the nine numbers.

(b) Let n be the number at the top left hand corner of the rectangle. Express the sum of the nine numbers in terms of n.

(c) Let m be the middle number in the rectangle. Express the sum of the nine numbers in terms of m.

(d) Write down an equation relating m and n.

(e) Describe some other interesting properties about the numbers within the rectangle.

Solution

(a) Sum of the nine numbers
$\quad = (7 + 8 + 9) + (14 + 15 + 16) + (21 + 22 + 23)$
$\quad = 3 \times 8 + 3 \times 15 + 3 \times 22$
$\quad = 24 + 45 + 66$
$\quad = 135$

OR

Sum of the nine numbers
$= 9 \times 15$
$= 135$
15 is the mean of the nine numbers.

(b) Sum of the nine numbers

$= n + (n + 1) + (n + 2) + (n + 7) + (n + 8)$
$\quad + (n + 9) + (n + 14) + (n + 15) + (n + 16)$
$= 9n + 72$

(c) Sum of the nine numbers

$= (m - 8) + (m - 7) + (m - 6) + (m - 1) + m$
$\quad + (m + 1) + (m + 6) + (m + 7) + (m + 8)$
$= 9m$

(d) $\quad 9m = 9n + 72$

or $\quad m = n + 8$

(e) Some other interesting properties include:
- **(i)** The sum of the nine numbers is a multiple of 9.
- **(ii)** The sum of the three numbers on each diagonal is equal.

Exercise 4.3

Basic Practice

1. Expand the following.

(a) $3(2 + a)$ **(b)** $4(7b + 5c)$

(c) $(2d - 6e)(5)$ **(d)** $(-3g - 4h)(2)$

(e) $-4(7 - 5n)$ **(f)** $-5(-3p + 9q)$

(g) $6(2r - 3s + 4t)$ **(h)** $a(-5x + 3y - 8z)$

(i) $\dfrac{2}{3}(6a - 18b - 24c)$ **(j)** $(4a - 8b + 12c)\left(-\dfrac{5}{2}b\right)$

Solution

(a) $3(2 + a) = 3(2) + 3(a)$
$\qquad\qquad = 6 + 3a$

(b) $4(7b + 5c) = 4(7b) + 4(5c)$
$\qquad\qquad\quad = 28b + 20c$

(c) $(2d - 6e)(5) = 10d - 30e$

(d) $(-3g - 4h)(2) = -6g - 8h$

(e) $(-4)(7 - 5n) = -28 + 20n = 20n - 28$

(f) $(-5)(-3p + 9q) = 15p - 45q$

(g) $6(2r - 3s + 4t) = 12r - 18s + 24t$

(h) $a(-5x + 3y - 8z) = -5ax + 3ay - 8az$

(i) $\dfrac{2}{3}(6a - 18b - 24c) = 4a - 12b - 16c$

(j) $(4a - 8b + 12c)\left(-\dfrac{5}{2}\right) = -10a + 20b - 30c$

2. Simplify the following expressions.

(a) $4(x + 7) + 3(x + 5)$

(b) $3(2a + 4b) + 9(3a - 2b)$

(c) $2(3u - 5) - 3(2u + 1)$

(d) $b(-5v - 4) - 2b(v + 4)$

(e) $-2(5m - p) + 5(-p + 2m)$

(f) $-7(2r - 3s) - 4(-3r - s)$

(g) $3(2a - 3b - 5c) - 5(a - 3c)$

(h) $(x - 3y)(-2) + (x - y + 3)(6)$

Solution

(a) $4(x + 7) + 3(x + 5) = 4x + 28 + 3x + 15$
$\qquad\qquad\qquad\qquad = 7x + 43$

(b) $3(2a + 4b) + 9(3a - 2b) = 6a + 12b + 27a - 18b$
$\qquad\qquad\qquad\qquad\qquad = 33a - 6b$

(c) $2(3u - 5) - 3(2u + 1) = 6u - 10 - 6u - 3$
$\qquad\qquad\qquad\qquad\quad = -13$

(d) $b(-5v - 4) - 2b(v + 4) = -5bv - 4b - 2bv - 8b$
$\qquad\qquad\qquad\qquad\qquad = -7bv - 12b$

(e) $-2(5m - p) + 5(-p + 2m) = -10m + 2p - 5p + 10m$
$\qquad\qquad\qquad\qquad\qquad\quad = -3p$

(f) $-7(2r - 3s) - 4(-3r - s) = -14r + 21s + 12r + 4s$
$\qquad\qquad\qquad\qquad\qquad = -2r + 25s$

(g) $3(2a - 3b - 5c) - 5(a - 3c)$
$= 6a - 9b - 15c - 5a + 15c$
$= a - 9b$

(h) $(x - 3y)(-2) + (x - y + 3)(6)$
$= -2x + 6y + 6x - 6y + 18$
$= 4x + 18$

3. Express each of the following as a single fraction in its simplest form.

(a) $-x + \dfrac{4x}{5}$ **(b)** $2 - \dfrac{3x}{8}$

(c) $1 + \dfrac{7x - 8}{6}$ **(d)** $\dfrac{4x + 1}{3} - 2x$

(e) $\dfrac{3x - 1}{4} - \dfrac{2x}{5}$ **(f)** $-2 + \dfrac{4x + 9}{3} - \dfrac{x}{2}$

Solution

(a) $-x + \dfrac{4x}{5} = \dfrac{-5(x) + 4x}{5}$

$\qquad\qquad\quad = \dfrac{-5x + 4x}{5}$

$\qquad\qquad\quad = -\dfrac{x}{5}$

(b) $2 - \dfrac{3x}{8} = \dfrac{2(8) - 3x}{8}$

$\qquad\qquad = \dfrac{16 - 3x}{8}$

(c) $1 + \dfrac{7x - 8}{6} = \dfrac{6 + 7x - 8}{6}$

$\qquad\qquad\quad = \dfrac{7x - 2}{6}$

(d) $\dfrac{4x + 1}{3} - 2x = \dfrac{4x + 1 - 3(2x)}{3}$

$\qquad\qquad\quad = \dfrac{4x + 1 - 3(2x)}{3}$

$\qquad\qquad\quad = \dfrac{-2x + 1}{3}$

(e) $\dfrac{3x - 1}{4} - \dfrac{2x}{5} = \dfrac{5(3x - 1) - 4(2x)}{20}$

$\qquad\qquad\quad = \dfrac{15x - 5 - 8x}{20}$

$\qquad\qquad\quad = \dfrac{7x - 5}{20}$

(f) $-2 + \dfrac{4x+9}{3} - \dfrac{x}{2} = \dfrac{-6(2)+2(4x+9)-3(x)}{6}$

$$= \dfrac{-12+8x+18-3x}{6}$$

$$= \dfrac{5x+6}{6}$$

Further Practice

4. Simplify the following.
   (a) $4a - [5a - (3 + 2a)]$
   (b) $7t - [5s + 8(s + 2t)]$
   (c) $4m + n + [5m - 6(m - n)]$
   (d) $5[a - (b - a)] + 7(-a + 2b)$
   (e) $9(y - z) - [5y - z - 3(2y - 4z)]$
   (f) $4[2p + 3q - (p + q)]$

Solution

(a) $4a - [5a - (3 + 2a)] = 4a - (5a - 3 - 2a)$
$= 4a - (3a - 3)$
$= 4a - 3a + 3$
$= a + 3$

(b) $7t - [5s + 8(s + 2t)] = 7t - (5s + 8s + 16t)$
$= 7t - 13s - 16t$
$= -13s - 9t$

(c) $4m + n + [5m - 6(m - n)]$
$= 4m + n + (5m - 6m + 6n)$
$= 4m + n - m + 6n$
$= 3m + 7n$

(d) $5[a - (b - a)] + 7(-a + 2b)$
$= 5(a - b + a) - 7a + 14b$
$= 10a - 5b - 7a + 14b$
$= 3a + 9b$

(e) $9(y - z) - [5y - z - 3(2y - 4z)]$
$= 9y - 9z - (5y - z - 6y + 12z)$
$= 9y - 9z + y - 11z$
$= 10y - 20z$

(f) $4[2p + 3q - (p + q)]$
$= 4(2p + 3q - p - q)$
$= 4(p + 2q)$
$= 4p + 8q$

5. Express each of the following as a single fraction in its simpelst form.
   (a) $\dfrac{x}{2} + \dfrac{x-8}{3}$
   (b) $-\dfrac{3t}{7} + \dfrac{4t+8}{2}$
   (c) $\dfrac{2x+1}{4} - \dfrac{x-3}{5}$
   (d) $\dfrac{5t-2}{5} - \dfrac{2(t+1)}{3}$
   (e) $-\dfrac{5(x-1)}{6} - \dfrac{3(2x+1)}{4}$

(f) $1 - \dfrac{x+2}{2} + \dfrac{4(3x-1)}{9}$

(g) $\dfrac{y+1}{3} + \dfrac{y+2}{2} - \dfrac{5y-1}{6}$

(h) $-\dfrac{y}{5} + \dfrac{3y-1}{2} - \dfrac{4y+7}{3}$

Solution

(a) $\dfrac{x}{2} + \dfrac{x-8}{3} = \dfrac{3x+2x-16}{6}$

$$= \dfrac{5x-16}{6}$$

(b) $-\dfrac{3t}{7} + \dfrac{4t+8}{2} = \dfrac{-2(3t)+7(t+8)}{14}$

$$= \dfrac{-6t+7t+56}{14}$$

$$= \dfrac{-9x+8}{20}$$

(c) $\dfrac{2x+1}{4} - \dfrac{x-3}{5} = \dfrac{5(2x+1)-4(x-3)}{20}$

$$= \dfrac{10x+5-4x+12}{20}$$

$$= \dfrac{6x+17}{20}$$

(d) $\dfrac{5t-2}{5} - \dfrac{2(t+1)}{3} = \dfrac{3(5t-2)-10(t+1)}{15}$

$$= \dfrac{15t-6-10t-10}{15}$$

$$= \dfrac{5x-16}{6}$$

(e) $-\dfrac{5(x-1)}{6} - \dfrac{3(2x+1)}{4} = \dfrac{-10(x-1)-9(2x+1)}{12}$

$$= \dfrac{-10x+10-18x-9}{12}$$

$$= \dfrac{-28x+1}{12}$$

(f) $1 - \dfrac{x+2}{2} + \dfrac{4(3x-1)}{9} = \dfrac{18-9(x+2)+8(3x-1)}{18}$

$$= \dfrac{18-9x-18+24x-8}{18}$$

$$= \dfrac{15x-8}{18}$$

(g) $\dfrac{y+1}{3} + \dfrac{y+2}{2} - \dfrac{5y-1}{6} = \dfrac{2(y+1)+3(y+2)-(5y-1)}{6}$

$$= \dfrac{2y+2+3y+6-5y+1}{6}$$

$$= \dfrac{9}{6}$$

$$= \dfrac{3}{2}$$

(h) $-\dfrac{y}{5} + \dfrac{3y-1}{2} - \dfrac{4y+7}{3}$

$= \dfrac{-12y + 30(3y-1) - 20(4y+7)}{60}$

$= \dfrac{-12y + 90y - 30 - 80y - 140}{60}$

$= \dfrac{-2y - 170}{60}$

$= \dfrac{-y - 85}{30}$

Math@Work

6. Let n be a number. Find the resulting expression after going through each step in order.
   (a) Add 10 to the number.
   (b) Multiply the sum by 2.
   (c) Subtract 4 from the result.
   (d) Divide the result in **(c)** by 2.
   (e) Subtract the number n from the result in **(d)**.
   (f) Simplify the expression in **(e)**.
   Note: This is the mathematics behind the number trick on the opening page of this chapter.

Solution
   (a) $n + 10$
   (b) $2(n + 10)$
   (c) $2(n + 10) - 4$
   (d) $[2(n + 10) - 4] \div 2$
   (e) $[2(n + 10) - 4] \div 2 - n$
   (f) Expression $= [2(n + 10) - 4] \div 2 - n$
   $= (2n + 20 - 4) \div 2 - n$
   $= (2n + 16) \div 2 - n$
   $= n + 8 - n$
   $= 8$

7. There are $(2a + b)$ books in a pile. The thickness of each book is 2 centimeters. Find the height of the pile of books in terms of a and b, expressing the answer in the simplest form.

Solution
Height of the pile of books $= 2(2a + b)$
$= (4a + 2b)$ cm

8. A grocer bought n eggs at $\$x$ each. He marked up the price of each egg by $\$y$ and sold all of them. Find the sales amount.

Solution
Sales amount $= \$(x + y)n$
$= \$(nx + ny)$

9. After arranging some oranges in 6 rows that each row holds $(2m - 3)$ oranges, there are 5 oranges left.
   (a) What is the total number of oranges?
   (b) Find the number of oranges when

Solution
   (a) Number of oranges $= 6(2m - 3) + 5$
   $= 12m - 18 + 5$
   $= 12m - 13$

   (b) When $m = 7$,
   $12m - 13 = 12(7) - 13$
   $= 84 - 13$
   $= 71$
   The number of oranges in the box is 71 when $m = 7$.

Brainworks

10. Design a number trick such that the final result is always 7.

Solution
The steps for the number trick can be:
   (a) Think of a number.
   (b) Add 9 to the number.
   (c) Multiply the sum by 3.
   (d) Subtract 6 from the result in **(c)**.
   (e) Divide the difference by 3.
   (f) Subtract your original number from the result in **(e)**.
   (g) You will get the number 7.

If the original number is n, the resulting expression
$= [(n + 9) \times 3 - 6] \div 3 - n$
$= (3n + 27 - 6) \div 3 - n$
$= (3n + 21) \div 3 - n$
$= n + 7 - n$
$= 7$

11. The distributive law can be applied to simplify some arithmetic calculations. For example,
$$37 \times 99 = 37 \times (100 - 1)$$
$$= 3,700 - 37$$
$$= 3,663.$$
Devise another two such calculators in which the distributive law is applied.

Solution
The following shows two short-cuts in Arithmetic that make use of the distributive law.
   (i) $56 \times 101 = 56 \times (100 + 1)$
   $= 5,600 + 56$
   $= 5,656$
   (ii) $387 \times 999 = 387 \times (1,000 - 1)$
   $= 387,00 - 387$
   $= 386,613$

12. Some matchsticks are used to form a pattern of n squares as shown below.

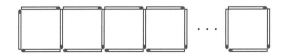

(a) Complete the following table.

n	1	2	3	4	5
Total number of matchsticks					

(b) Find the total number of matchsticks, in terms of n, used to form n squares.

(c) If each matchstick is 3 centimeters long, find the perimeter of the figure formed by n squares, in terms of n.

Solution

(a)

n	1	2	3	4	5
Total number of matchsticks	4	7	10	13	15

(b) Total number of matchsticks used to form n squares = $3n + 1$

(c) The perimeter of the figure is formed by $2n + 2$ matchsticks.

$$\text{Perimeter} = 3(2n + 2)$$
$$= (6n + 6) \text{ cm}$$

Exercise 4.4

Basic Practice

1. Factor each of the following expressions completely.

(a) $6a + 3b$ **(b)** $10c - 12d$
(c) $28e + 21$ **(d)** $6f - 6$
(e) $18ax - 15ay$ **(f)** $-5mx - 10my$
(g) $15ab - 3a$ **(h)** $12s + 48bs$
(i) $51cu + 17cv$ **(j)** $-56ay - 8a$

Solution

(a) $6a + 3b = 3(2a) + 3b$
            $= 3(2a + b)$
(b) $10c - 12d = 2(5c) - 2(6d)$
               $= 2(5c - 6d)$
(c) $28e + 21 = 7(4e) + 7(3)$
             $= 7(4e + 3)$
(d) $6f - 6 = 6(f - 1)$
(e) $18ax - 15ay = 3a(6x) - 3a(5y)$
                  $= 3a(6x - 5y)$
(f) $-5mx - 10my = -5m(x) + (-5m)(2y)$
                    $= -5m(x + 2y)$

(g) $15ab - 3a = 3a(5b - 1)$
(h) $12s + 48bs = 12s(1 + 4b)$
(i) $51cu + 17cv = 17c(3u + v)$
(j) $-56ay - 8a = -8a(7y + 1)$

Further Practice

2. Factor each of the following expressions completely.
(a) $7a + 7b + 7c$
(b) $12a - 8b + 20c$
(c) $5ax - 15bx - 30x$
(d) $-18 - 24ay - 6y$
(e) $mx + my + 3mz$
(f) $7bt - 21b - 35bt$
(g) $3a(x + y) - 4b(x + y)$
(h) $a(5m - 4) + b(5m - 4)$

Solution

(a) $7a + 7b + 7c = 7(a + b + c)$
(b) $12a - 8b + 20c = 4(3a - 2b + 5c)$
(c) $5ax - 15bx - 30x = 5x(a - 3b - 6)$
(d) $-18 - 24ay - 6y = -6(3 + 4ay + y)$
(e) $mx + my + 3mz = m(x + y + 3z)$
(f) $7bt - 21b - 35bt = 7b(t - 3 - 5t)$
                         $= -7b(3 + 4t)$
(g) $3a(x + y) - 4b(x + y) = (3a - 4b)(x + y)$
(h) $a(5m - 4) + b(5m - 4) = (5m - 4)(a + b)$

Math@Work

3. Compute each of the following without using calculators.
(a) $389 \times 57 + 389 \times 43$
(b) $86 \times 471 - 76 \times 471$

Solution

(a) $389 \times 57 + 389 \times 43 = 389 \times (57 + 43)$
                        $= 389 \times 100$
                        $= 38,900$
(b) $86 \times 471 - 76 \times 471 = (86 - 76) \times 471$
                          $= 10 \times 471$
                          $= 4,710$

Brainworks

4. Write three algebraic expressions, in expanded form, involving a, x, and y such that $(x + y)$ is one of their factors.

Solution

The following are some algebraic expressions, in expanded form, involving a, x, and y such that $(x + y)$ is a factor:

$$ax + ay, \ ax^2 + axy, \ -2a^2x - 2a^2y$$

5. Factorization can be used to simplify arithmetic calculations (refer to Q3). Write two situations in which you can apply this technique.

Solution

We can apply the technique as follows:

(i) $148 \times 4 - 123 \times 4 = (148 - 123) \times 4$
$$= 25 \times 4$$
$$= 100$$

(ii) $839 \times 537 + 839 \times 463 = 839 \times (537 + 463)$
$$= 839 \times 1,000$$
$$= 839,000$$

Exercise 4.5
Basic Practice

1. Factor the following completely.

(a) $(a + 3b)x + (a + 3b)y$
(b) $m(2p - q) - 3n(2p - q)$
(c) $5r + ar + 5s + as$
(d) $cv - c + v - 1$
(e) $ax + bx - ay - by$
(f) $1 + 2t - k - 2kt$
(g) $35mx - 7m + 5nx - n$
(h) $11x - px - 11y + py$
(i) $10px + 15qx + 8py + 12qy$
(j) $36ax - 63ay - 4bx + 7by$

Solution

(a) $(a + 3b)x + (a + 3b)y = (a + 3b)(x + y)$

(b) $m(2p - q) - 3n(2p - q) = (m - 3n)(2p - q)$

(c) $5r + ar + 5s + as = r(5 + a) + s(5 + a)$
$$= (5 + a)(r + s)$$

(d) $cv - c + v - 1 = c(v - 1) + v - 1$
$$= (c + 1)(v - 1)$$

(e) $ax + bx - ay - by = a(x - y) + b(x - y)$
$$= (a + b)(x - y)$$

(f) $1 + 2t - k - 2kt = 2t(1 - k) + 1 - k$
$$= (1 + 2t)(1 - k)$$

(g) $35mx - 7m + 5nx - n = 7m(5x - 1) + n(5x - 1)$
$$= (7m + n)(5x - 1)$$

(h) $11x - px - 11y + py = x(11 - p) - y(11 - p)$
$$= (11 - p)(x - y)$$

(i) $10px + 15qx + 8py + 12qy$
$$= 5x(2p + 3q) + 4y(2p + 3q)$$
$$= (2p + 3q)(5x + 4y)$$

(j) $36ax - 63ay - 4bx + 7by$
$$= 9a(4x - 7y) - b(4x - 7y)$$
$$= (9a - b)(4x - 7y)$$

Further Practice

2. Factor the following completely.

(a) $72 - 9a + 2ab - 16b$
(b) $-12nx + 21ny + 35y - 20x$
(c) $36qy - 16xq - 4px + 9py$
(d) $5ky - 15ym - 6xm + 2kx$
(e) $au - 5b + ab - 5u$
(f) $8qx + 21py + 6px + 28qy$
(g) $8bx - 15ay - 6by + 20ax$
(h) $3m - 6n + 36nt - 18mt$

Solution

(a) $72 - 9a + 2ab - 16b$
$$= 9(8 - a) - 2b(8 - a)$$
$$= (9 - 2b)(8 - a)$$

(b) $-12nx + 21ny + 35y - 20x$
$$= 3n(7y - 4x) + 5(7y - 4x)$$
$$= (3n + 5)(7y - 4x)$$

(c) $36qy - 16xq - 4px + 9py$
$$= 4q(9y - 4x) + p(9y - 4x)$$
$$= (4q + p)(9y - 4x)$$

(d) $5ky - 15ym - 6xm + 2kx$
$$= 5y(k - 3m) + 2x(k - 3m)$$
$$= (5y + 2x)(k - 3m)$$

(e) $au - 5b + ab - 5u$
$$= u(a - 5) + b(a - 5)$$
$$= (a - 5)(u + b)$$

(f) $8qx + 21py + 6px + 28qy$
$$= 6px + 8qx + 21py + 28qy$$
$$= 2x(3p + 4q) + 7y(3p + 4q)$$
$$= (3p + 4q)(2x + 7y)$$

(g) $8bx - 15ay - 6by + 20ax$
$$= 20ax + 8bx - 15ay - 6by$$
$$= 4x(5a + 2b) - 3y(5a + 2b)$$
$$= (5a + 2b)(4x - 3y)$$

(h) $3m - 6n + 36nt - 18mt$
$$= 3m - 18mt + 36nt - 6n$$
$$= 3m(1 - 6t) - 6n(1 - 6t)$$
$$= (3m - 6n)(1 - 6t)$$
$$= 3(m - 2n)(1 - 6t)$$

Math@Work

3. In the diagram, rectangle $ABCD$ is further divided into four rectangles by the lines PTQ and RTS. The areas of the four rectangles are $21ax$, $7bx$, $6ay$, and $2by$ respectively as shown in the diagram.

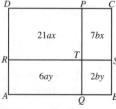

(a) Factor $21ax + 7bx + 6ay + 2by$ completely.
(b) Hence, find the lengths of AR and DP.

Solution

(a) $21ax + 7bx + 6ay + 2by$
$= 3a(7x + 2y) + b(7x + 2y)$
$= (3a + b)(7x + 2y)$

(b) $AR = 2y$ cm
$DP = 3a$ cm

Brainworks

4. (a) Can we factor the following expressions?
  (i) $3x + 4y$ (ii) $ax + ay - bx + by$
(b) What can you conclude from the results in (a)?
(c) Write a 4-term algebraic expression that cannot be factored.

Solution

(a) (i) $3x + 4y$ cannot be factored.
  (ii) $ax + ay - bx + by$ cannot be factored.
(b) Not all algebraic expressions can be factored.
(c) $x + y + z + 1$ cannot be factored.

Review Exercise 4

1. Simplify the following.
(a) $2a + 3b - 4a + 5b$
(b) $(2p - 7q - 6r) + (3p - 4q - r)$
(c) $(2x - 3y + 4) + (-3x + 6y - 1)$
(d) $(-3m - 8n + 2p) - (-4m + 7n - 3p)$

Solution

(a) $2a + 3b - 4a + 5b = -2a + 8b$

(b) $(2p - 7q - 6r) + (3p - 4q - r)$
$= 2p - 7q - 6r + 3p - 4q - r$
$= 5p - 11q - 7r$

(c) $(2x - 3y + 4) + (-3x + 6y - 1)$
$= 2x - 3y + 4 - 3x + 6y - 1$
$= -x + 3y + 3$

(d) $(-3m - 8n + 2p) - (-4m + 7n - 3p)$
$= -3m - 8n + 2p + 4m - 7n + 3p$
$= m - 15n + 5p$

2. Simplify the following.
(a) $4(2m - 1) + 3(4m + 1)$
(b) $3(2p - 7q) - 6(p + 3q)$
(c) $-3(4x + y) + 2(8x - 5y)$
(d) $-7(2x - y + 3) + -4(-3x + y - 5)$

Solution

(a) $4(2m - 1) + 3(4m + 1)$
$= 8m - 4 + 12m + 3$
$= 20m - 1$

(b) $3(2p - 7q) - 6(p + 3q)$
$= 6p - 21q - 6p - 18q$
$= -39q$

(c) $-3(4x + y) + 2(8x - 5y)$
$= -12x - 3y + 16x - 10y$
$= 4x - 13y$

(d) $-7(2x - y + 3) - 4(-3x + y - 5)$
$= -14x + 7y - 21 + 12x - 4y + 20$
$= -2x + 3y - 1$

3. Express each of the following as a single fraction in its simplest form.

(a) $\dfrac{3x}{4} + \dfrac{2(1 - 3x)}{5}$

(b) $\dfrac{4(2x - 1)}{7} - \dfrac{x - 3}{2}$

(c) $-\dfrac{2(5 - x)}{3} - \dfrac{7(2x + 1)}{9}$

(d) $1 - \dfrac{(x + 2)}{6} + \dfrac{4(1 - 2x)}{5}$

Solution

(a) $\dfrac{3x}{4} + \dfrac{2(1 - 3x)}{5} = \dfrac{5(3x) + 8(1 - 3x)}{20}$

$= \dfrac{15x + 8 - 24x}{20}$

$= \dfrac{-9x + 8}{20}$

(b) $\dfrac{4(2x - 1)}{7} - \dfrac{x - 3}{2} = \dfrac{8(2x - 1) - 7(x - 3)}{14}$

$= \dfrac{16x - 8 - 7x + 21}{14}$

$= \dfrac{9x + 13}{14}$

(c) $-\dfrac{2(5 - x)}{3} - \dfrac{7(2x + 1)}{9} = \dfrac{-6(5 - x) - 7(2x + 1)}{9}$

$= \dfrac{-30 + 6x - 14x - 7}{9}$

$= \dfrac{-8x - 37}{9}$

(d) $1 - \dfrac{(x + 2)}{6} + \dfrac{4(1 - 2x)}{5} = \dfrac{30 - 5(x + 2) + 24(1 - 2x)}{30}$

$= \dfrac{30 - 5x - 10 + 24 - 48x}{30}$

$= \dfrac{-53x + 44}{30}$

4. Factor the following completely.
(a) $5ac - c$
(b) $12xy + 36x$
(c) $-9pq - 15pr$
(d) $15ax - 20ay + 10az$

Solution

(a) $5ac - c = c(5a - 1)$
(b) $12xy + 36x = 12x(y + 3)$
(c) $-9pq - 15pr = -3p(3q + 5r)$
(d) $15ax - 20ay + 10az = 5a(3x - 4y + 2z)$

5. **(a)** Simplify $6(x + 2y) - 7(4x - 3y)$.
(b) Factor the result in **(a)**.
(c) When $x = -1$ and $y = 5$, find the value of the given expression.

Solution
(a) $6(x + 2y) - 7(4x - 3y) = 6x + 12y - 28x + 21y$
$$= -22x + 33y$$
(b) $-22x + 33y = -11(2x - 3y)$
(c) When $x = -1$ and $y = 5$,
$$-22x + 33y = -22(-1) + 33(5)$$
$$= 187$$

6. The numbers of marbles in two bags are $a(3x - y)$ and $2b(3x - y)$.
(a) Find the total number of marbles in the bags.
(b) Factor the result in **(a)**.
(c) All the marbles are arranged in rows and columns to form a rectangle. If one side of the rectangle has $(a + 2b)$ marbles, find the number of marbles on the other side.

Solution
(a) Total number of marbles
$$= a(3x - y) + 2b(3x - y)$$
$$= 3ax - ay + 6bx - 2by$$
(b) $3ax - ay + 6bx - 2by$
$$= 3ax + 6bx - ay - 2by$$
$$= 3x(a + 2b) - y(a + 2b)$$
$$= (a + 2b)(3x - y)$$
(c) The required number of marbles
$$= \frac{(a + 2b)(3x - y)}{a + 2b}$$
$$= 3x - y$$

7. A test consists of three parts. The minimum total score required to pass the test is $(8x + 4y)$ points. Jacob scores $(2x - y + 10)$ points and $(2x + 3y - 6)$ points in the first two parts.
(a) Find Jacob's total score in the first two parts.
(b) How many points does Jacob score in the third part if he just passes the test?
(c) Factor the result in **(b)**.

Solution
(a) Jacob's total score in the first two parts
$$= [(2x - y + 10) + (2x + 3y - 6)]$$
$$= (2x - y + 10 + 2x + 3y - 6)$$
$$= (4x + 2y + 4) \text{ points}$$
(b) The required score
$$= [(8x + 4y) - (4x + 2y + 4)]$$
$$= [8x + 4y - 4x - 2y - 4)$$
$$= (4x + 2y - 4) \text{ points}$$
(c) $4x + 2y - 4 = 2(2x + y - 2)$

8. In the diagram, n identical tables are joined end-to-end to form a long table. A single table can have 2 seats on each side and one seat at each end.

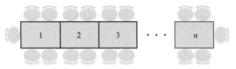

(a) Copy and complete the following table.

n	1	2	3	4	5
Total number of seats					

(b) If n tables are joined to form a long table, express the total number of seats in terms of n.

Solution

(a)

n	1	2	3	4	5
Total number of seats	6	10	14	18	22

(b) Total number of seats for n tables
$$= 6 + 4(n - 1)$$
$$= 6 + 4n - 4$$
$$= 4n + 2$$

Chapter 5 Simple Equations In One Variable

Class Activity 1

Objective: To formulate linear equations to solve problems.

Questions

A group of boys and girls planted a total of 148 trees. Each boy planted 7 trees and each girl planted 5 trees. There were 4 more boys than girls in the group. How many boys were there in the group?

1. Identify the unknown quantity that you are required to find in the problem.

    The number of boys in the group

2. Use a letter (e.g., x) to represent the unknown quantity.

    Let the number of boys in the group be x.

3. Express other quantities in terms of the letter that represents the unknown quantity. In this case, express each of the following in terms of x.

    (a) the number of girls = _____ $x - 4$ _____

    (b) the number of trees planted by all the boys = _____ $7x$ _____

    (c) the number of trees planted by all the girls = _____ $5(x - 4)$ _____

4. Form an equation required to solve the problem.

    $7x + 5(x - 4) = 148$

5. Solve the equation.

    $7x + 5(x - 4) = 148$

    $7x + 5x - 20 = 148$

    $12x = 168$

    $x = 14$

6. Write down the answer statement.

    There were 14 boys in the group.

Alternative Method:
We may use a model to formulate the problem.

Let the number of girls be y.

Girls: $\boxed{y}$

Boys: $\boxed{y}\boxed{4}$

Consider the numbers of trees planted by the girls and boys, denoted by GT and BT respectively, using the following model.

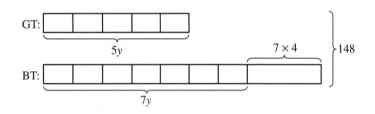

7. Form an equation to solve for y.

$5y + 7y + 28 = 148$

8. Hence, find the required number of boys.

$5y + 7y + 28 = 148$

$12y = 120$

$y = 10$

The required number of boys $= y + 4 = 14$.

Extend Your Learning Curve

Matchstick Triangle Patterns

Johnny uses matchsticks to form a pattern of triangles as shown below.

Suppose *m* matchsticks are required to form *n* triangles.

(a) Copy and complete the following table.

n	1	2	3	4	5	6
m	3					

(b) Find a formula connecting *m* and *n*.
(c) How many matchsticks are required to form 100 triangles?
(d) How many triangles can be formed with 2,005 matchsticks?
(e) Suppose the area of a triangle is $\sqrt{3}$ cm². Find the total area of the triangles formed in **(d)**. Give your answer correct to the closest whole number.

Suggested Answers

(a)

n	1	2	3	4	5	6
m	3	5	7	9	11	13

(b) Except for the first triangle, each triangle in a pattern of *n* triangles is formed by adding 2 matchsticks.
$\therefore$ $m = 3 + 2(n - 1)$ or $m = 2n + 1$

(c) When $n = 100$,
$$m = 2(100) + 1$$
$$= 201$$
$\therefore$ 201 matchsticks are required to form 100 triangles.

(d) When $m = 2,005$,
$$2,005 = 2n + 1$$
$$2,004 = 2n$$
$$\therefore n = 1,002$$
1,002 triangles can be formed with 2,005 matchsticks.

(e) Total area of 1,002 triangles $= 1,002 \times \sqrt{3}$
$$= 1,736 \text{ cm}^2 \quad \text{(correct to the closest whole number)}$$

Try It!

Section 5.1

1. Solve the equation $x - 2 = 7$.

   Solution
   $$x - 2 = 7$$
   $$x - 2 + 2 = 7 + 2$$
   $$x = 9$$

2. Solve the equation $x + 5 = 11$.

   Solution
   $$x + 5 = 11$$
   $$x + 5 - 5 = 11 - 5$$
   $$x = 6$$

3. Solve the equation $\frac{x}{3} = 5$.

   Solution
   $$\frac{x}{3} = 5$$
   $$\frac{x}{3} \times 3 = 5 \times 3$$
   $$x = 15$$

4. Solve the equation $-10x = 35$.

   Solution
   $$-10x = 35$$
   $$\frac{-10x}{-10} = \frac{35}{-10}$$
   $$x = -\frac{7}{2}$$
   $$= -3\frac{1}{2}$$

5. Solve the equation $7 - 10x = -2x - 5$.

   Solution
   $$7 - 10x = -2x - 5$$
   $$-10x + 2x = -5 - 7$$
   $$-8x = -12$$
   $$x = \frac{-12}{-8}$$
   $$= \frac{3}{2}$$
   $$= 1\frac{1}{2}$$

Section 5.2

6. Solve the equation $7(x + 2) = 2(2x + 9)$.

   Solution
   $$7(x + 2) = 2(2x + 9)$$
   $$7x + 14 = 4x + 18$$
   $$7x - 4x + 14 = 4x - 4x + 18$$
   $$3x + 14 - 14 = 18 - 14$$
   $$3x = 4$$
   $$x = \frac{4}{3}$$
   $$= 1\frac{1}{3}$$

7. Solve the equation $\frac{6(2x - 7)}{5} + 3 = x$.

   Solution
   $$\frac{6(2x - 7)}{5} + 3 = x$$
   $$6(2x - 7) + 15 = 5x$$
   $$12x - 42 + 15 = 5x$$
   $$12x - 5x - 27 = 0$$
   $$7x = 27$$
   $$x = \frac{27}{7}$$
   $$= 3\frac{6}{7}$$

8. Solve the equation $\frac{2x + 5}{7} = \frac{3x - 2}{4}$.

   Solution
   $$\frac{2x + 5}{7} = \frac{3x - 2}{4}$$
   $$4(2x + 5) = 7(3x - 2)$$
   $$8x + 20 = 21x - 14$$
   $$8x - 21x = -20 - 14$$
   $$-13x = -34$$
   $$x = \frac{34}{13}$$
   $$= 2\frac{8}{13}$$

9. Solve the equation $\frac{z}{3} + \frac{z - 6}{4} = 2$.

   Solution
   $$\frac{z}{3} + \frac{z - 6}{4} = 2$$
   $$4z + 3(z - 6) = 24$$
   $$4z + 3z - 18 = 24$$
   $$7z = 42$$
   $$z = 6$$

10. Given the formula $A = \frac{1}{2}(a + b)h$, find the value of a when $b = 13$, $h = 9$, and $A = 90$.

Solution

Substituting $b = 13$, $h = 9$, and $A = 90$ into
$$A = \frac{1}{2}(a + b)h,$$
we have the equation:
$$90 = \frac{1}{2}(a + 13) \times 9$$
$$90 \times \frac{2}{9} = a + 13$$
$$20 = a + 13$$
$$\therefore \ a = 7$$

Section 5.3

11. Solve the equation $\frac{8}{x + 1} = 4$.

Solution

$$\frac{8}{x + 1} = 4$$
$$8 = 4(x + 1)$$
$$8 = 4x + 4$$
$$4x = 4$$
$$x = 1$$

12. Solve the equation $\frac{y}{y + 4} - \frac{2}{3} = 0$.

Solution

$$\frac{y}{y + 4} = \frac{2}{3}$$
$$3y = 2(y + 4)$$
$$3y = 2y + 8$$
$$y = 8$$

Section 5.4

13. The sum of three consecutive integers is 144. Find the integers.

Solution

Let x be the smallest integer among these three consecutive integers.
$$x + (x + 1) + (x + 2) = 144$$
$$3x + 3 = 144$$
$$3x = 141$$
$$x = 47$$
The required integers are 47, 48, and 49.

14. Mr. Taylor is 4 times as old as his son. Four years ago, the sum of their ages was 37 years. Find the son's present age.

Solution

Let the son's present age be x years.
Mr. Taylor's present age = $4x$ years.
$$(4x - 4) + (x - 4) = 37$$
$$4x - 4 + x - 4 = 37$$
$$5x - 8 = 37$$
$$5x = 45$$
$$x = 9$$
The son's present age is 9 years.

15. The price of a book is \$1 more than twice the price of a pen. The total price of 5 books and 4 pens is \$47. Find the price of a pen and of a book.

Solution

Let the price of a pen be \$$x$.
The price of a book is \$$(2x + 1)$.
$$5(2x + 1) + 4x = 47$$
$$10x + 5 + 4x = 47$$
$$14x = 42$$
$$x = 3$$
$$\therefore \ 2x + 1 = 2(3) + 1$$
$$= 7$$
The price of a pen is \$3 and that of a book is \$7.

Exercise 5.1
Basic Practice

1. Solve the following equations.

    (a) $x + 8 = 9$ (b) $x + 36 = -40$

    (c) $x - 9 = 5$ (d) $x - 22 = -15$

    (e) $\frac{x}{2} = 3$ (f) $\frac{x}{5} = -4$

    (g) $4x = 24$ (h) $-9x = 21$

    (i) $2x - 3 = 7$ (j) $3x + 8 = -1$

    (k) $-5x + 2 = -3$ (l) $\frac{x}{3} - 2 = 0$

    (m) $\frac{1}{4}x + 9 = 6$ (n) $1 - \frac{1}{7}x = -8$

Solution

(a) $x + 8 = 9$
$$x + 8 - 8 = 9 - 8$$
$$x = 1$$

(b) $x + 36 = -40$
$$x + 36 - 36 = -40 - 36$$
$$x = -76$$

(c) $x - 9 = 5$
$$x - 9 + 9 = 5 + 9$$
$$x = 14$$

(d) $x - 22 = -15$
$$x - 22 + 22 = -15 + 22$$
$$x = 7$$

(e) $\frac{x}{2} = 3$
$$2 \times \frac{x}{2} = 2 \times 3$$
$$x = 6$$

(f) $\frac{x}{5} = -4$
$$5 \times \frac{x}{5} = 5 \times (-4)$$
$$x = -20$$

(g) $4x = 24$
$$\frac{4x}{4} = \frac{24}{4}$$
$$x = 6$$

(h) $-9x = 21$
$$\frac{-9x}{-9} = \frac{21}{-9}$$
$$x = -\frac{7}{3}$$
$$x = -2\frac{1}{3}$$

(i) $2x - 3 = 7$
$$2x - 3 + 3 = 7 + 3$$
$$2x = 10$$
$$\frac{2x}{2} = \frac{10}{2}$$
$$x = 5$$

(j) $3x + 8 = -1$
$$3x + 8 - 8 = -1 - 8$$
$$3x = -9$$
$$x = -\frac{9}{3}$$
$$x = -3$$

(k) $-5x + 2 = -3$
$$-5x = -5$$
$$x = 1$$

(l) $\frac{x}{3} - 2 = 0$
$$\frac{x}{3} = 2$$
$$x = 6$$

(m) $\frac{1}{4}x + 9 = 6$
$$\frac{1}{4}x = -3$$
$$x = -12$$

(n) $1 - \frac{1}{7}x = -8$
$$-\frac{1}{7}x = -9$$
$$x = (-9)(-7)$$
$$x = 63$$

Further Practice

2. Solve the following equations.

    (a) $12 + \frac{2}{5}x = 16$ (b) $9 - \frac{4}{3}x = -7$

    (c) $5x = x - 8$ (d) $2x - 10 = 6x$

    (e) $3x + 5 = -4x - 9$ (f) $4 - 3x = x + 8$

    (g) $-7x + 40 = -2x + 5$ (h) $-1 - 6x = 9 - 2x$

    (i) $6 + \frac{5}{7}x = x - 4$ (j) $2 - \frac{2}{3}x = \frac{5}{6}x + 8$

Solution

(a) $12 + \frac{2}{5}x = 16$
$$\frac{2}{5}x = 4$$
$$x = 4 \times \frac{5}{2}$$
$$x = 10$$

(b) $9 - \frac{4}{3}x = -7$

$$-\frac{4}{3}x = -16$$
$$x = -16 \times \left(-\frac{3}{4}\right)$$
$$x = 12$$

(c) $5x = x - 8$
$$5x - x = -8$$
$$4x = -8$$
$$x = -\frac{8}{4}$$
$$= -2$$

(d) $2x - 10 = 6x$
$$2x - 6x = 10$$
$$-4x = 10$$
$$x = \frac{10}{-4}$$
$$= -\frac{5}{2}$$
$$= -2\frac{1}{2}$$

(e) $3x + 5 = -4x - 9$
$$3x + 4x = -9 - 5$$
$$7x = -14$$
$$x = -\frac{14}{7}$$
$$= -2$$

(f) $4 - 3x = x + 8$
$$-3x - x = 8 - 4$$
$$-4x = 4$$
$$x = -1$$

(g) $-7x + 40 = -2x + 5$
$$-7x + 2x = 5 - 40$$
$$-5x = -35$$
$$x = 7$$

(h) $-1 - 6x = 9 - 2x$
$$-6x + 2x = 9 + 1$$
$$-4x = 10$$
$$x = \frac{10}{-4}$$
$$= -\frac{5}{2}$$
$$= -2\frac{1}{2}$$

(i) $6 + \frac{5}{7}x = x - 4$
$$\frac{5}{7}x - x = -4 - 6$$
$$-\frac{2}{7}x = -10$$
$$x = -10 \times \left(-\frac{7}{2}\right)$$
$$= 35$$

(j) $2 - \frac{2}{3}x = \frac{5}{6}x + 8$
$$-\frac{2}{3}x - \frac{5}{6}x = 6$$
$$-\frac{4}{6}x - \frac{5}{6}x = 6$$
$$-\frac{9}{6}x = 6$$
$$-\frac{3}{2}x = 6$$
$$x = 6 \times \left(-\frac{2}{3}\right)$$
$$= -4$$

Brainworks

3. Create an equation of the form $ax + b = c$, where a, b, and c are constants, such that the solution of the equation is $x = 4$.

Solution
The equation below is of the form $ax + b = c$, where $a = 4$, $b = 11$, and $c = 27$.
$$4x + 11 = 27$$
$$4x = 16$$
$$x = 4$$
The solution of the equation is $x = 4$.

Exercise 5.2
Basic Practice

1. Solve the following equations.
  (a) $3x + 4 = 2(2x + 7)$
  (b) $3(5x + 6) = 3x - 2$
  (c) $2(8x + 5) = 4(3x + 1)$
  (d) $3(4x - 1) = 7(2x - 5)$
  (e) $5(x + 3) - 4(2x - 9) = 0$
  (f) $3(3x - 1) - 4(5 - 2x) = -10$
  (g) $9x - 2(x + 8) = 5x - 11$
  (h) $1 - 4(2x + 3) = 5(x - 2) - 3(x - 1)$

Solution
(a) $3x + 4 = 2(2x + 7)$
$$3x + 4 = 4x + 14$$
$$3x - 4x = 14 - 4$$
$$-x = 10$$
$$x = -10$$

(b) $3(5x + 6) = 3x - 2$
$$15x + 18 = 3x - 2$$
$$15x - 3x = -2 - 18$$
$$12x = -20$$
$$x = -\frac{20}{12}$$
$$= -\frac{5}{3}$$
$$= -1\frac{2}{3}$$

(c) $2(8x + 5) = 4(3x + 1)$

$16x + 10 = 12x + 4$

$16x - 12x = 4 - 10$

$4x = -6$

$x = -\dfrac{6}{4}$

$= -\dfrac{3}{2}$

$= -1\dfrac{1}{2}$

(d) $3(4x - 1) = 7(2x - 5)$

$12x - 3 = 14x - 35$

$12x - 14x = -35 + 3$

$-2x = -32$

$x = 16$

(e) $5(x + 3) - 4(2x - 9) = 0$

$5x + 15 - 8x + 36 = 0$

$-3x + 51 = 0$

$3x = 51$

$x = 17$

(f) $3(3x - 1) - 4(5 - 2x) = -10$

$9x - 3 - 20 + 8x = -10$

$17x = -10 + 23$

$17x = 13$

$x = \dfrac{13}{17}$

(g) $9x - 2(x + 8) = 5x - 11$

$9x - 2x - 16 = 5x - 11$

$7x - 16 = 5x - 11$

$2x = 5$

$x = \dfrac{5}{2}$

$= 2\dfrac{1}{2}$

(h) $1 - 4(2x + 3) = 5(x - 2) - 3(x - 1)$

$1 - 8x - 12 = 5x - 10 - 3x + 3$

$-8x - 11 = 2x - 7$

$-8x - 2x = 11 - 7$

$-10x = 4$

$x = -\dfrac{4}{10}$

$= -\dfrac{2}{5}$

2. Solve the following equations.

(a) $\dfrac{2x + 9}{5} = 5$

(b) $\dfrac{3x - 11}{7} - 2 = 0$

(c) $\dfrac{7x - 2}{2} = \dfrac{5x - 3}{3}$

(d) $\dfrac{2x + 3}{3} = \dfrac{3x - 15}{11}$

(e) $\dfrac{3(5x - 6)}{4} + 2 = 4x$

(f) $\dfrac{2(1 - 4x)}{5} - 9 = 3(2 - x)$

Solution

(a) $\dfrac{2x + 9}{5} = 5$

$2x + 9 = 25$

$2x = 25 - 9$

$2x = 16$

$x = 8$

(b) $\dfrac{3x - 11}{7} - 2 = 0$

$\dfrac{3x - 11}{7} = 2$

$3x - 11 = 14$

$3x = 14 + 11$

$3x = 25$

$x = \dfrac{25}{3}$

$= 8\dfrac{1}{3}$

(c) $\dfrac{7x - 2}{2} = \dfrac{5x - 3}{3}$

$3(7x - 2) = 2(5x - 3)$

$21x - 6 = 10x - 6$

$11x = 0$

$x = 0$

(d) $\dfrac{2x + 3}{3} = \dfrac{3x - 15}{11}$

$11(2x + 3) = 3(3x - 15)$

$22x + 33 = 9x - 45$

$13x = -78$

$x = -6$

(e) $\dfrac{3(5x - 6)}{4} + 2 = 4x$

$3(5x - 6) + 8 = 16x$

$15x - 18 + 8 = 16x$

$-x = 10$

$x = -10$

(f) $\dfrac{2(1 - 4x)}{5} - 9 = 3(2 - x)$

$2(1 - 4x) - 45 = 15(2 - x)$

$2 - 8x - 45 = 30 - 15x$

$-8x - 43 = 30 - 15x$

$7x = 73$

$x = \dfrac{73}{7}$

$= 10\dfrac{3}{7}$

Further Practice

3. Solve the following equations.

(a) $x + \dfrac{x}{4} = 15$

(b) $\dfrac{x}{2} - \dfrac{x}{3} = 7$

(c) $\dfrac{t}{5} - \dfrac{t+2}{7} = 2$

(d) $\dfrac{2t-1}{3} + \dfrac{3t-4}{5} = t$

(e) $\dfrac{2y}{3} + \dfrac{5y}{4} = \dfrac{y}{6} - 8$

(f) $\dfrac{y+9}{2} = \dfrac{y-3}{4} - \dfrac{y}{3}$

(g) $\dfrac{z-7}{3} - \dfrac{z-5}{12} = \dfrac{2z-27}{15}$

(h) $\dfrac{4z+3}{5} - \dfrac{7z-1}{3} = \dfrac{2-19z}{10}$

Solution

(a) $x + \dfrac{x}{4} = 15$

$$4x + x = 60$$
$$5x = 60$$
$$x = 12$$

(b) $\dfrac{x}{2} - \dfrac{x}{3} = 7$

$$3x - 2x = 42$$
$$x = 42$$

(c) $\dfrac{t}{5} - \dfrac{t+2}{7} = 2$

$$7t - 5(t+2) = 70$$
$$7t - 5t - 10 = 70$$
$$2t = 80$$
$$t = 40$$

(d) $\dfrac{2t-1}{3} + \dfrac{3t-4}{5} = t$

$$5(2t-1) + 3(3t-4) = 15t$$
$$10t - 5 + 9t - 12 = 15t$$
$$19t - 17 = 15t$$
$$4t = 17$$
$$t = \dfrac{17}{4}$$
$$= 4\dfrac{1}{4}$$

(e) $\dfrac{2y}{3} + \dfrac{5y}{4} = \dfrac{y}{6} - 8$

$$4(2y) + 3(5y) = 2y - (12)8$$
$$8y + 15y = 2y - 96$$
$$21y = -96$$
$$y = -\dfrac{96}{21}$$
$$= -\dfrac{32}{7}$$
$$= -4\dfrac{4}{7}$$

(f) $\dfrac{y+9}{2} = \dfrac{y-3}{4} - \dfrac{y}{3}$

$$6(y+9) = 3(y-3) - 4y$$
$$6y + 54 = 3y - 9 - 4y$$
$$6y + 54 = -y - 9$$
$$7y = -63$$
$$y = -9$$

(g) $\dfrac{z-7}{3} - \dfrac{z-5}{12} = \dfrac{2z-27}{15}$

$$20(z-7) - 5(z-5) = 4(2z-27)$$
$$20z - 140 - 5z + 25 = 8z - 108$$
$$15z - 115 = 8z - 108$$
$$7z = 7$$
$$z = 1$$

(h) $\dfrac{4z+3}{5} - \dfrac{7z-1}{3} = \dfrac{2-19z}{10}$

$$6(4z+3) - 10(7z-1) = 3(2-19z)$$
$$24z + 18 - 70z + 10 = 6 - 57z$$
$$-46z + 28 = 6 - 57z$$
$$11z = -22$$
$$z = -2$$

Math@Work

4. Given the formula $A = P(1 + rt)$, find the value of r when $A = 27$, $P = 18$, and $t = 5$.

Solution

$$A = P(1 + rt)$$
$$27 = 18(1 + 5r)$$
$$27 = 18 + 90r$$
$$90r = 27 - 18$$
$$90r = 9$$
$$r = \dfrac{9}{90}$$
$$= \dfrac{1}{10}$$

5. The conversion formula for a temperature of f degree Fahrenheit (°F) and c degree Celsius (°C) is given by $c = \dfrac{5}{9}(f - 32)$. If the temperature in Montreal on one day in winter was −12°C, convert this temperature to degree Fahrenheit.

Solution

$$c = \dfrac{5}{9}(f - 32)$$
$$-12 = \dfrac{5}{9}(f - 32)$$
$$-12 = \dfrac{5}{9}f - \dfrac{160}{9}$$
$$\dfrac{5}{9}f = -12 + \dfrac{160}{9}$$
$$\dfrac{5}{9}f = \dfrac{52}{9}$$
$$f = \dfrac{52}{9} \times \dfrac{9}{5}$$
$$= 10.4°F$$

6. The distance, d miles, covered by a car in time, t hours, when it increases its speed gradually from u miles per hour to v miles per hour is given by $d = \frac{t}{2}(u + v)$. If $d = 290$, $t = 5$, and $u = 54$, find the value of v.

Solution

$$d = \frac{t}{2}(u + v)$$
$$290 = \frac{5}{2}(54 + v)$$
$$290 = 135 + \frac{5}{2}v$$
$$\frac{5}{2}v = 290 - 135$$
$$\frac{5}{2}v = 155$$
$$v = 155 \times \frac{2}{5}$$
$$= 62$$

7. The object distance, u units, and the image distance, v units, are related by the formula $f(u + v) = uv$ where f is the focal length of the lens in units. Find the value of v when $f = 20$ and $u = 30$.

Solution

$$f(u + v) = uv$$
$$20(30 + v) = 30v$$
$$600 + 20v = 30v$$
$$30v - 20v = 600$$
$$10v = 600$$
$$v = 60$$

Brainworks

8. What conclusions can you draw about the solutions of the following equations?
(a) $2(3x + 8) = 3(2x + 4)$
(b) $\dfrac{3x + 6}{3} = x + 2$

Solution
(a) $2(3x + 8) = 3(2x + 4)$
$6x + 16 = 6x + 12$
$16 = 12$
This is always false.
∴ the given equation has no solution.

(b) $\dfrac{3x + 6}{3} = x + 2$
$3x + 6 = 3(x + 2)$
$3x + 6 = 3x + 6$
$0 = 0$
This is always true.
∴ the solutions of the given equation are all the real numbers.

Exercise 5.3
Basic Practice

1. Solve the following equations.

(a) $\dfrac{15}{x} = 3$ (b) $\dfrac{7}{x} = -2$

(c) $\dfrac{1}{x} - 4 = 0$ (d) $9 - \dfrac{6}{x} = 0$

(e) $\dfrac{2}{x} - 3 = \dfrac{1}{2}$ (f) $\dfrac{2}{x - 3} = 4$

(g) $\dfrac{7}{2x + 5} = \dfrac{2}{3}$ (h) $\dfrac{7}{x - 9} - 5 = 0$

Solution

(a) $\dfrac{15}{x} = 3$
$15 = 3x$
$x = 5$

(b) $\dfrac{7}{x} = -2$
$7 = -2x$
$x = -\dfrac{7}{2}$
$= -3\dfrac{1}{2}$

(c) $\dfrac{1}{x} - 4 = 0$
$1 - 4x = 0$
$4x = 1$
$x = \dfrac{1}{4}$

(d) $9 - \dfrac{6}{x} = 0$
$9x - 6 = 0$
$9x = 6$
$x = \dfrac{2}{3}$

(e) $\dfrac{2}{x} - 3 = \dfrac{1}{2}$
$4 - 6x = x$
$-7x = -4$
$x = \dfrac{4}{7}$

(f) $\dfrac{2}{x - 3} = 4$
$2 = 4(x - 3)$
$2 = 4x - 12$
$4x = 14$
$x = \dfrac{14}{4}$
$= \dfrac{7}{2}$
$= 3\dfrac{1}{2}$

(g) $\dfrac{7}{2x+5} = \dfrac{2}{3}$

$$21 = 2(2x+5)$$
$$21 = 4x + 10$$
$$4x = 11$$
$$x = \dfrac{11}{4}$$
$$= 2\dfrac{3}{4}$$

(h) $\dfrac{7}{x-9} - 5 = 0$

$$7 - 5(x-9) = 0$$
$$7 - 5x + 45 = 0$$
$$5x = 52$$
$$x = \dfrac{52}{5}$$
$$= 10\dfrac{2}{5}$$

Further Practice

2. Solve the following equations.

(a) $\dfrac{3x}{x-1} = 2$ **(b)** $\dfrac{x}{x+3} = \dfrac{7}{10}$

(c) $\dfrac{3y+2}{2y-7} = 4$ **(d)** $\dfrac{y+1}{2y-5} = \dfrac{1}{3}$

(e) $\dfrac{1}{u+4} = \dfrac{5}{3u}$ **(f)** $\dfrac{3u+2}{u-1} = \dfrac{5}{u-1}$

Solution

(a) $\dfrac{3x}{x-1} = 2$

$$3x = 2(x-1)$$
$$3x = 2x - 2$$
$$x = -2$$

(b) $\dfrac{x}{x+3} = \dfrac{7}{10}$

$$10x = 7(x+3)$$
$$10x = 7x + 21$$
$$3x = 21$$
$$x = 7$$

(c) $\dfrac{3y+2}{2y-7} = 4$

$$3y + 2 = 4(2y-7)$$
$$3y + 2 = 8y - 28$$
$$-5y = -30$$
$$y = 6$$

(d) $\dfrac{y+1}{2y-5} = \dfrac{1}{3}$

$$3(y+1) = 2y - 5$$
$$3y + 3 = 2y - 5$$
$$y = -5 - 3$$
$$y = -8$$

(e) $\dfrac{1}{u+4} = \dfrac{5}{3u}$

$$3u = 5(u+4)$$
$$3u = 5u + 20$$
$$2u = -20$$
$$u = -10$$

(f) $\dfrac{3u+2}{u-1} = \dfrac{5}{u-1}$

$$3u + 2 = 5$$
$$3u = 3$$
$$u = 1$$

However, when $u = 1$, the denominator of the original equation, $u - 1$, is 0.

$\therefore$ there is no solution.

Math@Work

3. Given the formula $t = \dfrac{v-u}{a}$, find the value of a when $t = 4$, $u = 32$, and $v = 20$.

Solution

$t = \dfrac{v-u}{a}$

When $t = 4$, $u = 32$, and $v = 20$,

$$4 = \dfrac{20-32}{a}$$
$$4a = -12$$
$$a = -3$$

4. Given the formula $S = \dfrac{a}{1-r}$, find the value of r when $a = 3$ and $S = 1\dfrac{1}{3}$.

Solution

$S = \dfrac{a}{1-r}$

When $a = 3$ and $S = 1\dfrac{1}{3}$,

$$1\dfrac{1}{3} = \dfrac{3}{1-r}$$
$$\dfrac{4}{3} = \dfrac{3}{1-r}$$
$$4(1-r) = 9$$
$$4 - 4r = 9$$
$$-4r = 5$$
$$r = -\dfrac{5}{4}$$
$$= -1\dfrac{1}{4}$$

5. Given the formula $\dfrac{1}{u} + \dfrac{1}{v} = \dfrac{1}{f}$, find the value of v when $f = 20$ and $u = 30$.

Solution

$\dfrac{1}{u} + \dfrac{1}{v} = \dfrac{1}{f}$

When $f = 20$ and $u = 30$,

$\dfrac{1}{30} + \dfrac{1}{v} = \dfrac{1}{20}$

Multiplying both sides by $60v$,

$2v + 60 = 3v$

$v = 60$

6. Given the formula $T = \dfrac{km}{m + n}$, find the value of n when $k = 4$, $m = 5$, and $T = 2\dfrac{1}{2}$.

Solution

$T = \dfrac{km}{m + n}$

When $k = 4$, $m = 5$, and $T = 2\dfrac{1}{2}$,

$2\dfrac{1}{2} = \dfrac{4 \times 5}{5 + n}$

$\dfrac{5}{2} = \dfrac{20}{5 + n}$

$5(5 + n) = 40$

$25 + 5n = 40$

$5n = 15$

$n = 3$

Brainworks

7. Is $x \div x$ always equal to 1? If not, when is $x \div x$ not equal to 1? Explain briefly.

Solution

When $x \ne 0$, $\dfrac{x}{x} = 1$;

when $x = 0$, $\dfrac{x}{x}$ is undefined.

$\therefore$ $x \div x$ is NOT always equal to 1.

Exercise 5.4

Basic Practice

1. Tim is 5 pounds heavier than Amy. Let Amy's weight be x pounds.
   (a) Express Tim's weight in terms of x.
   (b) If Tim's weight is 126 pounds, what is Amy's weight?

Solution
   (a) Tim's weight $= (x + 5)$ pounds
   (b) $x + 5 = 126$
   $\qquad x = 121$
   Amy's weight is 121 pounds.

2. The price of a watch is \$50 more than twice the price of a gold ring. Let the price of the ring be \$$x$.
   (a) Express the price of the watch in terms of x.
   (b) If the price of the watch is \$208, what is the price of the ring?

Solution
   (a) Price of the watch $= \$(2x + 50)$
   (b) $2x + 50 = 208$
   $\qquad 2x = 158$
   $\qquad x = 79$
   The price of the ring is \$79.

3. Every week Rick works 3 times as many hours as Joseph. Let the number of hours Joseph works in a week be x hours.
   (a) Express the number of hours Rick works in a week in terms of x.
   (b) If their total number of working hours in a week is 56 hours, find the number of hours Joseph works in a week.

Solution
   (a) Number of hours Rick works in a week
   $\qquad = 3x$ hours
   (b) $3x + x = 56$
   $\qquad 4x = 56$
   $\qquad x = 14$
   Joseph works 14 hours in a week.

4. There are three consecutive even integers. Let x be the smallest one.
   (a) Express the other two integers in terms of x.
   (b) If the sum of these three integers is 66, find the integers.

Solution
   (a) The two integers are $x + 2$ and $x + 4$.
   (b) $x + (x + 2) + (x + 4) = 66$
   $\qquad x + x + 2 + x + 4 = 66$
   $\qquad 3x + 6 = 66$
   $\qquad 3x = 66 - 6$
   $\qquad 3x = 60$
   $\qquad x = 20$
   $\therefore$ the three integers are 20, 22, and 24.

5. Mrs. Clark buys three identical boxes of chocolates from a supermarket. She pays the cashier a \$50 bill and gets \$8 change. How much does each box of chocolates cost?

Solution
   Let the cost of each box of chocolates be \$$x$.
   $3x + 8 = 50$
   $\qquad 3x = 42$
   $\qquad x = 14$
   Each box of chocolates costs \$14.

6.
The total price of a teapot and 4 identical cups is $64. If the price of the teapot is $28, what is the price of a cup?

Solution
Let the price of a cup be x.
$28 + 4x = 64$
$\qquad 4x = 36$
$\qquad\ x = 9$
The price of a cup is $9.

Further Practice

7.
Tom is twice as old as Andy. In 4 years' time, the sum of their ages will be 32 years. Find Andy's present age.

Solution
Let Andy's present age be x years.
$(x + 4) + (2x + 4) = 32$
$\qquad 3x + 8 = 32$
$\qquad\quad 3x = 24$
$\qquad\quad\ x = 8$
Andy's present age is 8 years.

8.
Peter has four more $50 bills than $10 bills in his wallet. If the total amount of his money is $380, how many $10 bills does Peter have?

Solution
Let the number of $10 bills Peter have be x.
$\ 10x + 50(x + 4) = 380$
$10x + 50x + 200 = 380$
$\qquad\qquad 60x = 180$
$\qquad\qquad\ \ x = 3$
Peter has three $10 bills.

9.
In a mathematics competition, the winner won $100 more than twice the amount won by the runner-up. How much money did the runner-up win if both of them won $2,350 altogether?

Solution
Let x be the amount won by the runner-up.
$x + (2x + 100) = 2,350$
$\qquad\quad 3x = 2,250$
$\qquad\qquad x = 750$
The runner-up won $750.

10.
Aaron, Ben, and Charles shared 110 marbles. Ben received twice as many marbles as Aaron. Charles received 10 marbles more than Aaron. How many marbles did each boy receive?

Solution
Let Aaron's share be x marbles.
Ben's share = $2x$ marbles.
Charles's share = $(x + 10)$ marbles.

$x + 2x + (x + 10) = 110$
$\qquad\qquad\quad 4x = 100$
$\qquad\qquad\quad\ x = 25$
Aaron received 25 marbles, Ben received 50 marbles, and Charles received 35 marbles.

11.
144 coins are divided equally among some children. If there were 3 children fewer, each child would have 16 coins. How many children are there?

Solution
Let the number of children be x.
$$\frac{144}{x - 3} = 16$$
$$\frac{9}{x - 3} = 1$$
$$9 = x - 3$$
$$x = 12$$
There are 12 children.

12.
The denominator of a fraction is 3 more than its numerator. If 2 is added to both the numerator and the denominator, the new fraction is equivalent to $\frac{2}{3}$. Find the original fraction.
(*Hint:* Let the numerator of the original fraction be x.)

Solution
Let the numerator of the original fraction be x.
Thus, the denominator of the original fraction is $x + 3$.
$$\frac{x + 2}{(x + 3) + 2} = \frac{2}{3}$$
$$\frac{x + 2}{x + 5} = \frac{2}{3}$$
$$3(x + 2) = 2(x + 5)$$
$$3x + 6 = 2x + 10$$
$$x = 4$$
The original fraction is $\frac{4}{7}$.

Math@Work

13.
Mrs. Perry has a sum of money to buy fruits. She can buy n mangoes at $1.60 each and have $0.80 left. Alternatively, she can buy $(n + 10)$ apples at $0.70 each and have $0.10 left.
(a) Find the value of n.
(b) How much money does Mrs. Perry have for buying fruits?
(c) If Mrs. Perry buys 3 mangoes and uses the rest of the money to buy apples,
(i) how many apples can she buy?
(ii) how much money will she have left?

Solution

(a) Consider the sum of money for buying fruits.

$1.60n + 0.80 = 0.70(n + 10) + 0.10$

Multiplying the above equation by 10:

$$16n + 8 = 7(n + 10) + 1$$
$$16n + 8 = 7n + 70 + 1$$
$$9n = 63$$
$$n = 7$$

The value of n is 7.

(b) The required amount $= \$(1.60 \times 7 + 0.80)$
$$= \$12$$

(c) **(i)** The amount left after buying 3 mangoes
$$= \$12 - \$1.60 \times 3$$
$$= \$7.20$$

Since $\dfrac{\$7.20}{\$0.70} = 10\dfrac{2}{7}$,

$\therefore$ she can buy 10 apples.

(ii) The amount left $= \$7.20 - \$(0.70 \times 10)$
$$= \$0.20$$

14. George wants to participate in a triathlon competition where he has to swim, cycle, and run some distances. The cycling distance is 4 times the running distance. The swimming distance is 5.5 miles less than the running distance, and is 24 miles less than the cycling distance. Find the total distance of the race.

Solution

Let x be the running distance.

Cyling distance $= 4x$ miles

Swimming distance

$= (x - 5.5)$ miles and $(4x - 24)$ miles

$\therefore\ x - 5.5 = 4x - 24$
$$4x - x = -5.5 + 24$$
$$3x = 18.5$$
$$x = 6\frac{1}{6} \text{ miles}$$

Cycling distance $= 4x$

$$= 4 \times 6\frac{1}{6}$$

$$= 24\frac{2}{3} \text{ miles}$$

Swimming distance $= x - 5.5$

$$= 6\frac{1}{6} - 5\frac{1}{2}$$

$$= \frac{2}{3} \text{ miles}$$

Total distance $= 6\frac{1}{6} + 24\frac{2}{3} + \frac{2}{3}$

$$= 31\frac{1}{2} \text{ miles}$$

Brainworks

15. Write an application problem such that the equation to be formed for solving the problem is $5x + 4(x - 10) = 140$.

Solution

Consider the following problem.

In a class, the number of girls is 10 fewer than the number of boys. Each boy runs 5 laps and each girl runs 4 laps. The total number of laps run by the boys and girls is 140. Find the number of boys in the class.

The equation to be formed is as follows:

$$5x + 4(x - 10) = 140,$$

where x represents the number of boys and $x - 10$ represents the number of girls.

Review Exercise 5

1. Solve the following equations.

(a) $13x - 22 = 30$

(b) $2(5x - 8) + 6 = 11$

(c) $\dfrac{2x}{3} + \dfrac{x}{5} = 13$

(d) $1 - \dfrac{4}{7}x = 23 + x$

(e) $\dfrac{4x - 5}{2} = \dfrac{7x - 3}{9}$

(f) $\dfrac{x - 4}{3} - \dfrac{2x + 1}{6} = \dfrac{5x - 1}{2}$

(g) $\dfrac{2}{x - 7} = 6$

(h) $\dfrac{4x - 1}{5x + 1} = \dfrac{5}{7}$

Solution

(a) $13x - 22 = 30$
$$13x = 52$$
$$x = 4$$

(b) $2(5x - 8) + 6 = 11$
$$10x - 16 + 6 = 11$$
$$10x - 10 = 11$$
$$10x = 21$$
$$x = \frac{21}{10}$$
$$= 2\frac{1}{10}$$

(c) $\dfrac{2x}{3} + \dfrac{x}{5} = 13$
$$10x + 3x = 195$$
$$13x = 195$$
$$x = 15$$

(d)
$$1 - \frac{4}{7}x = 23 + x$$
$$7 - 4x = 161 + 7x$$
$$-11x = 154$$
$$x = -14$$

(e)
$$\frac{4x - 5}{2} = \frac{7x - 3}{9}$$
$$9(4x - 5) = 2(7x - 3)$$
$$36x - 45 = 14x - 6$$
$$22x = 39$$
$$x = \frac{39}{22}$$
$$= 1\frac{17}{22}$$

(f)
$$\frac{x - 4}{3} - \frac{2x + 1}{6} = \frac{5x - 1}{2}$$
$$2(x - 4) - (2x + 1) = 3(5x - 1)$$
$$2x - 8 - 2x - 1 = 15x - 3$$
$$-9 = 15x - 3$$
$$15x = -6$$
$$= -\frac{6}{15}$$
$$= -\frac{2}{5}$$

(g)
$$\frac{2}{x - 7} = 6$$
$$2 = 6(x - 7)$$
$$2 = 6x - 42$$
$$6x = 44$$
$$x = \frac{44}{6}$$
$$= \frac{22}{3}$$
$$= 7\frac{1}{3}$$

(h)
$$\frac{4x - 1}{5x + 1} = \frac{5}{7}$$
$$7(4x - 1) = 5(5x + 1)$$
$$28x - 7 = 25x + 5$$
$$3x = 12$$
$$x = 4$$

2. Given the formula $D = b^2 - 4ac$,
  (a) find the value of D when $a = 1$, $b = -5$, and $c = 3$,
  (b) find the value of c when $a = 2$, $b = 3$, and $D = 49$.

Solution
(a)
$$D = b^2 - 4ac$$
When $a = 1$, $b = -5$ and $c = 3$,
$$D = (-5)^2 - 4(1)(3)$$
$$= 25 - 12$$
$$= 13$$

(b) When $a = 2$, $b = 3$, and $D = 49$,
$$49 = 3^2 - 4(2)c$$
$$49 = 9 - 8c$$
$$8c = -40$$
$$c = -5$$

3. Given the formula $S = \frac{n(a + b)}{2}$,
  (a) find the value of S when $a = 1$, $b = 25$, and $n = 12$,
  (b) find the value of a when $b = 41$, $n = 15$, and $S = 330$.

Solution
(a)
$$S = \frac{n(a + b)}{2}$$
When $a = 1$, $b = 25$, and $n = 12$,
$$S = \frac{12(1 + 25)}{2}$$
$$= 156$$

(b) When $b = 41$, $n = 15$, and $S = 330$,
$$330 = \frac{15(a + 41)}{2}$$
$$a + 41 = 330 \times \frac{2}{15}$$
$$a + 41 = 44$$
$$a = 3$$

4. The lengths of the sides of a triangle are $(2x + 1)$ cm, $(3x + 2)$ cm, and $(4x - 1)$ cm.
  (a) Find the perimeter of the triangle in terms of x.
  (b) If the perimeter of the triangle is 47 cm, find the value of x.

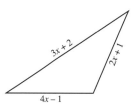

Solution
(a) Perimeter of the triangle
$$= (2x + 1) + (3x + 2) + (4x - 1)$$
$$= 2x + 1 + 3x + 2 + 4x - 1$$
$$= (9x + 2) \text{ cm}$$

(b)
$$9x + 2 = 47$$
$$9x = 45$$
$$x = 5$$
The value of x is 5.

5. Peter has 96 stamps and Sam has 63. How many stamps should Sam give Peter so that Peter will have twice as many stamps as Sam?

Solution
Let x be the number of stamps that Sam gives to Peter.
$96 + x = 2(63 - x)$
$96 + x = 126 - 2x$
$\qquad 3x = 30$
$\qquad\ x = 10$
Sam should give Peter 10 stamps so that Peter will have twice as many stamps as Sam.

6. A boy is 26 years younger than his father. In 3 years' time, his age will be $\frac{1}{3}$ his father's age. Find the boy's present age.

Solution
Let the boy's present age be x years.
His father's present age $= (x + 26)$ years.
$$x + 3 = \frac{1}{3}[(x + 26) + 3]$$
$$x + 3 = \frac{1}{3}(x + 29)$$
$3x + 9 = x + 29$
$\qquad 2x = 20$
$\qquad\ x = 10$
The boy's present age is 10 years.

7. The price of a skirt is \$25 more than the price of a T-shirt. The total price of 3 skirts and 8 T-shirts is \$339. Find the price of a skirt.

Solution
Let \$$x$ be the price of a skirt.
$3x + 8(x - 25) = 339$
$3x + 8x - 200 = 339$
$\qquad\qquad 11x = 539$
$\qquad\qquad\ \ x = 49$
The price of a skirt is \$49.

8. In a certain week, the amount of time Lisa spent on watching television was 3 hours more than twice the time she spent on doing her mathematics homework. If the total time she spent on these two activities was 30 hours in that week, how many hours did Lisa spend on doing her mathematics homework?

Solution
Let the amount of time Lisa spent on doing her mathematics homework be x hours.
$x + (2x + 3) = 30$
$\qquad 3x + 3 = 30$
$\qquad\quad 3x = 27$
$\qquad\quad\ x = 9$
Lisa spent 9 hours on doing her mathematics homework.

9. The number of books in a class library is 17 more than 3 times the number of students in the class. If 5 students are absent, each student can borrow exactly 4 books from the library. Find the number of students in the class.

Solution
Let x be the number of students in the class.
$$\frac{3x + 17}{x - 5} = 4$$
$3x + 17 = 4x - 20$
$\qquad\quad\ x = 37$
The number of students in the class is 37.

10. A number is 4 times greater than another number. By subtracting 3 from each number, the first number becomes 5 times greater than the second. What are the two numbers?

Solution
Let x be the first number.
$$x - 3 = 5\left(\frac{x}{4} - 3\right)$$
$$x - 3 = \frac{5}{4}x - 15$$
$$\frac{1}{4}x = 12$$
$$\qquad x = 48$$
$\therefore$ the two numbers are 12 and 48.

Chapter 6 Ratio, Rate, And Speed

Class Activity 1

Objective: To examine the pulse rate of the human body.

Tasks

Do the following:

(a) Jump up and down 10 times. Then, take your pulse for 15 seconds and record the result.

Number of pulses in 15 seconds = _____ 19 _____

(b) Calculate your pulse rate per minute.

Pulse rate per minute = _____ $19 \times 4 = 76$ pulses/min _____

(c) Take your pulse again for 1 minute and record the result.

Pulse rate per minute = _____ 73 pulses/min _____

Question

Are the results in **(b)** and **(c)** different? Why?

The results are different. This is because the pulse rate is not a constant and it will be faster immediately after jumping.

Class Activity 2

Objective: To explore the calculation of average speed.

The speed of a car for the first 2 hours of a journey is 50 miles per hour. Its speed for the next hour is 74 miles per hour. What is its average speed for the whole journey?

Questions

1. What would be a more accurate term to describe the word 'speed' in the first sentence? Why?

It is more accurate to use the term 'average speed' instead of 'speed'. This is because a car takes time to pick up the speed from rest to

50 miles per hour. Also, it cannot change its speed from 50 miles per hour to 74 miles per hour immediately.

2. Which one of the two solutions below is the correct method of obtaining the average speed for the whole journey, and why?

Solution (i):

Average speed = $\frac{1}{2}(50 + 74)$

= 62 mi/hr

Solution (ii):

Total distance traveled = $50 \times 2 + 74$

= 174 miles

Total time taken = 3 hr

Average speed = 174 mi ÷ 3 hr

= 58 mi/hr

By the definition of average speed, the correct solution would be (ii). Also, for an average speed of 62 mi/hr, the car would have traveled

186 mi in 3 hours. However, in this case, the total distance covered is only 174 mi.

Extend Your Learning Curve

Fastest Train

Find out the speed of the fastest train in the world in both km/hr and mph.

Suggested Answer:

The speed of the fastest train in the world is 581 km/hr (361 mph), set by a Japanese test train MLX01 on a magnetic levitation track.

Try It!

Section 6.1

1. A bag consists of 25 green balls and 15 red balls. Find the ratio of
   (a) the number of green balls to the number of red balls,
   (b) the number of red balls to the total number of balls in the bag.

   Solution
   (a) Number of green balls : Number of red balls
   $$= 25 : 15$$
   $$= 5 : 3$$
   (b) Number of red balls : Total number of balls
   $$= 15 : (25 + 15)$$
   $$= 15 : 40$$
   $$= 3 : 8$$

2. The masses of two bags of sugar, A and B, are 750 grams and 1 kilogram respectively. Find the ratio of the mass of B to the mass of A.

   Solution
   Mass of B : Mass of $A = 1$ kg : 750 g
   $$= 1,000 \text{ g} : 750 \text{ g}$$
   $$= 4 : 3$$

3. Express each ratio in its simplest form.
   (a) $1 : \dfrac{1}{2}$ (b) $1\dfrac{1}{3} : 4\dfrac{4}{7}$
   (c) $0.360 : 0.153$

   Solution
   (a) $1 : \dfrac{1}{2} = 1 \times 2 : \dfrac{1}{2} \times 2$
   $$= 2 : 1$$
   (b) $1\dfrac{1}{3} : 4\dfrac{4}{7} = \dfrac{4}{3} : \dfrac{32}{7}$
   $$= \dfrac{4}{3} \times \dfrac{21}{4} : \dfrac{32}{7} \times \dfrac{21}{4}$$
   $$= 7 : 24$$
   (c) $0.360 : 0.153 = 360 : 153$
   $$= \dfrac{360}{9} : \dfrac{153}{9}$$
   $$= 40 : 17$$

4. If $a : b = 7 : 10$ and $b : c = 15 : 8$, find $a : b : c$.

   Solution
   $a : b = 7 : 10$
   $$= 7 \times 3 : 10 \times 3$$
   $$= 21 : 30$$

$b : c = 15 : 8$
$$= 15 \times 2 : 8 \times 2$$
$$= 30 : 16$$
$\therefore \ a : b : c = 21 : 30 : 16$

5. Copper, zinc, and tin are combined in the ratio $2 : 3 : 4$ by mass to make an alloy. If the mass of a piece of the alloy is 2.7 kg, find the mass, in grams, of
   (a) copper,   (b) zinc,
   in the alloy.

   Solution
   (a) Mass of copper $= 2.7 \times \dfrac{2}{2 + 3 + 4} = 0.6$ kg $= 600$ g
   (b) Mass of zinc $= 2.7 \times \dfrac{3}{2 + 3 + 4} = 0.9$ kg $= 900$ g

6. Three boys X, Y, and Z share 132 computer games. The ratio of X's share to Y's share is $2 : 3$. The ratio of Y's share to Z's share is $1 : 2$. How many computer games does each boy get?

   Solution
   X's share : Y's share $= 2 : 3$
   Y's share : Z's share $= 1 : 2 = 3 : 6$
   $\therefore \ X$'s share : Y's share : Z's share $= 2 : 3 : 6$
   Number of copies that X gets $= 132 \times \dfrac{2}{2 + 3 + 6}$
   $$= 24$$
   Number of copies that Y gets $= 132 \times \dfrac{3}{2 + 3 + 6}$
   $$= 36$$
   Number of copies that Z gets $= 132 \times \dfrac{6}{2 + 3 + 6}$
   $$= 72$$

7. The weights of May and Terry are in the ratio $3 : 4$. If May's weight increases by 6 pounds while Terry's weight decreases by 4 pounds, the ratio of their weights become $24 : 29$. Find their original weights.

   Solution
   Let May's original weight and Terry's original weight be $3x$ pounds and $4x$ pounds respectively, where x is a constant.
   May's new weight $= (3x + 6)$ pounds
   Terry's new weight $= (4x - 4)$ pounds
   $$\frac{3x + 6}{4x - 4} = \frac{24}{29}$$
   $$29(3x + 6) = 24(4x - 4)$$
   $$87x + 174 = 96x - 96$$
   $$9x = 270$$
   $$x = 30$$
   $\therefore \ 3x = 90$
   $$4x = 120$$
   May's original weight is 90 pounds and Terry's original weight is 120 pounds.

Section 6.2

8. Find the rate in each case.
  (a) Joe ran 100 meters in 12.5 seconds. Give your answer in m/s.
  (b) 128 fluid ounce of apple juice cost $6.40. Give your answer in $/fl. oz.

Solution

  (a) Joe's rate of running $= \dfrac{100 \text{ m}}{12.5 \text{ s}}$

$= 8$ m/s

  (b) Cost rate of juice $= \dfrac{\$6.40}{128 \text{ fl. oz}}$

$= \$0.05/\text{fl. oz.}$

9. The price of a 50-square-meter apartment is $69,900. Find the price rate of the apartment in $/m^2.

Solution

Price rate $= \dfrac{\$69,900}{50}$

$= \$1,398/\text{m}^2$

10. A worker is paid $152 for 8 hours of work.
  (a) Find the hourly wage rate.
  (b) If the worker works for 5 hours, find his wage.

Solution

  (a) Hourly wage rate $= \dfrac{\$152}{8 \text{ hr}}$

$= \$19/\text{hr}$

  (b) His wage $= \$19 \times 5$

$= \$95$

Section 6.3

11. The average speed of a car for the first $1\frac{1}{2}$ hours of a journey is 64 miles per hour. Its average speed for the next $2\frac{1}{2}$ hours is 72 miles per hour. Find its average speed for the whole journey.

Solution

Total distance traveled $= 64 \times 1\frac{1}{2} + 72 \times 2\frac{1}{2}$

$= 276$ mi

Total time taken $= 1\frac{1}{2} + 2\frac{1}{2}$

$= 4$ hr

Its average speed for the whole journey $= \dfrac{276}{4}$

$= 69$ mph

12. Towns X and Y are 108 kilometers apart. Susan drives at an average speed of 72 kilometers per hour from X to Y and returns from Y to X at an average speed of 54 kilometers per hour. Find her average speed for the whole journey.

Solution

Total distance traveled $= 108 + 108$

$= 216$ km

Total time taken $= \dfrac{108}{72} + \dfrac{108}{54}$

$= 3.5$ hr

Her average speed for the whole journey $= \dfrac{216}{3.5}$

$= 61\frac{5}{7}$ km/hr

13. The speed limit for a road is 80 km/hr.
  (a) Express this speed limit in meters per second.
  (b) Taking 1 kilometer = 0.62 miles, express the speed limit in miles per hour, to the nearest 10 mi/hr.

Solution

  (a) Speed limit $= 80$ km/hr

$= 80 \times \dfrac{1,000}{3,600}$ m/s

$= 22\frac{2}{9}$ m/s

  (b) Speed limit $= 80$ km/hr

$= 80 \times 0.62$ mi/hr

$= 49.6$ mi/hr

$= 50$ mi/hr

(corrected to nearest 10 mi/hr)

14. The pronghorn antelope's exceptional speed is necessary in order to evade predators by outrunning them. The animal is considered to be the fastest land animal in the United States. The top speed is very difficult to measure accurately. However, the animal has been clocked at 61 mph. Express this speed in kilometers per hour.

Solution

Speed $= 61$ mph

$= 61 \text{ mph} \times \dfrac{1}{0.62}$ km/hr

$= 98.39$ km/hr (corrected to 2 d.p.)

Exercise 6.1

Basic Practice

1. Express each ratio in the simplest form.
   (a) $18 : 27$
   (b) $144 : 132$
   (c) $1\frac{1}{2} : 4\frac{1}{2}$
   (d) $2\frac{2}{3} : 1\frac{1}{5}$
   (e) $0.250 : 0.375$
   (f) $0.48 : 2\frac{2}{15}$
   (g) 1.6 feet : 36 inches
   (h) 850 grams : 3.4 kilograms
   (i) $1\frac{1}{3}$ hours : 20 minutes
   (j) 80¢ : $2

Solution

(a) $18 : 27 = \dfrac{18}{9} : \dfrac{27}{9}$
$\qquad\qquad = 2 : 3$

(b) $144 : 132 = \dfrac{144}{12} : \dfrac{132}{12}$
$\qquad\qquad\quad = 12 : 11$

(c) $1\frac{1}{2} : 4\frac{1}{2} = \dfrac{3}{2} : \dfrac{9}{2}$
$\qquad\qquad\quad = 1 : 3$

(d) $2\frac{2}{3} : 1\frac{1}{5} = \dfrac{8}{3} : \dfrac{6}{5}$
$\qquad\qquad\quad = 8 \times 5 : 6 \times 3$
$\qquad\qquad\quad = 40 : 18$
$\qquad\qquad\quad = 20 : 9$

(e) $0.250 : 0.375 = 250 : 375$
$\qquad\qquad\qquad = \dfrac{250}{125} : \dfrac{375}{125}$
$\qquad\qquad\qquad = 2 : 3$

(f) $0.48 : 2\frac{2}{15} = \dfrac{48}{100} : \dfrac{32}{15}$
$\qquad\qquad\quad = \dfrac{48}{100} \times \dfrac{300}{16} : \dfrac{32}{15} \times \dfrac{300}{16}$
$\qquad\qquad\quad = 9 : 40$

(g) 1.6 feet : 36 inches = 19.2 inches : 36 inches
$\qquad\qquad\qquad\qquad = \dfrac{19.2}{2.4} : \dfrac{36}{2.4}$
$\qquad\qquad\qquad\qquad = 8 : 15$

(h) 850 grams : 3.4 kilograms = 850 g : 3,400 g
$\qquad\qquad\qquad\qquad\qquad = 1 : 4$

(i) $1\frac{1}{3}$ hours : 20 minutes = 80 minutes : 20 minutes
$\qquad\qquad\qquad\qquad\qquad = 4 : 1$

(j) 80¢ : $2 = 80¢ : 200¢
$\qquad\qquad = \dfrac{80}{40} : \dfrac{200}{40}$
$\qquad\qquad = 2 : 5$

2. Given that $a : b : c = 20 : 35 : 15$,
   (a) simplify $a : b : c$,
   (b) find $a : b$,
   (c) find $c : b$.

Solution

(a) $a : b : c = 20 : 35 : 15$
$\qquad\qquad = \dfrac{20}{5} : \dfrac{35}{5} : \dfrac{15}{5}$
$\qquad\qquad = 4 : 7 : 3$

(b) $a : b = 4 : 7$

(c) $c : b = 3 : 7$

3. Given that $x : y : z = 5\frac{1}{2} : 4.62 : 33$,
   (a) simplify $x : y : z$,   (b) find $y : x$,
   (c) find $x : z$.

Solution

(a) $x : y : z = 5\frac{1}{2} : 4.62 : 33$
$\qquad\qquad = \dfrac{11}{2} : \dfrac{462}{100} : 33$
$\qquad\qquad = \dfrac{1}{2} : \dfrac{42}{100} : 3$
$\qquad\qquad = \dfrac{1}{2} \times 50 : \dfrac{42}{100} \times 50 : 3 \times 50$
$\qquad\qquad = 25 : 21 : 150$

(b) $y : x = 21 : 25$

(c) $x : z = 25 : 150 = 1 : 6$

4. Find the ratio of $a : b : c$.
   (a) $a : b = 3 : 4, b : c = 4 : 9$
   (b) $a : b = 5 : 3, b : c = 4 : 1$
   (c) $a : b = \dfrac{1}{2} : 1, b : c = 1 : \dfrac{1}{3}$
   (d) $a : b = 3 : 7, b : c = 3 : 7$

Solution

(a) $a : b = 3 : 4$
$\quad\ b : c = 4 : 9$
$\quad\ \therefore\ a : b : c = 3 : 4 : 9$

(b) $a : b = 5 : 3$
$\qquad\quad = 20 : 12$
$\quad\ b : c = 4 : 1$
$\qquad\quad = 12 : 3$
$\quad\ \therefore\ a : b : c = 20 : 12 : 3$

(c) $a : b = \dfrac{1}{2} : 1$
$\quad\ b : c = 1 : \dfrac{1}{3}$
$\quad\ \therefore\ a : b : c = \dfrac{1}{2} : 1 : \dfrac{1}{3}$
$\qquad\qquad\quad = \dfrac{1}{2} \times 6 : 1 \times 6 : \dfrac{1}{3} \times 6$
$\qquad\qquad\quad = 3 : 6 : 2$

(d) $a : b = 3 : 7$
$ = 9 : 21$
$b : c = 3 : 7$
$ = 21 : 49$
$\therefore\ a : b : c = 9 : 21 : 49$

Further Practice

5. If $a = 20$ and $b = 36$, find
   (a) $a : b$,
   (b) $a^2 : b^2$.

Solution
(a) $a : b = 20 : 36$
$ = 5 : 9$
(b) $a^2 : b^2 = 5^2 : 9^2$
$ = 25 : 81$

6. If $2x = 5y$, find $x : y$.

Solution
$2x = 5y$
$\dfrac{x}{y} = \dfrac{5}{2}$
$\therefore\ x : y = 5 : 2$

7. If $x : y = 0.75 : 0.90$ and $y : z = \dfrac{1}{3} : \dfrac{1}{4}$,
   (a)   simplify the ratios $x : y$ and $y : z$,
   (b)   find $x : y : z$.

Solution
(a) $x : y = 0.75 : 0.90$
$ = 75 : 90$
$ = \dfrac{75}{15} : \dfrac{90}{15}$
$ = 5 : 6$

$y : z = \dfrac{1}{3} : \dfrac{1}{4}$
$ = \dfrac{1}{3} \times 12 : \dfrac{1}{4} \times 12$
$ = 4 : 3$

(b) $x : y = 5 : 6$
$ = 10 : 12$
$y : z = 4 : 3$
$ = 12 : 9$
$\therefore\ x : y : z = 10 : 12 : 9$

8. If $x : y = 1\dfrac{1}{4} : \dfrac{2}{3}$ and $x : z = 1\dfrac{3}{7} : \dfrac{5}{6}$,
   (a)   simplify the ratios $x : y$ and $x : z$,
   (b)   find $x : y : z$.

Solution
(a) $x : y = 1\dfrac{1}{4} : \dfrac{2}{3}$
$ = \dfrac{5}{4} : \dfrac{2}{3}$
$ = 15 : 8$

$x : z = 1\dfrac{3}{7} : \dfrac{5}{6}$
$ = \dfrac{10}{7} : \dfrac{5}{6}$
$ = \dfrac{10}{7} \times \dfrac{42}{5} : \dfrac{5}{6} \times \dfrac{42}{5}$
$ = 12 : 7$

(b) $x : y = 15 : 8 = 60 : 32$
$x : z = 12 : 7 = 60 : 35$
$\therefore\ x : y : z = 60 : 32 : 35$

9. There are 42 male employees and 33 female employees in a company. Find the ratio of
   (a)   the number of male employees to the number of female employees,
   (b)   the number of female employees to the total number of employees.

Solution
(a) $\begin{array}{c}\text{Number of} \\ \text{male employees}\end{array} : \begin{array}{c}\text{Number of} \\ \text{female employees}\end{array}$
$= 42 : 33$
$= 14 : 11$

(b) $\begin{array}{c}\text{Number of} \\ \text{female employees}\end{array} : \begin{array}{c}\text{Total number of} \\ \text{employees}\end{array}$
$= 33 : (42 + 33)$
$= 33 : 75$
$= 11 : 25$

10. The sides of square A and square B are 15 inches and 20 inches respectively. Find the ratio of
   (a)   their sides,
   (b)   their perimeters,
   (c)   their areas.

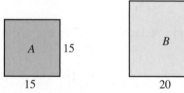

Solution
(a)   Ratio of their sides $= 15 : 20$
$ = 3 : 4$
(b)   Ratio of their perimeters $= 15 \times 4 : 20 \times 4$
$ = 3 : 4$
(c)   Ratio of their areas $= 15^2 : 20^2$
$ = 9 : 16$

11. In an alloy, copper and zinc are mixed in the ratio 5 : 3 by mass. If the mass of a block of the alloy is 4.8 kilograms, find the mass of copper in it.

Solution

Mass of copper $= 4.8 \times \dfrac{5}{5+3}$
$\qquad\qquad\qquad = 3 \text{ kg}$

12. The numbers of clerical and technical staff in a company are in the ratio 2 : 5. If the total number of staff in the company is 28, how many of them are technical staff?

Solution

Number of technical staff $= 28 \times \dfrac{5}{2+5}$
$\qquad\qquad\qquad\qquad\quad = 20$

13. In a solution, water and alcohol are mixed in the ratio 4 : 1 by volume. Find the amount of alcohol in 750 cubic centimeters of the solution.

Solution

Amount of alcohol $= 750 \times \dfrac{1}{4+1}$
$\qquad\qquad\qquad\quad = 150 \text{ cm}^3$

14. Two sisters share $4,200 in the ratio 5 : 7. How much money does each sister receive?

Solution

Amount received by one of the sisters
$= \$4{,}200 \times \dfrac{5}{5+7}$
$= \$1{,}750$
Amount received by the other sister
$= \$4{,}200 - \$1{,}750$
$= \$2{,}450$

Math@Work

15. In a recipe, chicken, potatoes, and onions are mixed in the ratio 7 : 3 : 2 by weight. If Mrs. Sanders follows the recipe and uses 6.3 pounds of chicken, how many pounds of
    (a) potatoes,
    (b) onions,
    does she use?

Solution

(a) Let x pounds be the weight of potatoes Mrs. Sanders uses.
$$\frac{x}{6.3} = \frac{3}{7}$$
$$x = 2.7$$
She uses 2.7 pounds of potatoes.

(b) Let y pounds be the weight of onions she uses.
$$\frac{y}{6.3} = \frac{2}{7}$$
$$y = 1.8$$
She uses 1.8 pounds of onions.

16. In a hydrocarbon compound, the atoms of carbon, hydrogen, and oxygen are bonded in the ratio 1 : 2 : 1. If the total number of atoms in the compound is 300, find the number of
    (a) carbon atoms,
    (b) hydrogen atoms,
    in the compound.

Solution

(a) Number of carbon atoms $= 300 \times \dfrac{1}{1+2+1}$
$\qquad\qquad\qquad\qquad\qquad = 75$

(b) Number of hydrogen atoms $= 300 \times \dfrac{2}{1+2+1}$
$\qquad\qquad\qquad\qquad\qquad\quad = 150$

17. A total of 165 students from schools P, Q, and R participated in a community carnival. The numbers of students from schools P and Q who participated in the carnival are in the ratio 5 : 6. The numbers of students from schools Q and R who participated are in the ratio 9 : 11. Find the number of students from
    (a) school P,
    (b) school Q,
    who had participated in the event.

Solution

(a) Number of students   Number of students
    from school P :   from school Q
    who participated   who participated
    $= 5 : 6$
    $= 15 : 18$

    Number of students   Number of students
    from school Q :   from school R
    who participated   who participated
    $= 9 : 11$
    $= 18 : 22$

    The numbers of students from schools P, Q, and R who participated are in the ratio 15 : 18 : 22.

    Number of students from school P
    $= 165 \times \dfrac{15}{15+18+22} = 45$

(b) Number of students from school Q
    $= 165 \times \dfrac{18}{15+18+22} = 54$

18. A wire 69 centimeters long is cut into 3 pieces of lengths x centimeters, y centimeters, and z centimeters. If $x : y = 2 : 5$, and x is 3 times as long as z, find
(a) $x : y : z$,
(b) the values of x, y, and z.
(c) Can the 3 pieces of wire form a triangle? Explain your answer.

Solution
(a) $x : y = 2 : 5 = 6 : 15$
$x : z = 3 : 1 = 6 : 2$
$\therefore x : y : z = 6 : 15 : 2$

(b) $x = 69 \times \dfrac{6}{6 + 15 + 2} = 18$

$y = 69 \times \dfrac{15}{6 + 15 + 2} = 45$

$z = 69 - x - z$
$= 69 - 18 - 45$
$= 6$

(c) $x + z = 18 + 6$
$= 24$
Notice that $x + z < y$.
In any triangle, the sum of two sides must be greater than the third side. (Triangle Inequality Theorem) As the lengths of the 3 pieces of wire do not provide sufficient condition to draw a triangle, the 3 pieces of wire cannot form a triangle.

19. Beth and Ruth are sisters and the ratio of Beth's age to Ruth's age is $\dfrac{2}{3} : \dfrac{3}{2}$. They want to buy a present for their mother's birthday, which costs $52. Ruth suggests that they split the cost in the ratio of their ages. How much would Beth pay in this situation?

Solution
Beth's age : Ruth's age $= \dfrac{2}{3} : \dfrac{3}{2}$
$= \dfrac{2}{3} \times 6 : \dfrac{3}{2} \times 6$
$= 4 : 9$
Amount Beth pays $= \$52 \times \dfrac{4}{4 + 9}$
$= \$16$

Brainworks
20. Find three numbers a, b, and c such that $a : b : c = 3 : 4 : 5$ and $c \neq 5$.

Solution
If $a = 3k$, $b = 4k$, and $c = 5k$, where $k \neq 0$, then $a : b : c = 3 : 4 : 5$.
When $k = 2$, $a = 6$, $b = 8$, and $c = 10$.
When $k = 3$, $a = 9$, $b = 12$, and $c = 15$.

21. Samantha, Rick, and Timothy contribute $20,000, $15,000, and $25,000 respectively to form a company. Their profit $\$P$ in the nth year is given by the formula
$$P = 9,000n - 10,800, \text{ for } n = 1, 2, 3, 4, \text{ and } 5.$$
(a) Find the ratio of Samantha's contribution to Rick's contribution to Timothy's contribution.
(b) Find the company's profits in the
(i) first year,
(ii) second year.
(c) Interpret the result in (b)(i).
(d) If the profits in the second year were given to them according to the ratio of their contributions, find the amount of money Samantha would receive.

Solution
(a) The ratio of Samantha's contribution to Rick's contribution to Timothy's contribution
$= 20,000 : 15,000 : 25,000$
$= 4 : 3 : 5$

(b) (i) Profit in the first year
$= \$[9,000(1) - 10,800]$
$= -\$1,800$
(ii) Profit in the second year
$= \$[9,000(2) - 10,800]$
$= \$7,200$

(c) $-\$1,800 < 0$
It indicates that the company made a loss in the first year.

(d) Amount received by Samantha
$= \$7,200 \times \dfrac{4}{4 + 3 + 5}$
$= \$2,400$

Exercise 6.2
Basic Practice
1. Find the rate in each case.
(a) A 48-fl. oz. bottle of corn oil costs $7.20
The price rate is $ ___ /fl. oz.
(b) A workshop produces 360 chairs in 5 days.
The rate of production is ___ chairs/day.
(c) Emily typed 376 words in 8 minutes.
Her rate of typing is ___ words/min.
(d) A carpet of area 30 square feet costs $240.
The price rate is $ ___ /ft^2.
(e) The mass of a 2.5-meter metal bar is 10 kilograms.
The rate of mass is ___ kg/m.
(f) The weight of 12 eggs is 27 ounces.
The rate of weight is ___ oz/egg.

Solution

(a) The price rate $= \dfrac{\$7.20}{48 \text{ fl. oz.}}$

$\qquad\qquad = \$0.15/\text{fl. oz.}$

(b) A workshop produces 360 chairs in 5 days.

Rate of production $= \dfrac{360 \text{ chairs}}{5 \text{ days}}$

$\qquad\qquad\quad = 72 \text{ chairs/day}$

(c) Emily typed 376 words in 8 minutes.

Rate of typing $= \dfrac{376 \text{ words}}{8 \text{ min}}$

$\qquad\qquad\quad = 47 \text{ words/min}$

(d) A carpet of area 30 square feet costs $240.

Price rate $= \dfrac{\$240}{30 \text{ ft}^2}$

$\qquad\quad = \$8/\text{ft}^2$

(e) The mass of a 2.5 meter metal bar is 10 kilograms.

Rate of mass $= \dfrac{10 \text{ kg}}{2.5 \text{ m}}$

$\qquad\qquad = 4 \text{ kg/m}$

(f) The mass of 12 eggs is 27 ounces.

Rate of weight $= \dfrac{27 \text{ oz}}{12 \text{ eggs}}$

$\qquad\qquad\quad = 2.25 \text{ oz/egg}$

2. Richard works 5 days a week and 8 hours a day. His daily wage is $184. Find
(a) his hourly wage rate,
(b) his weekly wage rate.

Solution

(a) Hourly wage rate $= \dfrac{\$184}{8 \text{ hr}}$

$\qquad\qquad\qquad = \$23/\text{hr}$

(b) Weekly wage rate $= \$184 \times 5/\text{week}$

$\qquad\qquad\qquad = \$920/\text{week}$

3. A car traveled 143 miles on 6.5 gallons of gasoline. The price of the gasoline consumed was $18.20.
(a) Find the rate of gasoline consumption in mi/gal.
(b) What was the price of gasoline per gallon?

Solution

(a) Rate of gasoline consumption $= \dfrac{143 \text{ mi}}{6.5 \text{ gal}}$

$\qquad\qquad\qquad\qquad\qquad = 22 \text{ mi/gal}$

(b) Price of gasoline $= \dfrac{\$18.20}{6.5 \text{ gal}}$

$\qquad\qquad\qquad\quad = \$2.80/\text{gal}$

4. There are 6 wooden cubes, each of side 5 centimeters. Their total mass is 525 grams. Find the mass per
(a) cube,
(b) cubic centimeter.

Solution

(a) Mass per cube $= \dfrac{525 \text{ g}}{6 \text{ cubes}}$

$\qquad\qquad\qquad = 87.5 \text{ g/cube}$

(b) Volume of a cube $= 5^3$

$\qquad\qquad\qquad\quad = 125 \text{ cm}^3$

Mass per cm$^3 = \dfrac{87.5 \text{ g}}{125 \text{ cm}^3}$

$\qquad\qquad\quad = 0.7 \text{ g/cm}^3$

Further Practice

5. John spent $120 on 8 concert tickets. Find
(a) the price per ticket,
(b) the price of 10 tickets.

Solution

(a) Price per ticket $= \dfrac{\$120}{8 \text{ tickets}}$

$\qquad\qquad\qquad = \$15/\text{ticket}$

(b) The price of 10 tickets $= \$15 \times 10$

$\qquad\qquad\qquad\qquad\quad = \$150$

6. The price of laying 12 square meters of floor tiles is $270. Find
(a) the price of laying floor tiles per square meter,
(b) the price of laying 20 square meters of floor tiles.

Solution

(a) The price of laying floor tiles per square meter

$\qquad = \dfrac{\$270}{12 \text{ m}^2}$

$\qquad = \$22.50/\text{m}^2$

(b) The price of laying 20 square meters of floor tiles

$\qquad = \$22.50 \times 20$

$\qquad = \$450$

7. A pipe delivers 9 liters of water in 20 seconds.
(a) Find the amount of water it delivers per minute.
(b) An empty fish tank is 60 centimeters long, 45 centimeters wide, and 30 centimeters high. How many minutes does it take for the pipe to fill the empty tank completely with water?
(1 liter = 1,000 cubic centimeters)

Solution

(a) Amount of water delivered per minute

$\qquad = \left(\dfrac{9}{20} \times 60 \right) \text{ L/min}$

$\qquad = 27 \text{ L/min}$

(b) Volume of the tank $= (60 \times 45 \times 30)$ cm^3

$$= 81{,}000 \text{ cm}^3$$

$$= \frac{81{,}000}{1{,}000} \text{ L}$$

$$= 81 \text{ L}$$

The required time taken $= \dfrac{81}{27}$

$$= 3 \text{ min}$$

Math@Work

8. A 500-gram pack of fertilizer that costs $13 can be applied to 20 square meters of lawn.
  (a) What is the cost of the fertilizer per kilogram?
  (b) Find the mass of the fertilizer that can be applied to 1 square meter of lawn.
  (c) A rectangular lawn measures 15 meters by 8 meters. Find the mass and cost of the fertilizer required for the lawn.

Solution

(a) Cost per kg $= \dfrac{\$13}{0.5 \text{ kg}} = \$26/\text{kg}$

(b) Amount of fertilizer required for 1 square meter of lawn

$$= \frac{500}{20}$$

$$= 25 \text{ g}$$

(c) Area of the lawn $= 15 \times 8$

$$= 120 \text{ m}^2$$

Mass of fertilizer required $= 25 \times 120$

$$= 3{,}000 \text{ g}$$

$$= 3 \text{ kg}$$

Cost of fertilizer required $= \$26 \times 3$

$$= \$78$$

9. The monthly rental price of an apartment of area 1,600 square feet is $1,040. Jenny and her friend shared the cost of such an apartment in the ratio 3 : 2.
  (a) How much did Jenny pay per month?
  (b) What was the rental cost per square foot of the apartment?

Solution

(a) Amount Jenny paid $= \$1{,}040 \times \dfrac{3}{3+2}$

$$= \$624$$

(b) Rental cost per square foot $= \dfrac{\$1{,}040}{1{,}600 \text{ ft}^2}$

$$= \$0.65/\text{ft}^2$$

10. A pure gold cube of side 3 centimeters has a mass of 521.1 grams.
  (a) Find the mass of pure gold per cubic centimeter.
  (b) Another gold cube is of side 2 centimeters. Its mass is 120 grams. Is it made of pure gold? Explain briefly.

Solution

(a) Mass of pure gold per cubic centimeter

$$= \frac{521.1 \text{ g}}{3^3 \text{ cm}^3}$$

$$= 19.3 \text{ g/cm}^3$$

(b) If the gold cube is made of pure gold,

its mass $= 19.3 \times 2^3$

$$= 154.4 \text{ g}$$

However, now its mass is only 120 g.

120 g $<$ 154.4 g

$\therefore$ it is NOT made of pure gold.

Brainworks

11. Work in groups and write down 10 examples of average rates that you can identify.

Solution

Some examples of average rates are:

rate of walking, pulse rate, failure rate, computation rate, rate of scoring goals, wage rate, rate of painting a wall, birth rate, audience rate, growth rate of an investment fund.

Exercise 6.3
Basic Practice

1. Copy and complete the following table.

	Distance traveled	Time taken	Average speed
(a)	64 km	2 hr	32 km/hr
(b)	200 m	25 s	8 m/s
(c)	345 mi	6 hr	57.5 mph
(d)	66 km	3 hr	22 km/hr
(e)	35 m	7 s	5 m/s
(f)	310 mi	5 hr	62 mph
(g)	75 km	1.5 hr	50 km/hr
(h)	39 m	13 s	3 m/s
(i)	145 mi	2.5 hr	58 mph

Solution

(a) Average speed $= \dfrac{64}{2} = 32$ km/hr

(b) Average speed $= \dfrac{200}{25} = 8$ m/s

(c) Average speed $= \dfrac{345 \text{ mi}}{6 \text{ hr}} = 57.5$ mph

(d) Distance traveled $= 22 \times 3 = 66$ km

(e) Distance traveled $= 5 \times 7 = 35$ m

(f) Distance traveled $= 62 \times 5 = 310$ mi

(g) Time taken $= \dfrac{75}{50} = 1.5$ hr

(h) Time taken $= \dfrac{39}{3} = 13$ s

(i) Time taken $= \dfrac{145}{58} = 2.5$ hr

2. Convert the following speeds to m/s and mph. Take 1 km = 0.62 mi.
   (a) 24 km/hr   **(b)** 50 km/hr
   (c) 80 km/h   **(d)** 126 km/h

Solution

(a) 24 km/hr $= 24 \times \dfrac{1,000}{3,600}$ m/s

$\qquad = 6\dfrac{2}{3}$ m/s

24 km/hr $= 24 \times 0.62$ mph
$\qquad = 14.88$ mph

(b) 50 km/hr $= 50 \times \dfrac{1,000}{3,600}$ m/s

$\qquad = 13\dfrac{8}{9}$ m/s

50 km/hr $= 50 \times 0.62$ mph
$\qquad = 31$ mph

(c) 80 km/hr $= 80 \times \dfrac{1,000}{3,600}$ m/s

$\qquad = 22\dfrac{2}{9}$ m/s

80 km/hr $= 80 \times 0.62$ mph
$\qquad = 49.6$ mph

(d) 126 km/hr $= 126 \times \dfrac{1,000}{3,600}$ m/s

$\qquad = 35$ m/s

126 km/hr $= 126 \times 0.62$ mph
$\qquad = 78.12$ mph

3. Convert the following speeds to km/hr and mph. Take 1 km = 0.62 mi.
   (a) 2 m/s   **(b)** 5 m/s
   (c) 13 m/s   **(d)** 20 m/s

Solution

(a) 2 m/s $= 2 \times \dfrac{3,600}{1,000}$ km/hr

$\qquad = 7.2$ km/hr

7.2 km/hr $= 7.2 \times 0.62$ mph
$\qquad = 4.464$ mph

(b) 5 m/s $= 5 \times \dfrac{3,600}{1,000}$ km/hr

$\qquad = 18$ km/hr

18 km/hr $= 18 \times 0.62$ mph
$\qquad = 11.16$ mph

(c) 13 m/s $= 13 \times \dfrac{3,600}{1,000}$ km/hr

$\qquad = 46.8$ km/hr

46.8 km/hr $= 46.8 \times 0.62$ mph
$\qquad = 29.016$ mph

(d) 20 m/s $= 20 \times \dfrac{3,600}{1,000}$ km/hr

$\qquad = 72$ km/hr

72 km/hr $= 72 \times 0.62$ mph
$\qquad = 44.64$ mph

4. Convert the following speeds to km/hr. Take 1 mi = 1.61 km.
   (a) 22 mph   **(b)** 48 mph
   (c) 65 mph   **(d)** 80 mph

Solution

(a) 22 mph $= 22 \times 1.61$ km/hr
$\qquad = 35.42$ km/hr

(b) 48 mph $= 48 \times 1.61$ km/hr
$\qquad = 77.28$ km/hr

(c) 65 mph $= 65 \times 1.61$ km/hr
$\qquad = 104.65$ km/hr

(d) 80 mph $= 80 \times 1.61$ km/hr
$\qquad = 128.8$ km/hr

Further Practice

5. Mr. Johnson took 40 minutes to drive from Town A to Town B at an average speed of 60 miles per hour.
   (a) Find the distance between A and B.
   (b) If he increased his speed by 12 mph, how long would he take to travel the same distance?

Solution

(a) Distance between A and $B = 60 \times \dfrac{40}{60}$

$\qquad = 40$ mi

(b) New speed = 60 + 12

= 72 mph

New time taken = $\dfrac{40 \text{ mi}}{72 \text{ mph}}$

= $\dfrac{5}{9}$ hr

= $33\dfrac{1}{3}$ min

6. Thomas ran at a uniform speed for 50 minutes. He covered 9 kilometers during that period of time.

(a) Find his speed in meters per second.

(b) If he reduced his speed by 1 meter per second, how long would he take to cover the same distance?

Solution

(a) His speed = $\dfrac{9 \times 1{,}000 \text{ m}}{50 \times 60 \text{ s}}$ = 3 m/s

(b) New speed = 3 − 1 = 2 m/s

New time taken = $\dfrac{9 \times 1{,}000 \text{ m}}{2 \text{ m/s}}$

= 4,500 s

= $\dfrac{4{,}500}{60}$ min

= 75 min

7. The average speed of a ship for the first hour of a journey is 32 km/hr. Its average speed for the next 2 hours is 41 km/hr. Find its average speed for the whole journey.

Solution

Total distance traveled = 32 × 1 + 41 × 2

= 114 km

Total time taken = 1 + 2

= 3 hr

Average speed = $\dfrac{114}{3}$

= 38 km/hr

8. Jack runs at an average speed of 4 miles per hour for one hour. He then cycles 6 miles at 12 miles per hour. Find his average speed for the whole journey.

Solution

Total distance traveled = 4 × 1 + 6

= 10 mi

Total time taken = 1 + $\dfrac{6}{12}$ = 1.5 hr

Average speed = $\dfrac{10}{1.5}$

= $6\dfrac{2}{3}$ mph

9. Mr. White ran from his home to a book store 400 meters away at an average speed of 2 meters per second. He walked back to his home at an average speed of 1 meter per second. Find his average speed for the whole journey if

(a) he did not speed any time in the store,

(b) he stayed in the store for 5 minutes.

Solution

(a) Total time taken = $\dfrac{400}{2}$ + $\dfrac{400}{1}$

= 600 s

Average speed = $\dfrac{2 \times 400}{600}$

= $1\dfrac{1}{3}$ m/s

(b) Total time taken = 600 + 5 × 60

= 900 s

Average speed = $\dfrac{2 \times 400}{900}$

= $\dfrac{8}{9}$ m/s

Math@Work

10. Sound travels at 340 meters per second in air.

(a) Find the distance traveled by sound in air in 7 seconds. Give your answer correct to the nearest 0.1 kilometer.

(b) A boy clapped his hands near a cliff. He could hear the echo of his claps 3 seconds later. Find his distance from the cliff.

Solution

(a) Distance traveled in 7 s

= 340 × 7

= 2,380

= 2.4 km   (correct to the nearest 0.1 km)

(b) Distance from the cliff = 340 × $\dfrac{3}{2}$

= 510 m

11. The flight distance between Singapore and New York is about 9,531 miles. A plane takes 19 hours and 4 minutes to fly from Singapore to New York.

(a) Find the average speed of the plane from Singapore to New York, giving your answer correct to the nearest mph.

(b) In February, New York's time is 13 hours behind Singapore's time. If the plane departs from Singapore at 9:55 A.M., find its time of arrival in New York.

Solution

(a) Average speed of the plane

$$= \frac{9{,}531}{19\frac{4}{60}}$$

$= 500$ mph (correct to the nearest mph)

(b)

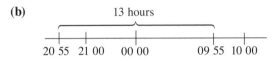

13 hours

20 55 21 00   00 00   09 55 10 00

Since New York is 13 hours behind Singapore, the
∴ time at New York at departure = 20 55.

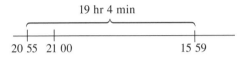

19 hr 4 min

20 55 21 00   15 59

∴ time of arrival at New York = 15 59
                              = 3:59 P.M.

---

12. Along a road, point X and point Y are 1,150 meters apart. Ann walks along the road from X to Y at $\frac{2}{3}$ m/s. Yohan walks along the same road from Y to X at $1\frac{1}{4}$ m/s. Both Ann and Yohan start walking at the same time.
(a) How many minutes later will they meet?
(b) How far from X will they meet?

Solution
(a) Let the time that Ann and Yohan will meet be t min later.
$$\frac{2}{3} \times (60t) + 1\frac{1}{4} \times (60t) = 1{,}150$$
$$115t = 1{,}150$$
$$t = 10$$
They will meet 10 min later.

(b) The required distance $= \frac{2}{3} \times 60 \times 10$
$$= 400 \text{ m}$$

Brainworks

13. A car travels at an average speed of x miles per hour for the first 2 hours. It travels at an average speed of y miles per hour for the next 3 hours. Its average speed for the whole journey is 40 miles per hour. Find two possible sets of values of x and y.

Solution
Total time taken $= 2 + 3$
$$= 5 \text{ hr}$$

Considering the total distance traveled, we have the equation
$$2x + 3y = 40 \times 5$$
i.e., $2x + 3y = 200.$

Two possible sets of x and y are:
$$x = 10,\ y = 60$$
and $\qquad x = 40,\ y = 40.$

14. The drivers of cars A and B drove uniformly in the same direction along a road. At a certain moment, B was 2 miles in front of A, which was moving at a speed of 60 miles per hour. The ratio of the speeds of A and B was 4 : 3.
(a) Find the speed of B.
(b) Describe the change in the distance between the cars.
(c) Will these two cars meet? If so, when?

Solution
(a) $\dfrac{\text{Speed of } A}{\text{Speed of } B} = \dfrac{4}{3}$

$\dfrac{60}{\text{Speed of } B} = \dfrac{4}{3}$

Speed of $B = 60 \times \dfrac{3}{4}$
$$= 45 \text{ mph}$$

(b) Since speed of $A >$ speed of B,
the distance between the cars is decreasing.

(c) Yes, the two cars will meet.
Let the time the two cars meet be t hours later.
$$60t = 45t + 2$$
$$15t = 2$$
$$t = \frac{2}{15}$$
$$\frac{2}{15} \text{ hr} = \frac{2}{15} \times 60 \text{ min}$$
$$= 8 \text{ min}$$
The two cars will meet 8 min later.

Review Exercise 6

1. Two cubes are of sides 6 inches and 8 inches respectively. Find the ratio of
(a) their sides,
(b) their areas on one face,
(c) their volumes.

Solution
(a) Ratio of their sides $= 6 : 8$
$$= 3 : 4$$

(b) Ratio of their areas on one face $= 6^2 : 8^2$
$$= 9 : 16$$

(c) Ratio of their volumes $= 6^3 : 8^3$

$\quad\quad\quad\quad\quad\quad\quad\quad\quad = 27 : 64$

2. Car X travels 60 miles in 45 minutes. Car Y travels 72 miles in 1 hour and 20 minutes. Find
   (a) the average speed of car X in mph,
   (b) the average speed of car Y in mph,
   (c) the ratio of the average speed of car X to that of car Y.

Solution

(a) Average speed of car $X = \dfrac{60}{\frac{45}{60}}$

$\quad\quad\quad\quad\quad\quad\quad\quad = 80$ mph

(b) Average speed of car $Y = \dfrac{72}{1\frac{20}{60}}$

$\quad\quad\quad\quad\quad\quad\quad\quad = 54$ mph

(c) Ratio of their average speeds $= 80 : 54$

$\quad\quad\quad\quad\quad\quad\quad\quad\quad\quad\quad = 40 : 27$

3. There are a total of 240 pieces of \$5 bills and \$10 bills. The numbers of \$5 and \$10 bills are in the ratio 3 : 2. Find
   (a) the number of \$5 bills,
   (b) the number of \$10 bills,
   (c) the ratio of the value of the \$5 bills to that of the \$10 bills.

Solution

(a) Number of \$5 bills $= 240 \times \dfrac{3}{3+2} = 144$

(b) Number of \$10 bills $= 240 \times \dfrac{2}{3+2} = 96$

(c) Ratio of value of \$5 bills and \$10 bills
$\quad = 144 \times 5 : 96 \times 10$
$\quad = 3 : 4$

4. Syrup and water are mixed in the ratio 1 : 4 by volume. If the volume of the solution is 600 gallons,
   (a) find the volume of syrup in the solution,
   (b) find the volume of water in the solution,
   (c) how much syrup must be added to the solution so that the ratio of volume of syrup to volume of water in the solution becomes 1 : 3?

Solution

(a) Volume of syrup $= 600 \times \dfrac{1}{1+4}$

$\quad\quad\quad\quad\quad\quad\quad\quad = 120$ gallons

(b) Volume of water $= 600 - 120$
$\quad\quad\quad\quad\quad\quad\quad\quad = 480$ gallons

(c) Let x cm^3 be the volume of syrup added.

$\quad\dfrac{120 + x}{480} = \dfrac{1}{3}$

$\quad 120 + x = 160$

$\quad\quad\quad\quad x = 40$

$\quad\therefore$ 40 gallons of syrup must be added.

5. A metal bar of mass 3.6 kilograms is cut into two pieces in the ratio 3 : 5. The length of the shorter piece is 45 centimeters. Find
   (a) the length of the longer piece,
   (b) the length of the original metal bar,
   (c) the mass per unit length of the bar in kg/m,
   (d) the mass of the shorter piece.

Solution

(a) Let x cm be the length of the longer piece.

$\quad\dfrac{45}{x} = \dfrac{3}{5}$

$\quad\quad x = 45 \times \dfrac{5}{3}$

$\quad\quad\quad = 75$

$\quad\therefore$ the length of the longer piece is 75 cm.

(b) Length of the original metal bar $= 45 + 75$

$\quad\quad\quad\quad\quad\quad\quad\quad\quad\quad\quad\quad = 120$ cm

(c) Mass per unit length $= \dfrac{3.6 \text{ kg}}{1.2 \text{ m}}$

$\quad\quad\quad\quad\quad\quad\quad\quad\quad\quad = 3$ kg/m

(d) Mass of the shorter piece $= 3 \times \dfrac{45}{100}$

$\quad\quad\quad\quad\quad\quad\quad\quad\quad\quad\quad = 1.35$ kg

6. **(a)** Simplify each of the following ratios.
   (i) $a : b = 1\dfrac{1}{2} : 2\dfrac{2}{5}$
   (ii) $b : c = 0.105 : 0.350$
   (b) Find the ratio $a : b : c$.
   (c) Alan, Bob, and Cathy share \$500 in the ratio $a : b : c$ found in **(b)**. Find Alan's share, correct to 2 decimal places.

Solution

(a) **(i)** $a : b = 1\dfrac{1}{2} : 2\dfrac{2}{5}$

$\quad\quad\quad\quad\quad = \dfrac{3}{2} : \dfrac{12}{5}$

$\quad\quad\quad\quad\quad = 15 : 24$

$\quad\quad\quad\quad\quad = 5 : 8$

(ii) $b : c = 0.105 : 0.350$

$\quad\quad\quad\quad = 105 : 350$

$\quad\quad\quad\quad = 3 : 10$

(b) $a : b = 5 : 8$
$ = 15 : 24$
$b : c = 3 : 10$
$ = 24 : 80$
$\therefore a : b : c = 15 : 24 : 80$

(c) Alan's share $= \$500 \times \dfrac{15}{15 + 24 + 80}$

$ = \$500 \times \dfrac{15}{119}$

$ = \$63.03 \quad$ (correct to 2 d.p.)

---

7. The prices of two stocks, A and B, are in the ratio $2 : 3$. If the price of A increases by \$12 while the price of B decreases by \$6, the ratio of their prices becomes $10 : 11$. Find the original prices of the stocks.

Solution

Let the price of stocks A and B be \$$2x$ and \$$3x$ respectively.
$$\frac{2x + 12}{3x - 6} = \frac{10}{11}$$
$$11(2x + 12) = 10(3x - 6)$$
$$22x + 132 = 30x - 60$$
$$8x = 192$$
$$x = 24$$
$$2x = 48$$
$$3x = 72$$
The original price of stock A is \$48 and the original price of stock B is \$72.

---

8. A 2-liter bottle of canola oil is sold for \$15. A $2\frac{1}{2}$-liter bottle of olive oil is sold for \$30.
(a) Find the unit price x of canola oil in \$/L.
(b) Find the unit price y of olive oil in \$/L.
(c) Find the ratio $x : y$.
(d) Suppose both types of oil are equally good for cooking, which one is a better buy?
(e) The bottle of canola oil can be used for 16 days. Find its consumption rate in L/day.
(f) If the consumption rate of the bottle of olive oil is the same as that of canola oil, how many days can it last?

Solution

(a) Unit price x of canola oil $= \dfrac{\$15}{2\,L}$

$ = \$7.50/L$

(b) Unit price y of olive oil $= \dfrac{\$30}{2\frac{1}{2}\,L}$

$ = \$12/L$

(c) $x : y = 7.5 : 12$
$ = 75 : 120$
$ = 5 : 8$

(d) Canola oil is cheaper. It is a better buy.

(e) Consumption rate $= \dfrac{2\,L}{16\,days}$

$ = \dfrac{1}{8}$ L/day

(f) Required number of days $= 2\frac{1}{2} \div \dfrac{1}{8}$

$ = 20$

---

9. A man took $2\frac{1}{2}$ hours to drive 195 km from San Diego to Los Angeles. He used 20 liters of gasoline for the entire journey.
(a) Find his average speed.
(b) Find the gasoline consumption rate in km/L.
(c) If he drove at an average speed of 110 km/hr on a highway for 45 minutes during his journey, find his average speed for the remaining part of his journey.

Solution

(a) Average speed $= \dfrac{195}{2\frac{1}{2}}$

$ = 78$ km/hr

(b) Gasoline consumption rate $= \dfrac{195}{20}$

$ = 9.75$ km/L

(c) Let x km/hr be the required average speed. Consider the total distance traveled.
$$110 \times \frac{45}{60} + \left(2\frac{1}{2} - \frac{45}{60}\right)x = 195$$
$$82.5 + \frac{7}{4}x = 195$$
$$\frac{7}{4}x = \frac{225}{2}$$
$$x = \frac{225}{2} \times \frac{4}{7}$$
$$= 64\frac{2}{7}$$
$\therefore$ his average speed for the remaining part of his journey is $64\frac{2}{7}$ km/hr.

---

10. A car starts from rest. After traveling 125 meters in 10 seconds, its speed picks up to 25 m/s. It travels at this speed for 20 seconds. Then brakes are applied. The car stops in 6 seconds and the braking distance is 95 meters.
(a) Express the speed 25 m/s in km/h.
(b) Find the average speed of the car during the period at which its speed increases.
(c) Find the average speed of the car during the period the brakes were applied.
(d) Find the average speed of the car for the whole journey.

Solution

(a) $25 \text{ m/s} = 25 \times \dfrac{3,600}{1,000}$ km/hr

$\qquad\qquad = 90$ km/hr

(b) Required average speed $= \dfrac{125}{10}$

$\qquad\qquad\qquad = 12.5$ m/s

(c) Required average speed $= \dfrac{95}{6}$

$\qquad\qquad\qquad = 15\dfrac{5}{6}$ m/s

(d) Total distance traveled
$\qquad = 125 + 25 \times 20 + 95$
$\qquad = 720$ m
Total time taken $= 10 + 20 + 6$
$\qquad\qquad\qquad = 36$ s
$\therefore$ average speed for the whole journey

$\qquad = \dfrac{720}{36}$

$\qquad = 20$ m/s

---

11. Towns P and Q are 120 miles apart. Mr. Miller drove from P to Q and was scheduled to reach Q after 2 hours. His average speed was 54 mph for the first 40 minutes.

(a) What was his average speed for the remaining journey if he managed to arrive just on time?

(b) The time taken for his return journey is 2 hours and 10 minutes. Find his average speed for
(i) the return journey,
(ii) the whole trip.

Solution

(a) Let x mph be the required average speed.

$$54 \times \frac{40}{60} + x\left(2 - \frac{40}{60}\right) = 120$$

$$36 + \frac{4}{3}x = 120$$

$$\frac{4}{3}x = 84$$

$$x = 63$$

His average speed for the remaining journey is 63 mph.

(b) (i) Average speed for the return journey

$\qquad = \dfrac{120}{2\frac{10}{60}}$

$\qquad = 55\dfrac{5}{13}$ mph

(ii) Average speed for the whole trip

$\qquad = \dfrac{120 + 120}{2 + 2\frac{10}{60}}$

$\qquad = 240 \times \dfrac{6}{25}$

$\qquad = 57.6$ mph

Chapter 7 Percentage

Extend Your Learning Curve

Compound Discount

1. A retired couple books a room in a motel for 7 nights. The usual price for accommodation per night is $200. However, the couple is entitled to all the following discounts.
   Find the couple's actual expenditure for the 7 nights' accommodation.

Suggested Answer:

The couple's actual expenditure = [$200 × (100% − 20%) × (100% − 5%) × (100% − 10%)] × 7
$$= \$136.80 \times 7$$
$$= \$957.60$$

2. Find out how batting averages are computed. Compare it to the use of percentages to allow us to communicate information and compare data on a fair basis.

Suggested Answer:

A batting average represents the percentage of at bats that result in hits for a particular baseball player. The formula is:

$$\frac{\text{Hits}}{\text{At Bats}} \times 100\% = \text{Batting Average}$$

The batting average provides a measure of individual batting ability.

A batting average of 100% means that the player gets a hit every time he comes to bat, and an average of 0% means the player has no hits. However, batting average is often presented as a decimal number instead of percentage.

Since the number of runs a player scores and how often he gets out varies between different players, we cannot simply compare number of hits in order to compare the batting skills between different players. Since batting average is a good metric for an individual player's skill as a batsman and it takes into account the number of times at bat, it allows us to compare batting skills between players. This is similar to comparing results of different tests that may have a different total, so we cannot just simply compare the numbers directly.

Try It!

Section 7.1

1. Express each of the following as a percentage.

   (a) $\dfrac{3}{4}$ (b) $2\dfrac{2}{3}$ (c) 0.871

   Solution

   (a) $\dfrac{3}{4} = \dfrac{3}{4} \times 100\%$

          $= 75\%$

   (b) $2\dfrac{2}{3} = \dfrac{8}{3} \times 100\%$

          $= 266\dfrac{2}{3}\%$

   (c) $0.871 = 0.871 \times 100\%$

          $= 87.1\%$

2. Express the following percentages as decimals.

   (a) 0.34% (b) 126%

   Solution

   (a) $0.34\% = \dfrac{0.34}{100} = 0.0034$

   (b) $126\% = \dfrac{126}{100} = 1.26$

3. A company has 50 employees and 34 of them are women. Find the percentage of

   (a) female employees,

   (b) male employees.

   Solution

   (a) Percentage of female employees $= \dfrac{34}{50} \times 100\%$

          $= 68\%$

   (b) Percentage of male employees $= 100\% - 68\%$

          $= 32\%$

4. The following table shows the test results of 3 groups of students.

Group	Total number of students	Number of students who pass
A	20	13
B	24	15
C	25	16

   Which group has the highest percentage of students who pass the test?

   Solution

   Percentage of students who pass in group A

   $= \dfrac{13}{20} \times 100\%$

   $= 65\%$

   Percentage of students who pass in group B

   $= \dfrac{15}{24} \times 100\%$

   $= 62.5\%$

   Percentage of students who pass in group C

   $= \dfrac{16}{25} \times 100\%$

   $= 64\%$

   Group A has the highest percentage of students who pass the test.

5. 650 people attended a family-day function organized by a community council. If 24% of them are men, 32% of them are women, and the rest are children, find the number of

   (a) men,   (b) women,   (c) children,

   attending the function.

   Solution

   (a) Number of men $= 650 \times 24\%$

          $= 156$

   (b) Number of women $= 650 \times 32\%$

          $= 208$

   (c) Number of children $= 650 - 156 - 208$

          $= 286$

6. Alan's height is 135 cm and Nicole's height is 150 cm. Express Alan's height as a percentage of Nicole's height.

   Solution

   The required percentage $= \dfrac{\text{Alan's height}}{\text{Nicole's height}} \times 100\%$

          $= \dfrac{135}{150} \times 100\%$

          $= 90\%$

Section 7.2

7. In a class, 25% of the students wear glasses. If there are 8 students wearing glasses, find the number of students in the class.

   Solution

   Let n be the number of students in the class.

   $n \times 25\% = 8$

        $n = \dfrac{8}{0.25}$

          $= 32$

   The number of students in the class is 32.

8. Kumar was fined \$187 for traffic speeding. If the fine was 110% of his daily wage, find Kumar's daily wage.

Solution

Let \$$w$ be Kumar's daily wage.

$w \times 110\% = 187$

$$w = \frac{187}{1.1}$$

$$= 170$$

Kumar's daily wage is \$170.

Section 7.3

9. Mrs. Lee's monthly expenses increased from \$3,200 to \$3,400. Find the percentage increase in her expenses.

Solution

Percentage increase in her expenses

$$= \frac{3,400 - 3,200}{3,200} \times 100\%$$

$$= \frac{200}{3,200} \times 100\%$$

$$= 6.25\%$$

10. A store sold 250 shirts last week. The sales of shirts increased by 16% this week. Find the sales volume for this week.

Solution

Method 1:

$\text{Percentage increase} = \frac{\text{Increase}}{\text{Original value}} \times 100\%$

$\text{Increase} = 250 \times 16\%$

$\qquad = 40$

Sales volume for this week $= 250 + 40$

$\qquad\qquad\qquad\qquad = 290$ shirts

Method 2:

Sales volume for this week $= (100 + 16)\% \times 250$

$$= \frac{116}{100} \times 250$$

$$= 290 \text{ shirts}$$

11. A boy's height is 133 cm at the end of a year. His height increased by 6.4% during the year. Find his height at the beginning of the year.

Solution

Let the boy's height at the beginning of the year be h cm.

$133 = h \times (100\% + 6.4\%)$

$$= h \times \frac{106.4}{100}$$

$$h = \frac{133}{1.064} = 125$$

His height at the beginning of the year was 125 cm.

12. The water level in a tank decreased from 30 inches to 25.5 inches. Find the percentage decrease in the water level.

Solution

Decrease in height of water level $= 30 - 25.5$

$\qquad\qquad\qquad\qquad\qquad = 4.5$ inches

Percentage decrease in height of water level

$$= \frac{4.5}{30} \times 100\%$$

$$= 15\%$$

13. The air temperature of a town was 32 °C. It decreased by 12.5% after a heavy rain. What was the new temperature?

Solution

The new temperature $= 32 \text{ °C} \times (100\% - 12.5\%)$

$\qquad\qquad\qquad\qquad = 32 \text{ °C} \times 0.875$

$\qquad\qquad\qquad\qquad = 28 \text{ °C}$

14. Mrs. Austin's weight dropped to 62 kg after her weight decreased by 7%. What was her original weight? Give your answer correct to the nearest kg.

Solution

Let Mrs. Austin's original weight be m kg.

$62 = m \times (100\% - 7\%)$

$\qquad = m \times \frac{93}{100}$

$m = \frac{62}{0.93} = 66.7 = 67$ (correct to the nearest kg)

Mrs. Austin's original weight was 67 kg.

Section 7.4

15. During a sale, a watch was sold for \$784. If the marked price of the watch is \$980, find the percentage discount.

Solution

Discount $= \$980 - \$784 = \$196$

Percentage discount $= \frac{196}{980} \times 100\% = 20\%$

16. The marked price of a microwave oven is \$380. If the oven is sold at a discount of 25%, find
    (a) its discount,   (b) its selling price.

Solution

(a) Discount $= \$380 \times 25\% = \$95$

(b) **Method 1:**

Selling price $= \$380 - \$95 = \$285$

Method 2:

Selling price

$= \text{Marked price} \times (100\% - \text{Discount } \%)$

$$= \$380 \times \frac{75}{100} = \$285$$

17. A TV set is sold at $570 after a 24% discount.
  (a) Find the marked price of the TV set.
  (b) If the TV set were sold at a 15% discount and then at a further 9% discount on the discounted price, how much more or less would this selling price be?

Solution
  (a) Let M be the marked price of the TV set.
  Selling price = Marked price × (100% − Discount %)
  $$570 = M \times (100\% - 24\%)$$
  $$= M \times \frac{76}{100}$$
  $$M = 570 \times \frac{100}{76}$$
  $$= 750$$
  The marked price of the TV set is $750.

  (b) The new selling price
  $$= \$750 \times (100\% - 15\%) \times (100\% - 9\%)$$
  $$= \$750 \times 0.85 \times 0.91$$
  $$= \$580.125$$
  Increase in the selling price
  $$= \$580.125 - \$570$$
  $$= \$10.125$$
  $$= \$10.13 \quad \text{(correct to 2 d.p.)}$$

18. A hairdresser charges $20 for a haircut excluding sales tax. If the sales tax rate is 7%,
  (a) how much is the sales tax for the service provided?
  (b) how much does a customer have to pay for the service provided inclusive of sales tax?

Solution
  (a) Sales tax $= \$20 \times 7\%$
  $$= \$1.40$$
  (b) The required amount $= \$20 + \$1.40$
  $$= \$21.40$$

19. In a store, the marked price, inclusive of sales tax, of a vacuum cleaner is $210. If the sales tax rate is 5%, find
  (a) its price before the sales tax,
  (b) the amount of sales tax levied on it.

Solution
  (a) Let the price before sales tax be P.
  $$P \times (100\% + 5\%) = 210$$
  $$P = \frac{210}{1.05}$$
  $$= 200$$
  Its price before the sales tax is $200.

  (b) Sales tax $= \$210 - \$200$
  $$= \$10$$

Exercise 7.1

Basic Practice

1. Express each of the following fractions as percentages.

   (a) $\dfrac{1}{4}$ (b) $\dfrac{5}{6}$ (c) $2\dfrac{3}{40}$

   Solution

   (a) $\dfrac{1}{4} = \dfrac{1}{4} \times 100\% = 25\%$

   (b) $\dfrac{5}{6} = \dfrac{5}{6} \times 100\% = 83\dfrac{1}{3}\%$

   (c) $2\dfrac{3}{40} = \dfrac{83}{40} \times 100\% = 207\dfrac{1}{2}\%$

2. Express each of the following decimals as percentages.

   (a) 0.67   (b) 0.0456   (c) 3.81

   Solution

   (a) $0.67 = 0.67 \times 100\% = 67\%$

   (b) $0.0456 = 0.0456 \times 100\% = 4.56\%$

   (c) $3.81 = 3.81 \times 100\% = 381\%$

3. Express each of the following percentages as fractions.

   (a) $5\dfrac{1}{3}\%$ (b) $82\dfrac{5}{8}\%$ (c) $109\dfrac{1}{11}\%$

   Solution

   (a) $5\dfrac{1}{3}\% = \dfrac{16}{3} \times \dfrac{1}{100}$

   $\quad = \dfrac{4}{75}$

   (b) $82\dfrac{5}{8}\% = \dfrac{661}{8} \times \dfrac{1}{100}$

   $\quad = \dfrac{661}{800}$

   (c) $109\dfrac{1}{11}\% = \dfrac{1,200}{11} \times \dfrac{1}{100}$

   $\quad = \dfrac{12}{11}$

   $\quad = 1\dfrac{1}{11}$

4. Express each of the following percentages as decimals.

   (a) 3%   (b) 44%   (c) 685%

   Solution

   (a) $3\% = \dfrac{3}{100} = 0.03$

   (b) $44\% = \dfrac{44}{100} = 0.44$

   (c) $685\% = \dfrac{685}{100} = 6.85$

5. Express the first quantity as a percentage of the second quantity.

   (a) $33 of $50   (b) 75 cm of 1.2 m

   Solution

   (a) The required percentage $= \dfrac{33}{50} \times 100\%$

   $\quad = 66\%$

   (b) The required percentage $= \dfrac{75}{120} \times 100\%$

   $\quad = 62.5\%$

6. Find the value for each of the following.

   (a) $66\dfrac{2}{3}\%$ of 54 gal   (b) 108% of 15 lb

   Solution

   (a) The required value $= 54 \text{ s} \times 66\dfrac{2}{3}\%$

   $\quad = 36$ gal

   (b) The required value $= 15 \text{ kg} \times 108\%$

   $\quad = 16.2$ lb

Further Practice

7. Gary's income and expenses in a month are $4,000 and $3,360 respectively.

   (a) What percentage of his income is his expenses?

   (b) What percentage of his income is his savings?

   Solution

   (a) The required percentage $= \dfrac{3,360}{4,000} \times 100\%$

   $\quad = 84\%$

   (b) The required percentage $= 100\% - 84\%$

   $\quad = 16\%$

8. There are 80 books on a bookshelf. 28 of them are english books, 32 of them are mathematics books and the rest are science books. Find the percentage of

   (a) english books,

   (b) mathematics books,

   (c) science books,

   on the shelf.

   Solution

   (a) Percentage of english books $= \dfrac{28}{80} \times 100\%$

   $\quad = 35\%$

   (b) Percentage of mathematics books $= \dfrac{32}{80} \times 100\%$

   $\quad = 40\%$

   (c) Percentage of science books

   $\quad = 100\% - 35\% - 40\%$

   $\quad = 25\%$

9. 135 students go for a vision test. 20% of them are found to be near-sighted. How many students are near-sighted?

Solution
Number of near-sighted students = $135 \times 20\%$
$= 27$

10. In a 400-millimeters can of mixed juice, 41% is mango juice, 32.5% is pineapple juice and the rest is water. Find the volume of
(a) mango juice,   (b) pineapple juice,
(c) water,
in the can.

Solution
(a) Volume of mango juice $= 400 \text{ ml} \times 41\%$
$= 164 \text{ ml}$
(b) Volume of pineapple juice $= 400 \text{ ml} \times 32.5\%$
$= 130 \text{ ml}$
(c) Volume of water $= (400 - 164 - 130) \text{ ml}$
$= 106 \text{ ml}$

11. Justin weighs 90 lb and April weighs 80 lb.
(a) Express Justin's weight as a percentage of April's weight.
(b) Express April's weight as a percentage of Justin's weight.

Solution
(a) The required percentage
$= \frac{90}{80} \times 100\%$
$= 112.5\%$
(b) The required percentage
$= \frac{80}{90} \times 100\%$
$= 88.9\%$ (correct to 3 sig. fig.)

Math@Work

12. At a shooting practice, Peter hit the target 18 times out of 25 shots and Cliff hit it 15 times out of 20 shots. Who is better at shooting?

Solution
Peter's percentage of shots that hit targets
$= \frac{18}{25} \times 100\%$
$= 72\%$

Cliff's percentage of shots that hit targets
$= \frac{15}{20} \times 100\%$
$= 75\%$

Cliff is better at shooting.

13. The vases produced by three production lines are inspected. The following table shows the results.

Line	Number of vases inspected	Number of defective vases
1	30	3
2	50	4
3	21	2

Which production line had the lowest percentage of defective vases?

Solution
Percentage of defective vases from Line 1
$= \frac{3}{30} \times 100\% = 10\%$

Percentage of defective vases from Line 2
$= \frac{4}{50} \times 100\% = 8\%$

Percentage of defective vases from Line 3
$= \frac{2}{21} \times 100\% = 9\frac{11}{21}\%$

Production line 2 has the lowest percentage of defective vases.

14. A breakfast cereal is classified as 'low fat'. Its label on nutrition provides the information below.

Nutrition Information	
Serving Package: 10 **Serving size: 30 g**	
	Per serving
Energy	156 kcal (655 kJ)
Protein	4 g
Fat	2.7 g
Cholesterol	0 mg
Carbohydrate	29 g
Dietary fibre	3 g
Sodium	168 mg
Calcium	70 mg

(a) The amount of energy can be measured in two different units. One of them is kilocalorie (kcal) and the other is kilojoule (kJ). Based on the nutrition information given, find the conversion rate between them in kJ/kcal. Give your answer correct to 1 decimal place.
(b) Find the percentage of fat per serving.
(c) According to the health requirements guidelines, any solid food that is considered 'low fat' should contain not more than 3 g of fat per 100 g of food. Is this breakfast cereal correctly classified as a 'low fat' food?

Solution

(a) 156 kcal = 655 kJ

$$1 \text{ kcal} = \frac{655}{156} \text{ kJ}$$
$$= 4.2 \text{ kJ} \quad \text{(correct to 1 d.p.)}$$

The conversion rate is 4.2 kJ/kcal.

(b) Percentage of fat per serving $= \frac{2.7}{30} \times 100\%$
$$= 9\%$$

(c) 'Low fat' maximum percentage of fat

$$= \frac{3}{100} \times 100\%$$
$$= 3\%$$

As 9% > 3%, the oat cereal is NOT a 'low fat' food.

Brainworks

15. (a) Suppose you are given the following information.

> In Glamour Town, 68% of the adults work in the town, 25% of them work outside the town and 12% of them are unemployed.

Is the above situation possible? Explain your answer.

(b) Visit the U.S. Bureau of Labor Statistics website, http://www.bls.gov/cps/, to find the percentage of people in the labor force and the unemployment rate in the previous year.

Solution

(a) 68% + 25% + 12% = 105%
$$\geqslant 100\%$$

Since the sum of the three percentages exceeds 100%, the above situation is impossible.

(b) In the year 2011, the percentage of people in the labor force is 64%.

The unemployment rate is 8.9%.

Exercise 7.2

Basic Practice

1. Find the unknown quantity in each case.

(a) 30% of a is 18.

(b) 37.5% of b is $108.

(c) $22\frac{2}{9}\%$ of c kg is 44 kg.

(d) 150% of d cm² is 126 cm².

(e) 0.5% of e °C is 7 °C.

(f) $\frac{1}{3}\%$ of f hours is 12 hours.

Solution

(a) $a \times 30\% = 18$
$$a = \frac{18}{0.3}$$
$$= 60$$

The required quantity is 60.

(b) $b \times 37.5\% = 108$
$$b = \frac{108}{0.375}$$
$$= 288$$

The required quantity is $288.

(c) $c \times 22\frac{2}{9}\% = 44$
$$c = \frac{44}{\frac{200}{9} \times \frac{1}{100}}$$
$$= 44 \times \frac{9}{2}$$
$$= 198$$

The required quantity is 198 kg.

(d) $d \times 150\% = 126$
$$d = \frac{126}{1.5}$$
$$= 84$$

The required quantity is 84 cm².

(e) $e \times 0.5\% = 7$
$$e = \frac{7}{0.005}$$
$$= 1,400$$

The required quantity is 1,400 °C.

(f) $f \times \frac{1}{3}\% = 12$
$$f = \frac{12}{\frac{1}{3} \times \frac{1}{100}}$$
$$= 3,600$$

The required quantity is 3,600 hours.

Further Practice

2. Adam attempts 65% of the questions in a test. If he attempts 52 questions, find the total number of questions in the test.

Solution

Let the number of questions in the test be n.
$$n \times 65\% = 52$$
$$n = \frac{52}{0.65}$$
$$= 80$$

There are 80 questions in the test.

3. 45% of the members in a council are women. There are 72 female council members. Find
   (a) the total number of council members,
   (b) the number of male council members.

Solution

(a) Let n be the total number of council members.
$$n \times 45\% = 72$$
$$n = \frac{72}{0.45}$$
$$= 160$$
The total number of council members is 160.

(b) Number of male council members $= 160 - 72$
$$= 88$$

4. 85% of the customers of a supermarket were residents of the neighborhood. Given that 2,380 of the customers on a particular day were residents, find
   (a) the total number of customers,
   (b) the number of customers who were not residents of the neighborhood on that day.

Solution

(a) Let N be the total number of customers.
$$N \times 85\% = 2,380$$
$$N = \frac{2,380}{0.85}$$
$$= 2,800$$
The total number of customers is 2,800.

(b) Number of customers who were not residents
$$= 2,800 - 2,380$$
$$= 420$$

5. After cycling 18 km at an average speed of 12 km/hr, Lucy finds that she still has to cycle 55% of the total distance. She then completes the rest of her journey at an average speed of 16.5 km/hr. Find
   (a) the total distance of her journey,
   (b) the remaining distance she needs to cycle to complete the journey,
   (c) the time taken for the whole journey,
   (d) the average speed for the whole journey.

Solution

(a) Let d km be the total distance.
$$d \times (100\% - 55\%) = 18$$
$$d = \frac{18}{0.45}$$
$$= 40$$
The total distance is 40 km.

(b) The distance of the rest of her journey
$$= 40 - 18$$
$$= 22 \text{ km}$$

(c) Time taken $= \dfrac{18}{12} + \dfrac{22}{16.5}$
$$= 2\frac{5}{6} \text{ hr}$$

(d) Average speed $= \dfrac{40}{2\frac{5}{6}}$
$$= 14\frac{2}{17} \text{ km/hr}$$

Math@Work

6. A drink stall in the mall sells bottled water, juice and soda. On a particular day, it sold 175 out of its 200 bottled water, 85% of its 220 bottled juice and 180 bottles of soda which is 80% of its original stock of bottled soda.
   (a) Which drink has the highest number of bottles sold? How many bottles of this drink were sold?
   (b) Which drink has sold the highest percentage of its stock? What was the percent figure?
   (c) Which drink has the greatest number of bottles in its original stock? What was the figure?

Solution

(a) Number of bottled water sold = 175
Number of bottled juice sold $= 220 \times 85\% = 187$
Number of bottled soda sold = 180
∴ The highest number of drinks sold is bottled juice.
The number of bottled juice sold was 187.

(b) Percentage of bottled water sold $= \dfrac{175}{200} \times 100\%$
$$= 87.5\%$$
Percentage of bottled juice drinks sold = 85%
Percentage of bottled soda sold = 80%
The highest percentage of the stock is bottled water.
This percentage figure was 87.5%.

(c) Number of bottled water prepared = 200
Number of bottled juice prepared = 220
Number of bottled soda prepared $= 180 \div 80\%$
$$= 225$$
Bottled soda has the highest number of bottles in its original stock. The stall prepared 225 bottles of soda.

7. 38% of Sumiko's music CDs are Chinese music CDs, 44% of them are English music CDs and the rest are Japanese music CDs. There are 45 Japanese music CDs.
   (a) Find the total number of CDs in the collection.
   (b) Find the number of Chinese music CDs.
   (c) If 60% of the English music CDs are CDs with pop songs, find the number of CDs with English pop songs.

Solution

(a) Percentage of Japanese music CDs
   $= 100\% - 38\% - 44\%$
   $= 18\%$
   Total number of CDs $= 45 \div 18\%$
                                $= 250$

(b) Number of Chinese music CDs $= 250 \times 38\%$
                                         $= 95$

(c) Number of CDs with English pop songs
   $= 250 \times 44\% \times 60\%$
   $= 250 \times 0.44 \times 60 \times \dfrac{1}{100}$
   $= 66$

Brainworks

8. (a) Is 60% of 30 equal to 30% of 60? Explain your answer. Generalize your findings using variables x and y.
   (b) If 60% of x is 30 and 30% of y is 60, is x equal to y? Explain your answer.
   (c) Write a real-life problem that involves the mathematics in (a).

Solution

(a) 60% of $30 = 30 \times 60\% = 18$
   30% of $60 = 60 \times 30\% = 18$
   $\therefore$ 60% of 30 and 30% of 60 are equal.
   In general,
       $x\%$ of $y = xy\%$
   and $y\%$ of $x = xy\%$
   $\therefore$ $x\%$ of y and $y\%$ of x are equal.

(b) $x \times 60\% = 30$
          $x = \dfrac{30}{0.6}$
           $= 50$
   $y \times 30\% = 60$
          $y = \dfrac{60}{0.3}$
           $= 200$
   $\therefore$ $x \neq y$

(c) A club P has 30 members. If 60% of the members are male, then there are 18 male members.
A club Q has 60 members. If 30% of the members are male, then there are 18 male members.
The number of male members of these two clubs are equal.

Exercise 7.3
Basic Practice

1. Copy and complete the following table.

	Original value	Increased value	Increase	Percentage increase
(a)	$25	$28	$3	12%
(b)	16 s	20 s	4 s	25%
(c)	40 oz	52 oz	12 oz	30%
(d)	20 ft	23 ft	3 ft	15%
(e)	50 °C	55 °C	5 °C	10%
(f)	60 copies	69 copies	9 copies	15%

Solution

(a) Increase $= \$28 - \$25$
            $= \$3$
   Percentage increase $= \dfrac{3}{25} \times 100\%$
                        $= 12\%$

(b) Increased value $= 16 + 4$
                 $= 20$ s
   Percentage increase $= \dfrac{4}{16} \times 100\%$
                        $= 25\%$

(c) Increased value $= 40 \times (100\% + 30\%)$
                 $= 52$ oz
   Increase $= 40 \times 30\%$
           $= 12$ oz

(d) Original value $= 23 - 3$
               $= 20$ ft
   Percentage increase $= \dfrac{3}{20} \times 100\%$
                        $= 15\%$

(e) $55 = $ Original value $\times (100\% + 10\%)$
   Original value $= 55$ °C $\div 1.1$
                 $= 50$ °C
   Increase $= 55$ °C $- 50$ °C
           $= 5$ °C

(f) Original value $= 9 \div 15\%$
               $= 60$ copies
   Increased value $= 60 + 9$
                 $= 69$ copies

2. Copy and complete the following table.

	Original value	Decreased value	Decrease	Percentage decrease
(a)	36 lb	30 lb	6 lb	$16\frac{2}{3}$%
(b)	2 h	1.5 h	0.5 h	25%
(c)	80 miles	64.8 miles	15.2 miles	19%
(d)	15 cm³	12 cm³	3 cm³	20%
(e)	$70	$49	$21	30%
(f)	55 pint	44 pint	11 pint	20%

Solution

(a) Decrease = 36 – 30
         = 6 lb

Percentage decrease = $\frac{6}{36}$ × 100%

            = $16\frac{2}{3}$ %

(b) Decreased value = 2 – 0.5
              = 1.5 h

Percentage decrease = $\frac{0.5}{2}$ × 100%

            = 25%

(c) Decreased value = 80 m × (100% – 19%)
              = 64.8 miles
Decrease = 80 m × 19%
       = 15.2 miles

(d) Original value = 12 + 3
            = 15 cm³

Percentage decrease = $\frac{3}{15}$ × 100%

            = 20%

(e) $49 = Original value × (100% – 30%)
Original value = $49 ÷ 0.7
          = $70
Decrease = $70 – $49
       = $21

(f) Original value = 11 pint ÷ 20%
            = 55 pint
Decreased value = 55 – 11
            = 44 pint

3. Ronald's previous monthly salary was $3,000. Find his new monthly salary if it increased by 6%.

Solution
New salary = $3,000 × (100% + 6%)
        = $3,180

4. The price of a printer increased by 8% to $777.60. Find the original price of the printer.

Solution
Let $P be the original price of the printer.
$P × (100\% + 8\%) = 777.60$
$P = 777.60 ÷ 1.08$
$= 720$
The original price of the printer was $720.

5. The price of a computer system decreases from $1,250 to $1,050. Find the percentage decrease in price.

Solution
Decrease = $1,250 – $1,050
      = $200

Percentage decrease in price = $\frac{200}{1,250}$ × 100%

               = 16%

6. Jacob's monthly expenses is $2,464 after it decreased by 12%. Find his original monthly expenses.

Solution
Let $P be the original monthly expenses.
$P × (100\% - 12\%) = 2,464$
$P = \frac{2,464}{0.88}$
$= 2,800$
His original monthly expenses was $2,800.

Further Practice

7. The mass of a baby boy at birth was 3.6 kg. When he was 6 months old and 12 months old, his masses were 7.2 kg and 10.0 kg respectively. What was the percentage increase in his mass at 12 months old when compared with
   (a) his mass at birth,
   (b) his mass at 6 months old?

Solution
(a) Increase = 10 – 3.6
         = 6.4 kg

Percentage increase = $\frac{6.4}{3.6}$ × 100%

            = $177\frac{7}{9}$%

(b) Increase = 10 – 7.2
         = 2.8 kg

Percentage increase = $\frac{2.8}{7.2}$ × 100%

            = $38\frac{8}{9}$%

8. The regular price of an airline ticket is $960.
   (a) Its price increases by 30% during the peak season. Find the price of the ticket during the peak season.
   (b) Find the percentage decrease in its price if it drops to $748.80.

Solution
   (a) Price of ticket during the peak season
   $= \$960 \times (100\% + 30\%)$
   $= \$1,248$
   (b) Decrease $= \$960 - \$748.80$
   $\qquad\quad\ = \$211.20$

   Percentage decrease $= \dfrac{211.20}{960} \times 100\%$
   $\qquad\qquad\qquad\quad = 22\%$

9. The original height of a plant was 25 inches. One month later, its height increased by 20%. In the second month, it increased by 15% of the plant's height at the end of the first month. Find its height after
   (a) 1 month,
   (b) 2 months.

Solution
   (a) Plant's height after 1 month
   $= 25 \text{ in.} \times (100\% + 20\%)$
   $= 30 \text{ in.}$
   (b) Plant's height after 2 months
   $= 30 \text{ in.} \times (100\% + 15\%)$
   $= 34.5 \text{ in.}$

Math@Work

10. The population of a city in 2000 and 2010 was 3,264,000 people and 3,508,800 people respectively.
   (a) Find the percentage increase in the population during the 10 years.
   (b) If the current growth rate is the same as that in the next 10 years, find the population of the city in the year 2020.

Solution
   (a) Increase $= 3,508,800 - 3,264,000$
   $\qquad\qquad\ = 244,800$

   Percentage increase
   $= \dfrac{244,800}{3,624,000} \times 100\%$
   $= 7.5\%$
   (b) Population in the year 2020
   $= 3,508,800 \times (100\% + 7.5\%)$
   $= 3,771,960$

11. The cost of producing a batch of books can be broken down as follows:

   Typesetting: $4,000, Paper: $6,000, Printing: $2,500
   Suppose the costs of typesetting and printing increase by 15% and 8% respectively, and the cost of paper decreases by 10%.
   (a) Find the new cost of
       (i) typesetting,
       (ii) paper,
       (iii) printing,
       (iv) producing the books.
   (b) Find the percentage change in the cost of producing the books.

Solution
   (a) **(i)** New cost of typesetting
   $\qquad\qquad = \$4,000 \times (100\% + 15\%)$
   $\qquad\qquad = \$4,600$
       (ii) New cost of paper
   $\qquad\qquad = \$6,000 \times (100\% - 10\%)$
   $\qquad\qquad = \$5,400$
       (iii) New cost of printing
   $\qquad\qquad = \$2,500 \times (100\% + 8\%)$
   $\qquad\qquad = \$2,700$
       (iv) New cost of producing the books
   $\qquad\qquad = \$(4,600 + 5,400 + 2,700)$
   $\qquad\qquad = \$12,700$
   (b) Original cost of producing the books
   $= \$(4,000 + 6,000 + 2,500)$
   $= \$12,500$
   Increase in cost $= \$12,700 - \$12,500$
   $\qquad\qquad\qquad\ = \$200$

   Percentage increase $= \dfrac{200}{12,500} \times 100\%$
   $\qquad\qquad\qquad\qquad = 1.6\%$

Brainworks

12. Consider a rectangle of length 50 cm and width 40 cm.

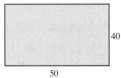

   (a) Find its area.
   (b) Find its area when the length is increased by 10% and the width is decreased by 10%.
   (c) Find its area when the length is decreased by 10% and the width is increased by 10%.
   (d) Compare the results in **(a)**, **(b)** and **(c)**.
   (e) Find its area when the length is increased by 20% and the width is decreased by 20%.

(f) Find its area when the length is decreased by 20% and the width is increased by 20%.

(g) Compare all the above results. What can you conclude?

(h) Susan proposed that the new area of A cm^2 when the length is increased by $x\%$ and the width is decreased by $x\%$ is given by

$$A = 2{,}000 \times \left(1 - \frac{x^2}{100}\right).$$

Is she right in saying so? If not, can you identify the mistake in the formula?

Solution

(a) Area of the rectangle $= 50 \times 40$
$$= 2{,}000 \text{ cm}^2$$

(b) New area
$= 50 \times (100\% + 10\%) \times 40 \times (100\% - 10\%)$
$= 1{,}980 \text{ cm}^2$

(c) New area
$= 50 \times (100\% - 10\%) \times 40 \times (100\% + 10\%)$
$= 1{,}980 \text{ cm}^2$

(d) The results in **(b)** and **(c)** are the same. They are both 20 cm^2 less than the original area in **(a)**.

(e) New area
$= 50 \times (100\% + 20\%) \times 40 \times (100\% - 20\%)$
$= 1{,}920 \text{ cm}^2$

(f) New area
$= 50 \times (100\% - 20\%) \times 40 \times (100\% + 20\%)$
$= 1{,}920 \text{ cm}^2$

(g) The results in **(e)** and **(f)** are the same. They are both 80 cm^2 less than the original area in **(a)**.
We see that when the length of a rectangle is increased by $x\%$ while its width is decreased by $x\%$, the resulting area is the same as when the length is decreased by $x\%$ while the width is increased by $x\%$. These two areas are less than the original.

(h) $A = 50 \times (100\% + x\%) \times 40 \times (100\% - x\%)$

$$= 2{,}000 \times \left(\frac{100 + x}{100}\right)\left(\frac{100 - x}{100}\right)$$

$$= 2{,}000 \times \left(1 + \frac{x}{100}\right)\left(1 - \frac{x}{100}\right)$$

$$= 2{,}000 \times \left(1 - \frac{x^2}{10{,}000}\right)$$

The mistake in the given formula is the term $\dfrac{x^2}{100}$.

Exercise 7.4

Basic Practice

1. Copy and complete the following table.

	Marked price	Selling price	Discount	Discount %
(a)	$125	$100	**$25**	20%
(b)	$70	$49	$21	**30%**
(c)	$240	$204	**$36**	15%
(d)	$320	$256	$64	**20%**
(e)	**$450**	$351	**$99**	22%
(f)	**$500**	**$345**	$155	31%

Solution

(a) Discount $= \$125 - \$100$
$$= \$25$$
Discount % $= \dfrac{25}{125} \times 100\%$
$$= 20\%$$

(b) Selling price $= \$70 - \$21$
$$= \$49$$
Discount % $= \dfrac{21}{70} \times 100\%$
$$= 30\%$$

(c) Selling price $= \$240 \times (100\% - 15\%)$
$$= \$204$$
Discount $= \$240 \times 15\%$
$$= \$36$$

(d) Marked price $= \$256 + \$64$
$$= \$320$$
Discount % $= \dfrac{64}{320} \times 100\%$
$$= 20\%$$

(e) $351 = $ Marked price $\times (100\% - 22\%)$
Marked price $= \dfrac{\$351}{0.78}$
$$= \$450$$
Discount $= \$450 - \$351$
$$= \$99$$

(f) Marked price $= \$155 \div 31\%$
$$= \$500$$
Selling price $= \$500 - \$155$
$$= \$345$$

2. A table is sold at a discount of 20% of its marked price. Find its selling price if its marked price is $980.

Solution
Selling price $= \$980 \times (100\% - 20\%)$
$$= \$784$$

3. A rice cooker is sold at a discount of 15%. If the discount is $24, find
  (a) its marked price,
  (b) its selling price.

Solution
(a) Let $M be the marked price.
$$M \times 15\% = 24$$
$$M = \frac{24}{0.15}$$
$$= 160$$
The marked price is $160.
(b) Selling price = $160 − $24 = $136

4. When a pair of shoes is sold at 12.5% discount, the selling price is $78.75. Find
  (a) the marked price of the pair of shoes,
  (b) the amount of discount.

Solution
(a) Let $M be the marked price.
$$M \times (100\% - 12.5\%) = 78.75$$
$$M = \frac{78.75}{0.875}$$
$$= 90$$
The marked price is $90.
(b) Amount of discount = $(90 − 78.75) = $11.25

5. Copy and complete the following table.

	Marked price	Price before sales tax	Amount of sales tax
(a)	$210	$200	$10
(b)	$378	$360	$18
(c)	$105	$100	$5
(d)	$493.50	$470	$23.50
(e)	$420	$400	$20
(f)	$546	$520	$26

Solution
(a) Marked price = $200 × (100% + 5%)
$$= \$210$$
Sales tax = $200 × 5%
$$= \$10$$
(b) Marked price = $360 × (100% + 5%)
$$= \$378$$
Sales tax = $360 × 5%
$$= \$18$$
(c) Price before sales tax = $5 ÷ 0.05
$$= \$100$$
Marked price = $100 + $5
$$= \$105$$

(d) Price before sales tax = $23.50 ÷ 0.05
$$= \$470$$
Marked price = $470 + $23.50
$$= \$493.50$$
(e) Price before sales tax = $420 ÷ 1.05
$$= \$400$$
Sales tax = $420 − $400
$$= \$20$$
(f) Price before sales tax = $546 ÷ 1.05
$$= \$520$$
Sales tax = $546 − $520
$$= \$26$$

6. An electrician charges Mr. Reed $300, before sales tax, for wiring his home.
  (a) What is the amount of sales tax that Mr. Reed has to pay for the service rendered?
  (b) What is the total amount, inclusive of sales tax, that Mr. Reed has to pay?

Solution
(a) Amount of sales tax = $300 × 5%
$$= \$15$$
(b) Total amount = $300 + $15
$$= \$315$$

7. The marked price, inclusive of sales tax, of a color laser printer in a computer store is $840. Find
  (a) its price before the sales tax,
  (b) the amount of sales tax charged.

Solution
(a) Price before sales tax = $840 ÷ 1.05
$$= \$800$$
(b) Amount of sales tax = $840 − $800
$$= \$40$$

Further Practice
8. At a sale in a department store, goods are sold at 10% discount. The VIP members of the store are entitled to a further discount of 5% on the discounted price. If the marked price of a sofa set is $1,200, how much does a VIP member have to pay?

Solution
Amount a VIP member has to pay
$$= \$1,200 \times (100\% - 10\%) \times (100\% - 5\%)$$
$$= \$1,026$$

9. In a store, the price of a shirt is $30. During a promotion, a customer can buy two shirts and get one free. Find the actual discount percentage when a customer buys
   (a) 1 shirt,   (b) 3 shirts.

   Solution
   (a) Discount = $0 for one shirt.
       Discount percentage = 0%

   (b) Original price of 3 shirts = $30 × 3
                                  = $90
       Selling price of 3 shirts = $30 × 2
                                 = $60
       Discount percentage = $\frac{90-60}{90} \times 100\%$

       $= 33\frac{1}{3}\%$

10. At a jewelry store, the manager increases the price of a diamond ring marked at $3,500 by 10%. He then sells it to a customer at a discount of 10%. Find
    (a) the new marked price,
    (b) the selling price of the ring,
    (c) the actual discount percentage based on the original marked price.

    Solution
    (a) New marked price = $3,500 × (100% + 10%)
                         = $3,850
    (b) Selling price = $3,850 × (100% − 10%)
                      = $3,465
    (c) Discount percentage = $\frac{3,500-3,465}{3,500} \times 100\%$

        $= 1\%$

11. The marked price, inclusive of sales tax, of a notebook computer is $1,680. It is sold at 10% discount.
    (a) Find its marked price before the sales tax.
    (b) Find the original sales tax on it.
    (c) What is the selling price of the computer?
    (d) Find the sales tax after discount.
    (e) What is the percentage decrease in the sales tax?

    Solution
    (a) Marked price before sales tax = $1,680 ÷ 1.05
                                      = $1,600
    (b) Original sales tax = $1,680 − $1,600
                           = $80
    (c) Selling price = $1,680 × (100% − 10%)
                      = $1,512
    (d) Sales tax after discount = $1,512 ÷ 1.05 × 5%
                                 = $72
    (e) Percentage decrease in sales tax = $\frac{80-72}{80} \times 100\%$

        $= 10\%$

Math@Work

12. During a Christmas sale in a department store, electrical appliances were sold at 5% discount and clothing at 20% discount storewide. Mrs. Ford bought a hair dryer with a marked price of $50 and two skirts at a discounted price of $120 each. Find
    (a) the selling price of the hair dryer,
    (b) the marked price of each skirt,
    (c) the total amount of discount Mrs. Ford received,
    (d) the average percentage discount on Mrs. Ford's purchases.

    Solution
    (a) Selling price of the hair dryer
        = $50 × (100% − 5%)
        = $47.50
    (b) Marked price of each skirt
        = $120 ÷ (100% − 20%)
        = $150
    (c) Total amount of discount
        = $[(50 − 47.50) + 2 × (150 − 120)]
        = $62.50
    (d) Original price of all the goods = $(50 + 2 × 150)
                                        = $350

        Average percentage discount = $\frac{62.50}{350} \times 100\%$

        $= 17\frac{6}{7}\%$

13. On average, a bakery sells 500 pecan rolls at $1.50 each a day. When the price of each roll increases by 20%, the total sales volume drops by 25%.
    (a) Find the new price of each pecan roll.
    (b) Find the number of pecan roll sold at the new price.
    (c) What is the percentage change in the revenue with the increase in the price?
    (d) Find the percentage discount required on the new price to adjust the price to its original value.

    Solution
    (a) New price of each pecan rolls
        = $1.50 × (100% + 20%)
        = $1.80
    (b) Number of pecan rolls sold = 500 × (100% − 25%)
                                   = 375
    (c) Total revenue under new price = $1.80 × 375
                                      = $675

        Original revenue = $1.50 × 500
                         = $750

        Percentage decrease in revenue
        $= \frac{750-675}{750} \times 100\% = 10\%$

(d) Discount required = $1.80 − $1.50
$$= \$0.30$$
Required percentage discount

$$= \frac{0.3}{1.8} \times 100\%$$

$$= 16\frac{2}{3}\%$$

Brainworks

14. George wants to buy a digital camera advertised in a poster. He is given three options to choose from.

(a) Find the selling price for Option 2.
(b) Find the selling price of each camera if George chooses Option 3.
(c) Which option offers the cheapest price for one digital camera?

Solution
(a) Selling price for option 2
$$= \$388 \times (100\% - 30\%)$$
$$= \$271.60$$

(b) Selling price for each camera under option 3
$$= \$388 \times 2 \div 3$$
$$= \$258.70 \quad \text{(correct to the nearest 10 cents)}$$

(c) Option 3 is the cheapest price for one digital camera.

Review Exercise 7

1. In a particular month, Mr. Clark spent $900 on food which was 30% of his monthly salary.
(a) Find his monthly salary.
(b) If he saved 12% of his monthly salary, find his monthly savings.

Solution
(a) His monthly salary = $900 ÷ 30%
$$= \$3,000$$

(b) His monthly savings = $3,000 × 12%
$$= \$360$$

2. A piece of alloy contains 60% copper and 40% zinc by weight. The weight of the alloy is 25 kg.
(a) Find the weight of
  (i) copper,
  (ii) zinc,
  in the alloy.
(b) If 5 kg of tin is added to the alloy, find the ratio of the weights of copper, zinc and tin in the new alloy.

Solution
(a) **(i)** Weight of copper = 25 × 60%
$$= 15 \text{ kg}$$
  (ii) Weight of zinc = 25 × 40%
$$= 10 \text{ kg}$$

(b) Ratio of weights of copper, zinc and tin
$$= 15 : 10 : 5$$
$$= 3 : 2 : 1$$

3. In a box of pens, 26% of them are red, 38% are blue and the remaining ones are black. There are 57 blue pens in the box.
(a) Find the total number of pens in the box.
(b) How many of them are black?
(c) If 10 more blue pens were put into the box, what would the new percentage of blue pens be?

Solution
(a) Total number of pens = 57 ÷ 38%
$$= 150$$

(b) Percentage of black pens
$$= 100\% - 26\% - 38\%$$
$$= 36\%$$
Number of black pens = 150 × 36%
$$= 54$$

(c) New percentage of blue pens
$$= \frac{57 + 10}{150 + 10} \times 100\%$$
$$= \frac{67}{160} \times 100\%$$
$$= 41.875\%$$

4. 30% of the members of a club are female and 20% of them own cars. 30 female members in the club own cars.
(a) How many female members are there?
(b) What is the total number of members?
(c) How many new female members have to be recruited to increase the percentage of female members to 37.5%?

Solution
(a) Number of female members = 30 ÷ 20%
$$= 150$$

(b) Total number of members = 150 ÷ 30%
$$= 500$$

(c) Let n be the number of new female members required.
$$150 + n = (500 + n) \times 37.5\%$$
$$150 + n = 187.5 + 0.375n$$
$$0.625n = 37.5$$
$$n = 60$$
60 new female members have to be recruited.

5. Richard earned $36,000 in the year 2010 and $38,880 in the year 2011.
  (a) Find the percentage increase in his annual income in the year 2011.
  (b) If Richard's income in the year 2010 was 10% less than that of the previous year, what was his annual income in the year 2009?

Solution

  (a) Percentage increase = $\dfrac{38,880 - 36,000}{36,000} \times 100\%$

$= \dfrac{2,880}{36,000} \times 100\%$

$= 8\%$

  (b) Income in the year 2009
    $= \$36,000 \div (100\% - 10\%)$
    $= \$40,000$

6. Mr. Wood's monthly expenses was $2,125 after he had reduced it by 15%. The original monthly expenses was 80% of his monthly income.
  (a) Find the original monthly expenses.
  (b) Find his monthly income.

Solution

  (a) Original monthly expenditure
    $= \$2,125 \div (100\% - 15\%)$
    $= \$2,500$

  (b) Monthly income $= \$2,500 \div 80\%$
    $= \$3,125$

7. Mrs. Delano's weight increased by 20% to 132 lb.
  (a) Find her original weight.
  (b) If her weight then dropped by 15%, find her new weight.
  (c) What percentage is her new weight of her original weight?

Solution

  (a) Original weight $= 132 \div (100\% + 20\%)$
    $= 110$ lb

  (b) New weight $= 132 \times (100\% - 15\%)$
    $= 112.2$ lb

  (c) Required percentage $= \dfrac{112.2}{110} \times 100\%$
    $= 102\%$

8. The costs of labor and material used in making a table are in the ratio 2 : 3. The cost of the table, which is $600, is the sum of these two costs.
  (a) Find the cost of
    (i) labor,
    (ii) material used.

  (b) If the cost of labor is increased by 15% while the cost of material is decreased by 20%, find the percentage change in the cost of making the table.

Solution

  (a) **(i)** Cost of labor $= \$600 \times \dfrac{2}{2 + 3} = \$240$

  (ii) Cost of material used $= \$600 \times \dfrac{3}{2 + 3}$
    $= \$360$

  (b) New cost of labor $= \$240 \times (100\% + 15\%)$
    $= \$276$
    New cost of material used
    $= \$360 \times (100\% - 20\%)$
    $= \$288$
    New cost of making the table $= \$(276 + 288)$
    $= \$564$

  Percentage decrease in the cost of making the table
    $= \dfrac{600 - 564}{600} \times 100\%$
    $= \dfrac{36}{600} \times 100\%$
    $= 6\%$

9. A newsagent overstocks 10 copies of a magazine. Eight of these copies are sold at 30% discount and the selling price is $5.60 each. The remaining two copies are sold at 40% discount.
  (a) Find the marked price of the magazine.
  (b) Find the selling price of each of the last two copies.
  (c) What is the overall percentage discount for the 10 copies of these magazines?

Solution

  (a) Marked price of the magazine
    $= \$5.60 \div (100\% - 30\%)$
    $= \$8$

  (b) Selling price of each of the last two copies
    $= \$8 \times (100\% - 40\%)$
    $= \$4.80$

  (c) Selling price for the 10 copies
    $= \$5.60 \times 8 + \$4.80 \times 2$
    $= \$54.40$
    Original marked price for 10 copies $= \$8 \times 10$
    $= \$80$

  Discount $= \$80 - \$54.40$
    $= \$25.60$

  Percentage discount $= \dfrac{25.60}{80} \times 100\% = 32\%$

10. In 500 cm^3 of alcohol solution, the percentage of alcohol by volume is 80%.
  (a) Find the volume of alcohol in the solution.
  (b) Find the volume of water that must be added to the solution so that the ratio of the volume of alcohol to that of water becomes 5 : 2.

Solution

(a) Volume of alcohol = 500 × 80%
  = 400 cm^3

(b) Let the volume of water that must be added to the solution be x cm^3.

$$\frac{400}{100 + x} = \frac{5}{2}$$

$$500 + 5x = 800$$

$$5x = 800 - 500$$

$$= 300$$

$$x = \frac{300}{5}$$

$$= 60$$

The volume of water that must be added to the solution is 60 cm^3.

11. At a clearance sale of a department store, handbags were sold at 40% discount and skirts at 25% discount. Jenny bought 2 handbags for $144 each and 3 skirts which were marked at $60 each.
  (a) Find the marked price of each handbag.
  (b) Find the selling price of each skirt.
  (c) What was the total discount on Jenny's purchases?
  (d) Find the overall percentage discount.
  (e) Find the total amount of the sales tax on the handbags and skirts bought if all purchases are subjected to a sales tax of 6%.

Solution

(a) Marked price for each handbag
  = $144 ÷ (100% − 40%) = $240

(b) Selling price of each skirt
  = $60 × (100% − 25%) = $45

(c) Total marked price
  = $(240 × 2 + 60 × 3)
  = $660
  Total selling price
  = $(144 × 2 + 45 × 3) = $423
  Total discount = $660 − $423
  = $237

(d) Overall percentage discount = $\frac{237}{660} \times 100\%$

$$= 35\frac{10}{11}\%$$

(e) Total amount of sales tax = $423 × 6%
  = $25.38

12. A store has a total of 84 gold, silver and bronze coins for sale. The number of gold, silver and bronze coins are in the ratio 1 : 2 : 3.
  (a) Find the number of
    (i) gold, **(ii)** silver, **(iii)** bronze, coins in the shop.
  (b) The marked price of the gold coins is $25 each. They are sold at 20% discount. Find the selling price of each gold coin.
  (c) The silver coins are sold for $17 each at 15% discount. Find the marked price of each silver coin.
  (d) Three bronze coins are sold for the price of 2 bronze coins. The marked price of each bronze coin is $15. Find
    (i) the total price of getting all the bronze coins,
    (ii) the percentage discount on the bronze coins.
  (e) What is the overall percentage discount on all the coins?

Solution

(a) **(i)** Number of gold coins = $84 \times \dfrac{1}{1 + 2 + 3}$
    = 14

  (ii) Number of silver coins = $84 \times \dfrac{2}{1 + 2 + 3}$
    = 28

  (iii) Number of bronze coins = $84 \times \dfrac{3}{1 + 2 + 3}$
    = 42

(b) Selling price of each gold coin
  = $25 × (100% − 20%)
  = $20

(c) Marked price of each silver coin
  = $17 × (100% − 15%)
  = $20

(d) **(i)** Total price of the bronze coins
    = $15 \times 42 \times \dfrac{2}{3}$
    = $420

  (ii) Percentage discount on the bronze coins
    = $\dfrac{1}{3} \times 100\%$
    = $33\dfrac{1}{3}\%$

(e) Original price for all the coins
  = $(25 × 14 + 20 × 28 + 15 × 42)
  = $1,540
  Selling price for all the coins
  = $(20 × 14 + 17 × 28 + 15 × 28)
  = $1,176
  Overall percentage discount
  = $\dfrac{1,540 - 1,176}{1,540} \times 100\%$
  = $\dfrac{364}{1,540} \times 100\%$
  = $23\dfrac{7}{11}\%$

Chapter 8 Angles, Triangles, and Quadrilaterals

Class Activity 1

Objective: To draw points, lines, rays, and line segments using The Geometer's Sketchpad and explore their features.

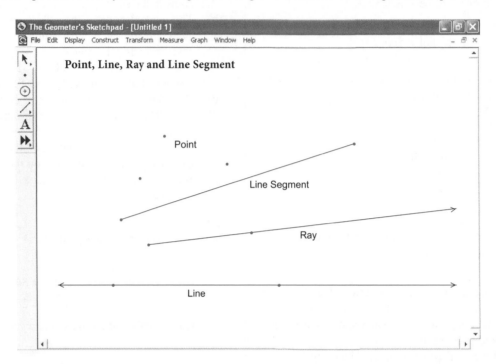

Tasks

(a) Start Sketchpad.

(b) Select the **Point tool** ✦ and click in a few places to construct some points.

(c) Select the **Segment tool** ╱. Click and drag to draw a line segment. Drag one end point on the line segment and observe what happens.

(d) Press and hold down the mouse button on the Segment tool. Without releasing your hand, drag to the right and select the **Ray tool** ⟋. Click and drag to draw a ray. Observe what happens when you drag one point on the ray at a time.

(e) Press and hold down the mouse button on the Ray tool. Without releasing your hand, drag to the right and select the **Line tool** ⟋. Drag to draw a line. Observe how dragging each point on the line at a time affects your construction.

Questions

1. What do you notice about the following objects that you have drawn?
   (a) point   **(b)** line segment
   (c) ray   **(d)** line

   (a) A point indicates a position and not a length.

   (b) A line segment has length with two end points.

   (c) A ray has length with one end point.

   (d) A line has an infinite number of points. It has no width and can be straight or curved.

2. Based on what you have observed, describe the relationship between point, line segment, ray and line.

   A line consists of infinitely many points. A ray is a part of a line and it has a fixed end. A line segment is a part of a line and it has two fixed ends.

3. On which geometrical object do the points and the line lie?

   The points and the line lie on a plane.

Class Activity 2

Objective: To explore the properties of angles at a point, complementary angles, supplementary angles, and vertically opposite angles.

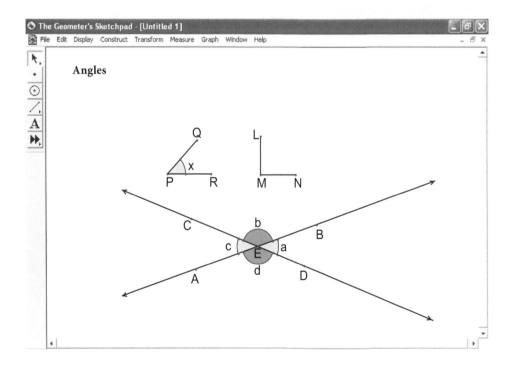

Tasks

(a) Start Sketchpad.

(b) Mark a point *P* anywhere on the screen and draw an acute angle *x*, an obtuse angle *y*, and a reflex angle *z* with the common vertex *P* such that each angle is adjacent to the other two angles.

(c) Measure ∠*x*, ∠*y*, and ∠*z* and find their sum.

(d) Construct a right angle, ∠*LMN*, and a pair of complementary angles.

(e) Construct a pair of supplementary angles.

(f) Draw two intersecting straight lines *AB* and *CD* as shown above.

(g) Measure all the four angles ∠*a*, ∠*b*, ∠*c*, and ∠*d* at their point of intersection *E*.

(h) Drag one of the lines and observe the changes in these angles and how they are related.

Questions

1. What can you say about the sum of *m*∠*x*, *m*∠*y*, and *m*∠*z* ?

$m\angle x + m\angle y + m\angle z = 360°$

2. Describe your way of drawing a pair of complementary angles.

To draw complementary angles:

Step 1: Construct a right angle.

Step 2: From the vertex of the right angle, draw a line segment to divide the right angle into two angles.

Then those two angles formed are complementary angles.

3. Describe your way of drawing a pair of supplementary angles.

To draw supplementary angles:

Step 1: Draw a straight line and mark a point on it.

Step 2: From the point, draw a line segment.

Then the two angles formed by the straight line and the line segment are supplementary angles.

4. What can you say about the relationship between ∠*a* and ∠*b*?

$m\angle a + m\angle b$ are angles next to each other on a straight line. $m\angle a + m\angle b = 180°$.

5. What can you say about the relationship between ∠*a* and ∠*c*?

∠*a* and ∠*c* are angles opposite each other on the two intersecting straight lines, *AB* and *CD*. $m\angle a = m\angle c$.

Class Activity 3

Objective: To draw a perpendicular bisector of a line segment and explore its property using The Geometer's Sketchpad.

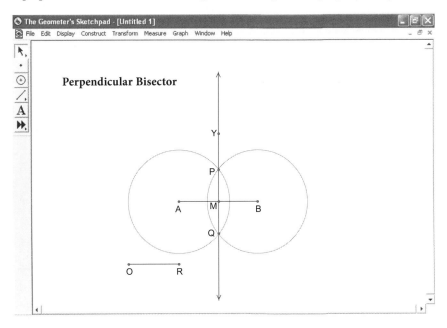

Tasks

(a) Draw a line segment *AB*.

(b) Draw a line segment *OR* greater than $\frac{1}{2}$ *AB* at the bottom part of the screen.

(c) Select the point *A* and the line segment *OR*. Select **Construct | Circle by Center + Radius** to draw a circle with center *A* and radius *OR*.

(d) Similarly, draw a circle with center *B* and radius *OR*.

(e) Plot the intersecting points of the circles as *P* and *Q*.

(f) Draw the line *PQ*. Then *PQ* is the perpendicular bisector of *AB*.

(g) Plot the intersecting point of *AB* and *PQ* as *M*. Plot a point *Y* on the line *PQ*.

(h) Measure ∠*AMP* and the lengths *AM*, *BM*, *AY*, and *BY*.

Questions

1. Slide the point *Y* along *PQ*. What do you observe?

AY is always equal to BY.

2. Drag the point *R* around. Does the line *PQ* change?

No, it does not change.

3. Drag the point *B* around.

(a) What do you observe about the line *PQ*?

The line *PQ* changes as *B* moves. *PQ* ⊥ *AB*.

(b) Make a conjecture about the measurements.

m∠*AMP* = 90°, *AM* = *BM*, *AY* = BY

Class Activity 4

Objective: To construct the angle bisector of an angle and explore its property using The Geometer's Sketchpad.

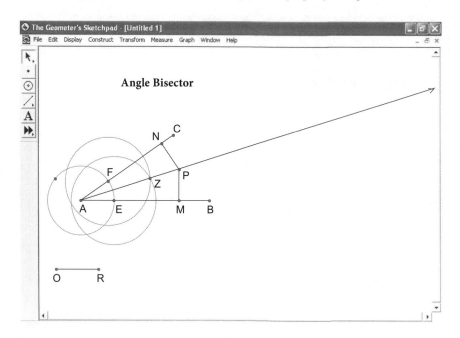

Tasks

(a) Draw line segments *AB* and *AC* to form an angle *BAC*.

(b) Select the **Compass** tool to create a circle with centre at *A*.

(c) Plot the points where the circle cuts *AB* and *AC* as *E* and *F* respectively.

(d) Draw a line segment *OR* at the bottom of the screen.

(e) With *E* and *F* as centers and *OR* as radius, draw two circles.

(f) Mark the intersecting point of these two circles within ∠*BAC* as *Z*.

(g) Draw the ray *AZ*. Then *AZ* is the angle bisector of ∠*BAC*.

(h) Measure ∠*BAZ* and ∠*CAZ* and drag the point *C* around to verify it.

(i) Plot a point *P* on *AZ*.

(j) Select the point *P* and the line segment *AB*. Select **Construct | Perpendicular Line** to draw a perpendicular from *P* to meet *AB* at *M*.

(k) Create the line segment *PM*. Select the perpendicular line and then select **Hide | Perpendicular Line** to hide the perpendicular line.

(l) Similarly, draw a perpendicular line segment *PN* from *P* to meet *AC* at *N*.

Question

Drag the point *P* along *AZ* and the point *R* around. Name some equal parts in the diagram.

AM = AN, PM = PN

Class Activity 5

Objective: To investigate the sufficient conditions needed to draw unique triangles.

Tasks

You will need drinking straws (or pipe cleaners) and angle strips of different angle of pre-determine measures.

(a) Form a triangle using three pieces of drinking straws or pipe cleaners of lengths 5 cm, 7 cm, and 10 cm.
  (i) Compare your triangle with the triangles of your classmates.
  (ii) What do you observe? Are all the triangles the same?
  Try three different lengths of material (3 cm – 4 cm – 5 cm, 5cm – 5 cm – 5cm, and 7 cm – 7 cm – 5 cm) to see if the same conclusion holds true.

(b) Using the 5 cm and 7 cm pieces of straw and a 50° angle made from angle strips (or straws and pipe cleaners), form a triangle. The third side can be any length necessary to complete the triangle. Experiment by placing the 50° angle in different locations so that it is the angle between the two given sides and then as the angle opposite one of the given sides.
  (i) Sketch and label the triangles that you have formed.
  (ii) Compare your triangles with those of your classmates for each case explored, and to state the conclusions.
  (iii) Where must the 50° angle be placed relative to the other known sides in order to produce triangles that are the same for you and your classmates?
  Try three different combinations of lengths and angle measures of material to see if the same conclusion holds true.

(c) Using only the 7 cm straw and 2 angles of 50° and 60°, along with 2 other pieces of straw (cut to appropriate required lengths), explore possible ways of combining them to make a triangle.
  (i) Sketch and label the triangles that you have formed.
  (ii) Compare your triangles with those of your classmates and observe how two angles and one side should be arranged such that triangles that are alike will always be produced.
  Similarly, try three different combinations of lengths and angle measures of material to see if the same conclusion hold true.

(d) Explore using only 3 angles of 50°, 60°, and 70° to form triangles.
  Is it possible to form a unique triangle?

(e) Explore using three pieces of straws of lengths 3 cm, 4 cm, and 10 cm to form triangles. Also, try another different combination of lengths of material (3 cm – 5 cm – 10 cm or 4 cm – 5 cm – 10 cm).
  (i) Is it possible to form a unique triangle in each of the case?
  (ii) Find the sum of any two sides of each triangle in Task **(e)**.
  Compare the sum of any two sides of a triangle with the length of the third side of the triangle.
  (iii) Refer to the lengths of sides of the triangles formed in Task **(a)**. Find the sum of any two sides of each of those triangles in Task **(a)**. What do you notice about the sum of any two sides of a triangle with the length of the third side of the triangle?

Questions

1. Are you able to create a unique triangle in each case if you are given each of the following measures? Which are the sufficient conditions needed to create a unique triangle?

  (a) the lengths of three sides,

  It is sufficient to construct a unique triangle.
  _____

  (b) the length of two sides and the measure of the angle between the two sides,

  It is sufficient to construct a unique triangle.
  _____

  (c) the length of two sides and the measure of one angle that is not between these two sides,

  It is not sufficient to construct a unique triangle. More than one triangle can be drawn.
  _____

  (d) the measure of two angles and the length of one side,

  It is not sufficient to construct a unique triangle. More than one triangle can be drawn.
  _____

(e) the measure of three angles of a triangle.

It is sufficient to construct a unique triangle.

2. What can you conclude about the relationship among the lengths of the three sides of a unique triangle?

The sum of length of any two sides of a triangle is always greater than the length of the third side.

Class Activity 6

Objective: To construct a parallelogram and explore its properties using The Geometer's Sketchpad.

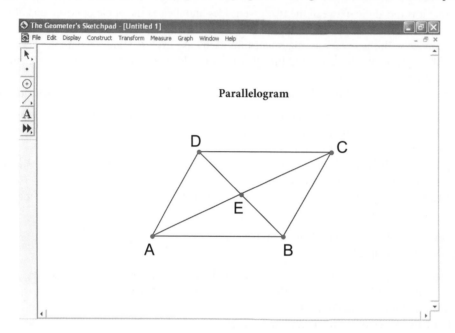

Tasks

(a) Construct the line segments *AB* and *AD* as shown above.

(b) Construct a line through *B* and parallel to *AD*. Then construct a line through *D* and parallel to *AB*. Mark the point of intersection of these two lines as *C*.

(c) Construct the line segments *BC* and *CD*. Hide the parallel lines created in **(b)**. Then *ABCD* is a parallelogram.

(d) Join the diagonals *AC* and *BD*. Mark their point of intersection as *E*.

Questions

1. Measure the sides and angles of the parallelogram. What do you observe?

Opposite sides and opposite angles of a parallelogram are equal.

2. Measure the lengths of *AE*, *BE*, *CE*, and *DE*. What do you observe?

AE = *CE* and *BE* = *DE*

Class Activity 7

Objective: To construct some special quadrilaterals and explore their properties using The Geometer's Sketchpad.

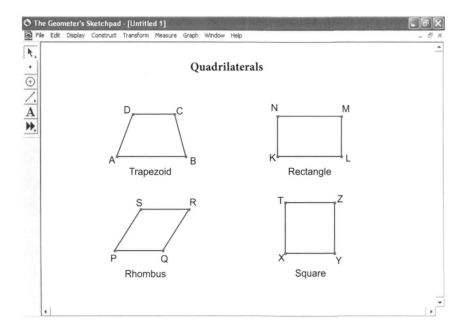

Tasks

(a) Construct a trapezoid *ABCD* with *AB* // *DC*.

(b) Draw a line segment *KL* and then a perpendicular line *KN* through *K*. Construct a rectangle *KLMN*.

(c) Construct a line segment *PQ*. Draw a circle with center *P* and passing through *Q*. Mark a point *S* on the circle. Then construct a rhombus *PQRS*.

(d) Construct a square *XYZT*.

(e) Construct the diagonals of each figure and explore their properties.

Questions

1. Consider the figures of a trapezoid, a parallelogram, a rectangle, a rhombus, and a square.

   (a) Which figures have the diagonals bisecting each other?

   Square, rhombus, rectangle, and parallelogram

   (b) Which figures have the diagonals equal in length?

   Square and rectangle

   (c) Which figures have the diagonals perpendicular to each other?

   Square and rhombus

2. Measure ∠*QPR* and ∠*SPR*. What do you observe?

m∠QPR = m∠SPR

3. Measure ∠*YXZ* and ∠*TXZ*. What do you observe?

m∠YXZ = m∠TXZ = 45°

4. Discuss the relationship between
   (a) a trapezoid and a parallelogram,

   A parallelogram is a special type of trapezoid with two pairs of parallel sides.

   (b) a rectangle, a rhombus, and a square.

   (i) A square is a special type of rectangle with four equal sides.

   (ii) A square is a special type of rhombus with four right angles.

Extend Your Learning Curve

Construction of Angles Using a Ruler and Compasses

Construction using primitive tools such as a ruler and compasses has been regarded as an art by mathematicians for a long time. The diagram shows a method of constructing 45°. Try to construct three other angles using a ruler and compasses.

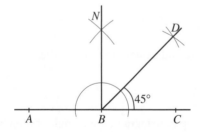

Suggested Answer

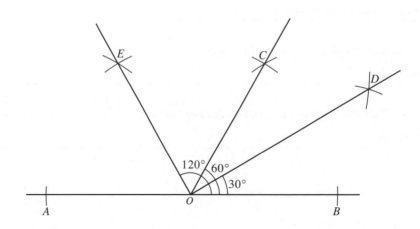

Try It!

Section 8.2

1. In the diagram, *XYZ* is a straight line. Find the value of *w*.

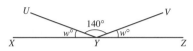

Solution

$w° + 140° + w° = 180°$ (adj. ∠s on a st. line)
$2w = 40$
$w = 20$

2. Find the value of *x* in the diagram.

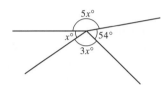

Solution

$5x° + x° + 3x° + 54° = 360°$ (∠s at a point)
$9x + 54 = 360$
$9x = 306$
$x = 34$

3. In the diagram, *EFG* and *HFK* are straight lines. Find $m∠x$ and $m∠y$.

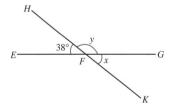

Solution

$m∠x = m∠EFH$ (vert. opp. ∠s)
$= 38°$
$m∠y + 38° = 180°$ (adj. ∠s on a st. line)
$m∠y = 142°$

4. In the diagram, *PS*, *QT* and *RU* are straight lines, intersecting at *V*. Find the value of *z*.

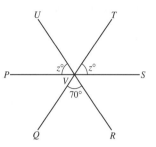

Solution

$m∠UVT = 70°$ (vert. opp. ∠s)
$z° + m∠UVT + z° = 180°$ (adj. ∠s on a st. line)
$z° + 70° + z° = 180°$
$2z = 110$
$z = 55$

Section 8.4

5. Construct △*LMN* with *LM* = 4 cm, *MN* = 4 cm, and ∠*LMN* = 30°. Measure and write down the length of *LN*.

Solution

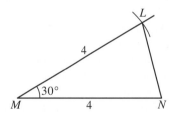

Construction Steps:
1. Construct a line segment *MN* 4 cm long.
2. Draw a ray with the end point *M* and making an angle of 30° with *MN* using a protractor.
3. With *M* as centre and 4 cm as radius, draw an arc to cut the ray at *L*.
4. Join *L* and *N*. △*LMN* is the required triangle.
   LN = 2 cm

Section 8.5

6. (a) Construct a parallelogram *EFGH* in which *EF* = 4 cm, *FG* = 5.5 cm, and *m∠EFG* = 80°.

(b) Measure and write down the length of the diagonal *EG*.

Solution

(a)

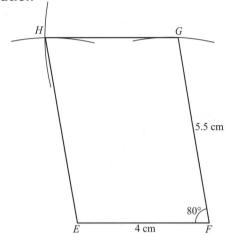

Construction Steps:

1. Draw a line segment *EF* 4 cm long.
2. Using a protractor, draw a ray with end point *F* making an angle of 80° with *EF*.
3. Mark a point *G* on the ray such that *FG* = 5.5 cm.
4. With *E* as center and 5.5 cm as radius, draw an arc above *EF*.
5. With *G* as center and 4 cm as radius, draw an arc to cut the previous arc at *H*.
6. Draw the line segments *EH* and *HG*. Then *EFGH* is the required parallelogram.

(b) *EG* = 6.2 cm

7. (a) Construct a quadrilateral *XYZT* in which *XY* = 3 cm, *YZ* = 3.5 cm, *XT* = 3 cm, *m∠X* = 130°, and *m∠Y* = 90°.

(b) Measure ∠*XTZ* and state its size, correct to the nearest degree.

Solution

(a)

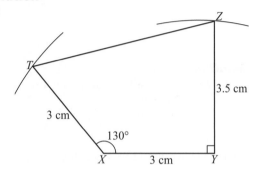

Construction Steps:

1. Draw a line segment *XY* 3 cm long
2. Using a protractor, draw a ray with end point *X* making an angle of 130° with *XY*.
3. Mark a point *T* on the ray such that *XT* = 3 cm.
4. Using a protractor, draw a ray with end point *Y* on the same side of *XY* as *XT* such that it makes an angle of 90° with *XY*.
5. Mark a point *Z* on the ray such that *YZ* = 3.5 cm.
6. Draw the line segment *TZ*. Then *XYZT* is the required quadrilateral.

(b) *m∠XTZ* = 64° (correct to the nearest degree)

Exercise 8.1
Basic Practice

1. In the diagram, A and B are two points on a plane. How many lines can be drawn passing through
(a) A,
(b) both A and B?

Solution
(a) infinite
(b) 1

2. In the diagram, C and D are two points on a plane. Draw the ray CD, where C is the end point.

Solution

Further Practice

3.

In the diagram, A, B, and C are three points on a straight line.
(a) Find the number of different line segments that can be formed by these points.
(b) Find the number of different rays that can be formed by these points.

Solution
(a) 3   **(b)** 6

Math@Work

4.

The above diagram shows a line segment $ABCD$ in which $AB = CD$.
(a) State the relation between AC and BD.
(b) Give the reason for the result.

Solution
(a) $AC = BD$
(b) $AB = CD$ (given)
$AB + BC = BC + CD$
$\therefore \quad AC = BD$

Brainworks

5.

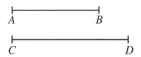

In the diagram, AB and CD are two line segments, and AB is shorter than CD.
(a) How many points are on the line segment
  (i) AB,
  (ii) CD?
(b) Is it true that there are more points on CD than on AB?

Solution
(a) **(i)** infinite
  (ii) infinite
(b) No

Exercise 8.2
Basic Practice

1. Which of the following pairs of angles are complementary?
(a) $31°$, $71°$ **(b)** $25°$, $65°$

Solution
(a) $31° + 71° = 102°$
$\neq 90°$
$\therefore$ $31°$ and $71°$ are not complementary angles.
(b) $25° + 65° = 90°$
$\therefore$ $25°$ and $65°$ are complementary angles.

2. In each case, find the angle that is complementary to the given angle.
(a) $20°$ **(b)** $42°$

Solution
(a) The required angle $= 90° - 20°$
$= 70°$
(b) The required angle $= 90° - 42°$
$= 48°$

3. Which of the following pairs of angles are supplementary?
(a) $128°$, $62°$ **(b)** $40°$, $140°$

Solution
(a) $128° + 62° = 190°$
$\neq 180°$
$\therefore$ $128°$ and $62°$ are not supplementary angles.
(b) $40° + 140° = 180°$
$\therefore$ $40°$ and $140°$ are supplementary angles.

4. In each case, find the angle that is supplementary to the given angle.

(a)   43°   **(b)**   76°

Solution
(a)   The required angle = 180° − 43°
                        = 137°
(b)   The required angle = 180° − 76°
                        = 104°

5. In each diagram, *AOB* is a straight line. Find the measure of each unknown marked angle.

(a) 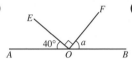   **(b)**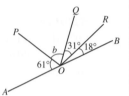

Solution
(a)   40° + 90° + *m∠a* = 180°   (adj. ∠s on a st. line)
                    m∠a = 50°
(b)   61° + *m∠b* + 31° + 18° = 180°
                            (adj. ∠s on a st. line)
                    m∠b = 70°

6. Find the measure of the unknown angle *x* in each diagram.

(a) 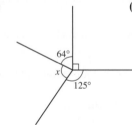   **(b)**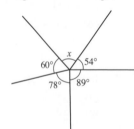

Solution
(a)   *m∠x* + 125° + 90° + 64° = 360°   (∠s at a point)
                    m∠x = 81°
(b)   *m∠x* + 60° + 78° + 89° + 54° = 360°
                            (∠s at a point)
                    m∠x = 79°

7. In each of the diagrams, the straight lines *AB* and *CD* intersect at a point. Find the measure of each unknown marked angle.

(a)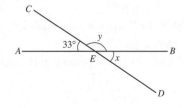

(b)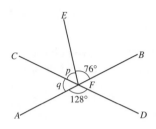

Solution
(a)   *m∠x* = 33°   (vert. opp. ∠s)
        33° + *m∠y* = 180°   (adj. ∠s on a st. line)
            m∠y = 147°

(b)   *m∠BFC* = *m∠AFD*   (vert. opp. ∠s)
        m∠p + 76° = 128°
                m∠p = 52°
        m∠q + 128° = 180°   (adj. ∠s on a st. line)
                m∠q = 52°

Further Practice

8. If the angles *x*° and 2*x*° are complementary, find the value of *x*.

Solution
x° + 2*x*° = 90°
        3*x* = 90
          x = 30

9. If the angles 2*y*° and 3*y*° are supplementary, find the value of *y*.

Solution
2*y*° + 3*y*° = 180°
        5*y* = 180
          y = 36

10. In the diagram, *ABC* is a straight line.
(a)   Find the value of *x*.
(b)   What type of angle is ∠*ABD*?

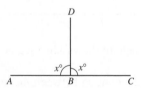

Solution
(a)   *x*° + *x*° = 180°   (adj. ∠s on a st. line)
                2*x* = 180
                  x = 90

(b)   ∠*ABD* is a right angle.

11. In the diagram, *LMN* is a straight line.
(a) Find the value of *y*.
(b) What type of angle is
   (i) ∠*PMN*,
   (ii) ∠*LMN*?

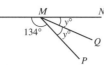

Solution
(a) $134° + y° + y° = 180°$ (adj. ∠s on a st. line)
$$2y = 46$$
$$y = 23$$

(b) (i) $m∠PMN = 2y°$
$$= 46°$$
∠*PMN* is an acute angle.

   (ii) $m∠LMN = 180°$
∠*LMN* is a straight angle.

12. In the diagram, *PQR* is a straight line.
(a) Find the value of *x*.
(b) What type of angle is ∠*SQT*?

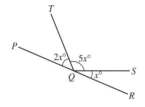

Solution
(a) $2x° + 5x° + x° = 180°$ (adj. ∠s on a st. line)
$$8x = 180$$
$$x = 22.5$$

(b) $m∠SQT = 5 × 22.5°$
$$= 112.5°$$
∴ ∠*SQT* is an obtuse angle.

13. Find the value of *x* in the diagram.

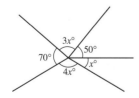

Solution
$x° + 50° + 3x° + 70° + 4x° = 360°$ (∠s at a point)
$$8x = 240$$
$$x = 30$$

14. In each diagram, three lines intersect at a point. Find the value of *x*.
(a)   (b)

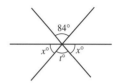

Solution
(a)

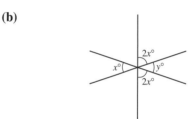

$$t° = 84°   \text{(vert. opp. ∠s)}$$
$$x° + t° + x° = 180   \text{(adj. ∠s on a st. line)}$$
$$2x = 96$$
$$x = 48$$

(b)

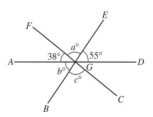

$$y° = x°   \text{(vert. opp. ∠s)}$$
$$2x° + y° + 2x° = 180°   \text{(adj. ∠s on a st. line)}$$
$$5x = 180$$
$$x = 36$$

15. In the diagram, the lines *AD*, *BE*, and *CF* intersect at the point *G*. Find the values of *a*, *b*, and *c*.

Solution
$38° + a° + 55° = 180°$ (adj. ∠s on a st. line)
$$a = 87$$
$$b° = 55°   \text{(vert. opp. ∠s)}$$
$$b = 55$$
$$c° = a°   \text{(vert. opp. ∠s)}$$
$$c = 87$$

Math@Work

16. In the diagram, an end of each wooden frame $ABCD$ and $EFGH$ is cut to form an angle x such that $\angle ABC$ and $\angle FGH$ are complementary. Find the value of x.

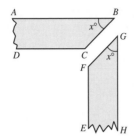

Solution

$x° + x° = 90°$

$\quad 2x = 90$

$\quad\quad x = 45$

17. The diagram represents a logo. Find the value of y.

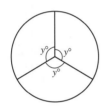

Solution

$y° + y° + y° = 360°$ $\quad$ ($\angle$s at a point)

$\quad\quad\quad 3y = 360$

$\quad\quad\quad\quad y = 120$

18. The diagram shows a pair of tongs. Find the values of x and y.

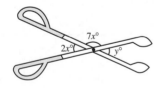

Solution

$2x° + 7x° = 180°$ $\quad$ (adj. $\angle$s on a st. line)

$\quad\quad\quad 9x = 180$

$\quad\quad\quad\quad x = 20$

$\quad\quad 2x° = y°$ $\quad$ (vert. opp. $\angle$s)

$\quad\quad\quad\quad y = 40$

Brainworks

19. In the diagram, ABC is a straight line. Name
   (a) 2 acute angles,
   (b) 2 obtuse angles,
   (c) 1 pair of complementary angles,
   (d) 2 pairs of supplementary angles.

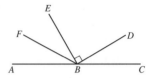

Solution

(a) $\angle ABF, \angle FBE, \angle ABE$, and $\angle CBD$ are acute angles.
(b) $\angle ABD, \angle FBD, \angle FBC$, and $\angle EBC$ are obtuse angles.
(c) $\angle ABE$ and $\angle CBD$ are complementary angles.
(d) $\angle ABF$ and $\angle CBF$,
$\angle ABE$ and $\angle CBE$, and
$\angle ABD$ and $\angle CBD$ are pairs of supplementary angles.

20. In the diagram, AD, BE, and CF are straight lines which intersect at G.
   (a) Find two pairs of possible values of x and y.
   (b) If y is 3 times of x, find the values of x and y.

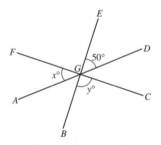

Solution

(a) $\quad\quad m\angle AGB = m\angle DGE$ $\quad$ (vert. opp. $\angle$s)

$\quad\quad\quad\quad\quad\quad = 50°$

$x° + m\angle AGB + y° = 180°$ $\quad$ (adj. $\angle$s on a st. line)

$\quad\quad x + 50 + y = 180$

$\quad\quad\quad\quad x + y = 130$

The two pairs of possible values of x and y are:

$x = 30$ and $y = 100$,

$x = 40$ and $y = 90$.

(b) If $y = 3x$, we have

$\quad x + 3x = 130$

$\quad\quad\quad 4x = 130$

$\therefore \quad\quad x = 32.5$

and $\quad y = 3 \times 32.5 = 97.5$

Exercise 8.3

Basic Practice

1. Draw a line segment AB 4 cm long and construct the perpendicular bisector of AB using a ruler and compasses.

Solution

(a)

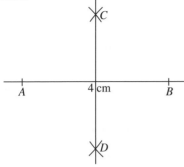

Steps for constructing the perpendicular bisector of AB:
1. With A as center and a radius $> \frac{1}{2}AB$, draw an arc on each side of AB.
2. With B as center and same radius as in step 1, draw two arcs to cut the previous arcs at C and D. Then CD is the $\perp$ bisector of AB.

2. Draw a line segment 6 cm long and divide it into 4 equal parts using a ruler and compasses.

Solution

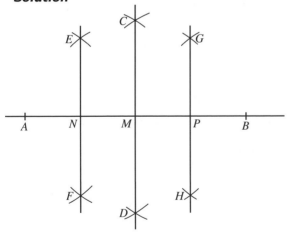

In the figure, $AB = 6$ cm.
Steps for dividing AB into 4 equal parts are:
1. Draw the $\perp$ bisector CD of AB to cut AB at its midpoint M.
2. Draw the $\perp$ bisector EF of AM to cut AM at its midpoint N.
3. Draw the $\perp$ bisector GH of MB to cut MB at its midpoint P.
4. Then $AN = NM = MP = PB$.

3. Draw each angle using a protractor and construct its angle bisector using a ruler and compasses.

(a) 　　(b)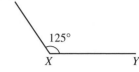

Solution

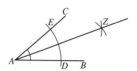

(a) Steps for constructing the angle bisector of $\angle BAC$:
1. With A as center, draw an arc to cut AB and AC at D and E respectively.
2. With D and E as centers and equal radii, draw arcs to cut at point Z.
3. Join AZ.
Then AZ is the angle bisector of $\angle BAC$.

(b)

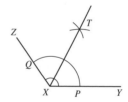

Steps are similar to those in (a).
XT is the angle bisector of $\angle YXZ$.

4. Draw an angle of 200° using a protractor and divide it into 4 equal angles using a ruler and compasses.

Solution

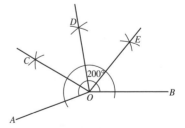

In the figure, reflex $\angle AOB = 200°$.
Steps for dividing reflex $\angle AOB$ into 4 equal angles are:
1. Construct OD to divide reflex $\angle AOB$ into 2 equal angles, $\angle AOD$ and $\angle BOD$.
2. Construct the angle bisectors OC and OE of $\angle AOD$ and $\angle BOD$ respectively.
3. Then $\angle AOC = \angle COD = \angle DOE$ and $\angle EOB$.

Further Practice

5.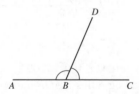

(a) Draw a line segment *ABC* with *AB* = 1.5 cm and *BC* = 2.5 cm as shown in the diagram.

(b) Construct the perpendiculars *PM* and *QN* of *AB* and *BC*, where *M* and *N* are the midpoints of *AB* and *BC* respectively.

(c) How are the lines *PM* and *QN* related geometrically?

(d) What is the relation between the lengths of *MN* and *AC*?

Solution

(a) and (b)

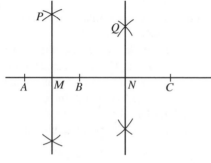

(c) *PM* and *QN* are parallel.

(d) $MB = \frac{1}{2}AB$

$= \frac{1}{2} \times 1.5$ cm

$= 0.75$ cm

$BN = \frac{1}{2}BC$

$= \frac{1}{2} \times 2.5$ cm

$= 1.25$ cm

$\therefore MN = MB + BN$

$= (0.75 + 1.25)$ cm

$= 2$ cm

Since *AC* = 4 cm,

$MN = \frac{1}{2}AC.$

6. In the diagram, *ABC* is a straight line.

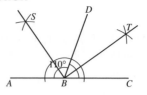

(a) Given that $m\angle ABD = 110°$, construct the bisectors *BS* and *BT* of $\angle ABD$ and $\angle CBD$ respectively using a ruler and compasses.

(b) What is the measure of $\angle SBT$? Give a reason for this.

Solution

(a)

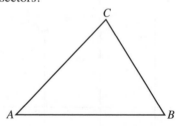

(b) $m\angle SBD = \frac{1}{2} m\angle ABD$

$= \frac{1}{2} \times 110°$

$= 55°$

$m\angle CBD = 180° - 110°$ (adj. $\angle$s on a st. line)

$= 70°$

$m\angle DBT = \frac{1}{2} m\angle CBD$

$= \frac{1}{2} \times 70°$

$= 35°$

$\therefore m\angle SBT = m\angle SBD + m\angle DBT$

$= 55° + 35°$

$= 90°$

Math@Work

7. **(a)** **(i)** Make a copy of the triangle *ABC* on a sheet of plain paper.

     (ii) Using a ruler and compasses, construct the perpendicular bisectors of the three sides of the triangle.

(b) What do you observe about the perpendicular bisectors?

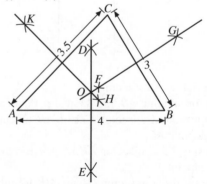

Solution

(a) **(i) and (ii)**

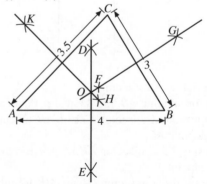

(b) The three perpendicular bisectors meet at a point *O*. If we draw a circle with center *O* and radius *OA*, the circle will touch the vertices *A*, *B*, and *C*.

8. (a) (i) Make a copy of the triangle *XYZ* on a sheet of plain paper.

(ii) Using a ruler and compasses, construct the angle bisectors of the three angles of the triangle.

(b) What do you observe about the angle bisectors?

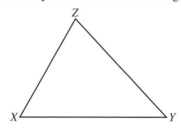

Solution

(a) (i) and **(ii)**

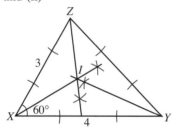

(b) The angle bisectors of the angles of △*XYZ* meet at a point *I*. If we draw a circle with center *I* and the perpendicular distance from *I* to *XY* as its radius, the circle will touch the three sides of △*XYZ*.

Brainworks

9. Using compasses, design some patterns involving circles and arcs.

Solution

Students may come up with various designs using circles and arcs. Those designs can be used as classroom display.

10. The diagram shows three towns *A*, *B*, and *C*. Where should the hospital be built if it is to be equidistant from the three towns?

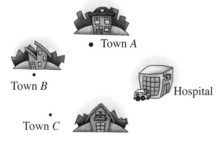

Solution

The hospital should be located at the point of intersection of the perpendicular bisectors of △*ABC*, where *A*, *B*, and *C* are the locations of the towns *A*, *B*, and *C* respectively.

Exercise 8.4

Basic Practice

1. Determine if the measurements given in each case are sufficient to create a unique triangle. If so, sketch the triangle and classify the triangle by its sides.

(a) △*ABC* with *AB* = 5 cm, *BC* = 3 cm, and *AC* = 5 cm

(b) △*DEF* with *DE* = 4 cm, *EF* = 4 cm, and *DF* = 4 cm

(c) △*GHK* with *GH* = 6 cm, *m*∠*GHK* = 37°, and *GK* = 4.5 cm

(d) △*LMN* with *LM* = 6 cm, *m*∠*LMN* = 120°, and *MN* = 6 cm

Solution

(a) Sufficient. Isosceles triangle

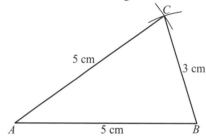

(b) Sufficient. Equilateral triangle

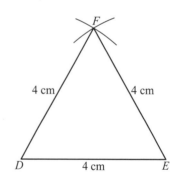

(c) Not sufficient

(d) Sufficient. Isosceles triangle

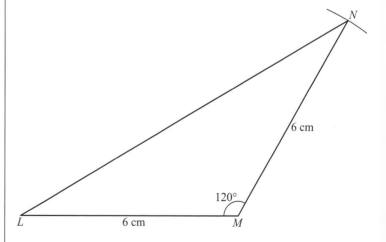

2. Determine if the measurements given in each case can create a unique triangle *PQR*. If so, sketch the triangle and classify the triangle

    (i) by its angles,   **(ii)** by its sides.

(For parts **(c)** to **(f)**, find $m\angle R$.)

(a) $m\angle P = 70°, m\angle Q = 40°, m\angle R = 70°$
(b) $m\angle P = 97°, m\angle Q = 13°, m\angle R = 90°$
(c) $m\angle P = 42°, m\angle Q = 48°, QR = 3$ cm
(d) $m\angle P = 34°, m\angle Q = 112°, PQ = 4$ cm
(e) $m\angle P = 65°, m\angle Q = 50°, PR = 5$ cm
(f) $m\angle P = 20°, m\angle Q = 60°, PQ = 6$ cm

Solution

(a) No unique triangle

(b) No unique triangle.

(c) No unique triangle. Side given must be in between the two given angles.

(d) Unique triangle.
    (i) Obtuse-angled
    (ii) Isosceles triangle. $m\angle R = 34°$

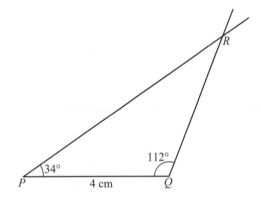

(e) No unique triangle
(f) Unique triangle.
    (i) Obtuse-angled
    (ii) Scalene triangle. $m\angle R = 100°$

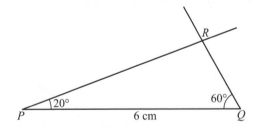

3. **(a)** Construct $\triangle ABC$ where $m\angle ABC = 90°$ and $AB = BC = 3$ cm.
    (b) What type of triangle is $\triangle ABC$?
    (c) Find $m\angle BAC$.

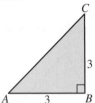

Solution
(a)

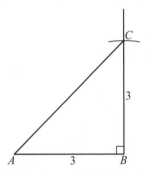

Construction Steps:
1. Draw a line segment *AB* 3 cm long.
2. Using a protractor, draw a ray with end point *B* making an angle of 90° with *AB*.
3. Mark a point *C* on the ray such that *BC* = 3 cm.
4. Draw the line segment *AC*. *ABC* is the required triangle.

(b) Right-angled isosceles
(c) 45°

4. **(a)** Construct $\triangle DEF$ in which $DE = 7$ cm, $EF = 6$ cm, and $DF = 5$ cm.
    (b) Measure all the angles of $\triangle DEF$ and give your answers correct to the nearest degree.
    (c) Classify $\triangle DEF$ by its angles.
    (d) Which angle is opposite the longest side?
    (e) Which side is opposite the smallest angle?

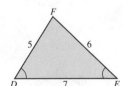

Solution

(a)

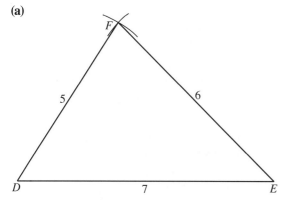

Construction Steps:
1. Construct a line segment *DE* 7 cm long.
2. With *D* as center and 5 cm as radius, draw an arc.
3. With *E* as center and 6 cm as radius, draw an arc to cut the previous arc at *F*.
4. Draw the line segments *DF* and *EF*. Then △*DEF* is the required triangle.

(b) $m\angle D = 57°$
$m\angle E = 44°$
$m\angle F = 79°$

(c) △*DEF* is an acute-angled triangle.

(d) ∠*DFE* is opposite the longest side *DE*.

(e) *DF* is opposite the smallest angle ∠*DEF*.

5. (a) Construct △*GHK* in which *GH* = 5 cm, *GK* = 4 cm and *m*∠*HGK* = 110°.

(b) Measure the length of *HK* and give your answer correct to the nearest 0.1 cm.

(c) Classify △*GHK* by its sides.

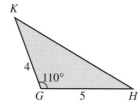

Solution

(a)

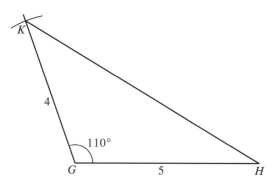

Construction Steps:
1. Draw a line segment *GH* 5 cm long.
2. Using a protractor, draw a ray through *G* making an angle of 110° with *GH*.
3. With *G* as center and 4 cm as radius, draw an arc to cut the ray at *K*.
4. Draw the line segment *HK*. Then △*GHK* is the required triangle.

(b) *HK* = 7.4 cm

(c) △*GHK* is a scalene triangle.

6. (a) Construct △*LMN* in which *LM* = 4 cm, and *m*∠*NLM* = *m*∠*LMN* = 45°.

(b) Measure ∠*LNM* and give your answer correct to the nearest degree.

(c) Measure the lengths of *LN* and *MN* and give your answers correct to the nearest 0.1 cm.

(d) What type of triangle is △*LMN*?

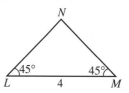

Solution

(a)

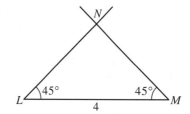

Construction Steps:
1. Draw a line segment *LM* 4 cm long.
2. Using a protractor, draw a ray with end point *L* and making an angle of 45° with *LM*.
3. Using a protractor, draw a ray with end point *M* and making an angle of 45° with *LM* such that it cuts the previous ray at *N*. Then △*LMN* is the required triangle.

(b) *m*∠*LNM* = 90° (correct to the nearest degree)

(c) *LN* = 2.8 cm (correct to the nearest 0.1 cm)
MN = 2.8 cm (correct to the nearest 0.1 cm)

(d) △*LMN* is a right-angled isosceles triangle.

Further Practice

7. (a) Construct $\triangle XYZ$ in which $YZ = 2.5$ cm, $XZ = 6.5$ cm, and $m\angle XYZ = 90°$.

(b) Measure the length of XY and give your answer correct to the nearest 0.1 cm.

(c) Classify $\triangle XYZ$ by its sides.

Solution

(a)

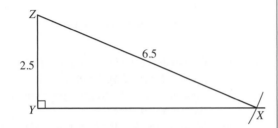

Construction Steps:
1. Draw a line segment YZ 2.5 cm long.
2. Using a protractor, draw a ray with end point Y and making an angle of 90° with YZ.
3. With Z as center and 6.5 cm as radius, draw an arc to cut the ray at X.
4. Join X and Z. Then $\triangle XYZ$ is the required triangle.

(b) $XY = 6.0$ cm (correct to the nearest 0.1 cm)

(c) $\triangle XYZ$ is a scalene triangle.

8. (a) Construct $\triangle ABC$ in which $AB = 4$ cm, $AC = 4$ cm, and $m\angle ABC = 30°$.

(b) Measure $\angle BAC$ and $\angle ACB$ and give your answers correct to the nearest degree.

(c) Classify $\triangle ABC$ by its sides.

Solution

(a)

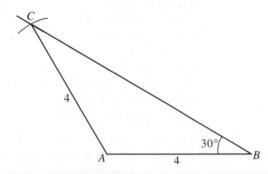

Construction Steps:
1. Draw a line segment AB 4 cm long.
2. Draw a ray with end point B and making an angle of 30° with AB.

3. With A as center and 4 cm as radius, draw an arc to cut the ray at C.
4. Join A and C. Then $\triangle ABC$ is the required triangle.

(b) $m\angle BAC = 120°$ (correct to the nearest degree)
$m\angle ACB = 30°$ (correct to the nearest degree)

(c) $\triangle ABC$ is an isosceles triangle.

9. (a) Construct $\triangle RST$ in which $RS = 4$ cm, $m\angle RST = 55°$, and $m\angle TRS = 70°$.

(b) Measure $\angle RTS$ and give your answer correct to the nearest degree.

(c) Measure the length of RT and give your answer correct to the nearest 0.1 cm.

(d) Classify $\triangle RST$ by its angles and sides.

Solution

(a)

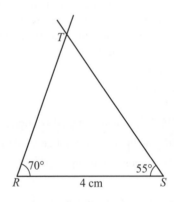

Construction Steps:
1. Draw a line segment RS 4 cm long.
2. Using a protractor, draw a ray with end point S making an angle of 55° with RS.
3. Using a protractor, draw a ray with end point R making an angle of 70° with RS such that it cuts the previous ray at T. Then, $\triangle RST$ is the required triangle.

(b) $m\angle RTS = 55°$

(c) $RT = 4$ cm

(d) Acute angled isosceles triangle.

10. (a) Construct $\triangle UVW$ in which $VW = 5.5$ cm, $m\angle UVW = 28°$, and $m\angle UWV = 52°$.

(b) Measure $\angle WUV$ and give your answer correct to the nearest degree.

(c) Classify $\triangle UVW$ by its angles and sides.

Solution

(a)

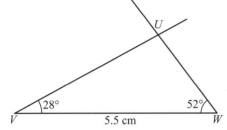

Construction Steps:
1. Draw a line segment *VW* 5.5 cm long.
2. Using a protractor, draw a ray with end point *V* making an angle of 28° with *VW*.
3. Using a protractor, draw a ray with end point *W* making an angle of 52° with *VW* such that it cuts the previous ray at *U*. Then, △*UVW* is the required triangle.

(b) *m∠WUV* = 100°

(c) Obtuse-angled scalene triangle.

Math@Work

11. (a) Construct △*ABC* in which *AB* = 4.5 cm, *AC* = 4.5 cm, and *m∠BAC* = 130° using Sketchpad.

(b) Measure ∠*ABC* and ∠*ACB* and give your answers correct to the nearest degree.

(c) Draw a perpendicular line from *A* to meet the line *BC* at *D*.

(d) Measure the lengths of *BD* and *CD* and give your answers correct to the nearest 0.1 cm.

(e) What do you observe from the result in **(d)**?

Solution

(a)

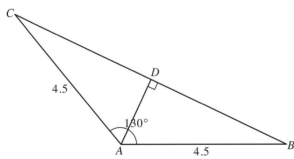

Construction Steps:
1. Draw a line segment *AB* 4.5 cm long.
2. Rotate *AB* about *A* for 130° to *AC*.
3. Join *B* and *C*. Then △*ABC* is the required triangle.

(b) *m∠ABC* = 25° (correct to the nearest degree)
m∠ACB = 25° (correct to the nearest degree)

(d) *BD* = 4.1 cm (correct to the nearest 0.1 cm)
CD = 4.1 cm (correct to the nearest 0.1 cm.)

(e) When *AB* = *AC*, the perpendicular *AD* from *A* to *BC* bisects *BC*.

12. (a) Draw an equilateral triangle *ABC* using Sketchpad.

(b) Plot the midpoints *D*, *E*, and *F* of the sides *AB*, *BC*, and *CA*.

(c) Draw △*DEF*.

(d) What type of triangle is △*DEF*?

(e) Find the value of $\frac{DE}{AB}$.

Solution

(a)

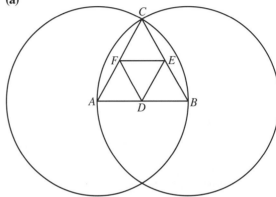

Construction Steps:
1. Draw a line segment *AB*.
2. Draw two circles with centers at *A* and *B* and equal radii *AB*.
3. Mark *C* as one of the intersecting points of the circles.
4. Draw the line segments *AC* and *BC*. Then △*ABC* is an equilateral triangle.

(b) Use the midpoint command to create the midpoints *D*, *E*, *F* of the sides *AB*, *BC*, and *CA*.

(c) Draw the line segments *DE*, *EF*, and *FD* to form △*DEF*.

(d) △*DEF* is an equilateral triangle.

(e) $\frac{DE}{AB}$ = 0.5

Brainworks

13. Is there a type of triangle where the lengths of two sides are sufficient to create a unique triangle?

Solution

No, it is not sufficient. We need to know the angle made by the two sides (included angle). Note that if we are only given one non-including angle, we can draw 2 different triangles so it will not be unique.

Exercise 8.5

Basic Practice

1. **(a)** Construct a rectangle *ABCD* of sides 5 cm and 3 cm.
   (b) Measure the length of the diagonal and give your answer correct to the nearest 0.1 cm.

Solution

(a)

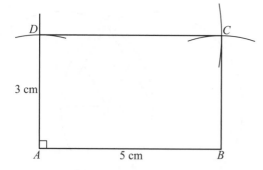

Construction Steps:
1. Draw a line segment *AB* 5 cm long.
2. Using a protractor, draw a ray with end point *A* making an angle of 90° with *AB*.
3. Mark a point *D* on the ray such that *AD* = 3 cm.
4. With *B* as center and 3 cm as radius, draw an arc above *AB*.
5. With *D* as center and 5 cm as radius, draw an arc to cut the previous arc at *C*.
6. Draw the line segments *DC* and *BC*. Then *ABCD* is the required rectangle.

(b) Length of diagonal = 5.8 cm (correct to the nearest 0.1 cm)

2. **(a)** Construct a parallelogram *EFGH* in which *EF* = 4.8 cm, *EH* = 3.5 cm, and *m∠E* = 70°.
   (b) Measure the length of *FH* and give your answer correct to the nearest 0.1 cm.

Solution

(a)

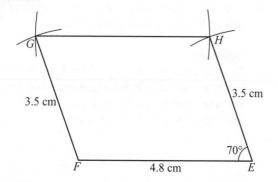

Construction Steps:

1. Draw a line segment *EF* 4.8 cm long.
2. Using a protractor, draw a ray with end point E making an angle of 70° with *EF*.
3. Mark a point *H* on the ray such that *EH* = 3.5 cm.
4. With F as center and 3.5 cm as radius, draw an arc above *EF*.
5. With *H* as center and 4.8 cm as radius, draw an arc to cut the previous arc at *G*.
6. Draw the line segments *HG* and *GF*. Then *EFGH* is the required parallelogram.

(b) *FH* = 6.8 cm (correct to the nearest 0.1 cm)

3.

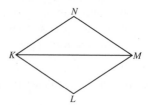

KLMN is a rhombus where *KM* = 5.5 cm and *LN* = 4 cm.

(a) Draw a line segment *KM* = 5.5 cm.
(b) Construct the perpendicular bisector of *KM*.
(c) Locate the points *L* and *N* by using only a pair of compasses and a ruler.
(d) Measure the length of a side of the rhombus and give your answer correct to the nearest 0.1 cm.

Solution

(a) – (c)

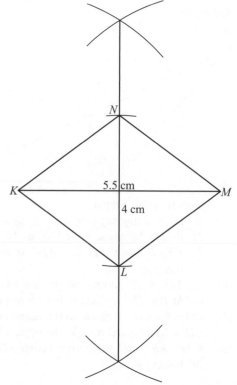

(b) Construction Steps:

With K as center and radius $> \frac{1}{2}$ KM, draw an arc on each side of KM.

With M as center and same radius as in step 1, draw an arc on each side of KM to cut the previous two arcs.

Draw the line segment connecting the two points where the two pair of arcs meet. This line segment is the perpendicular bisector of KM.

(c) Construction Steps:

With the point of intersection of the line segments in **(a)** and **(b)** as center, and 2 cm as radius, draw an arc on each side of KM.

The points of intersection of the arcs and the perpendicular bisector of KM in **(b)** are the points L and N of the rhombus.

(d) Length of a side of the rhombus = 3.4 cm (correct to the nearest 0.1 cm).

4. (a) Construct a quadrilateral $XYZT$ in which $XY = 3.5$ cm, $YZ = 4.5$ cm, $ZT = 2$ cm, $XT = 4$ cm, and $YT = 5$ cm.

(b) Measure $\angle YZT$ and $\angle XTZ$, and give your answers correct to the nearest degree.

Solution

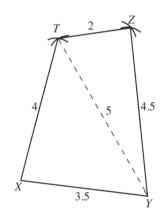

Construction Steps:

1. Draw a line segment XY 3.5 cm long.
2. With X as center and radius 4 cm, draw an arc.
3. With Y as center and radius 5 cm, draw an arc to cut the previous arc at T.
4. With T as center and radius 2 cm, draw an arc.
5. With Y as center and radius 4.5 cm, draw an arc to cut the previous arc at Z.
6. Draw the line segments YZ, ZT, and TX. Then $XYZT$ is the required quadrilateral.

(b) $m\angle YZT = 89°$ (correct to nearest degree)
$m\angle XTZ = 121°$ (correct to nearest degree)

Further Practice

5. (a) Construct a trapezoid $PQRS$ in which $PQ \mathbin{/\!/} SR$, $PQ = 4$ cm, $PS = 3$ cm, $SR = 5.5$ cm, and $m\angle P = 90°$.

(b) Measure and write down the length of QR and the size of $\angle PQR$.

Solution

(a)

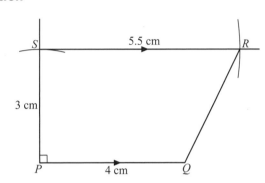

Construction Steps:

1. Draw a line segment PQ 4 cm long.
2. Using a protractor, draw a ray with end point P making an angle of 90° with PQ.
3. Mark a point S on the ray such that $PS = 3$ cm.
4. Using a protractor, draw a ray with end point S making an angle of 90° with PS and on the same side of PS as the line segment PQ.
5. Mark a point R on the ray such that $SR = 5.5$ cm.
6. Draw the line segment QR. Then, $PQRS$ is the required trapezoid.

(b) $QR = 3.35$ cm, $m\angle PQR = 116.6°$.

6. (a) Construct a rhombus $OXYZ$ of side 4 cm and diagonal $OY = 7$ cm.

(b) Measure the length of the other diagonal and give your answer correct to the nearest 0.1 cm.

Solution

(a)

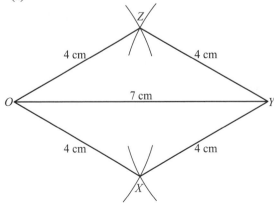

Construction Steps:
1. Draw a line segment *OY* 7 cm long.
2. With *O* as center and radius 4 cm, draw an arc on each side of *OY*.
3. With *Y* as center and radius 4 cm, draw an arc on each side of *OY* to cut the previous two arcs at *X* and *Z*.
4. Draw the line segments *OX*, *XY*, *YZ*, and *OZ*. Then, *OXYZ* is the required rhombus.

(b) *XZ* = 3.9 cm (correct to the nearest 0.1 cm)

7. (a) Construct a quadrilateral *ABCD* in which *AB* = 6.5 cm, *BC* = 3.5 cm, *CD* = 6 cm, *m∠B* = 75°, and *m∠C* = 115°.

(b) Measure ∠*A* and ∠*D*, and give your answers correct to the nearest degree.

Solution

(a)

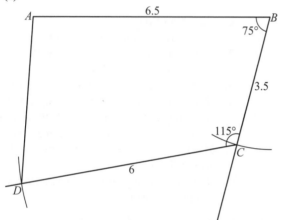

Construction Steps:
1. Draw a line segment *AB* 6.5 cm long.
2. Using a protractor, draw a ray with end point *B* making an angle of 75° with *AB*.
3. Mark a point *C* on the ray such that *BC* = 3.5 cm.
4. Using a protractor, draw a ray with end point *C* making an angle of 115° with BC.
5. Mark a point *D* on the ray such that *CD* = 6 cm.
6. Draw the line segment *AD*. *ABCD* is the required quadrilateral.

(b) *m∠A* = 93°, (correct to the nearest degree)
   m∠D = 77° (correct to the nearest degree).

8. (a) Construct a quadrilateral *ABCD* in which *AD* = 4 cm, *BC* = 2 cm, *CD* = 3 cm, *m∠C* = 120°, and *m∠D* = 100°.

(b) Measure the length of *AB* and give your answers correct to the nearest 0.1 cm.

Solution

(a)

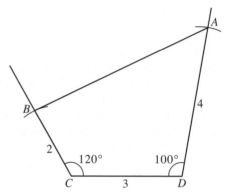

Construction Steps:
1. Draw a line segment *CD* 3 cm long.
2. Draw a ray with end point *C* and making an angle of 120° with *CD*.
3. Mark a point *B* on the ray such that *BC* = 2 cm.
4. Draw a ray with end point *D* on the same side of *CD* as *BC* such that it makes an angle of 100° with *CD*.
5. Mark a point *A* on the previous ray such that *AD* = 4 cm.
6. Join *A* and *B*. Then *ABCD* is the required quadrilateral.

(b) *AB* = 5.2 cm (correct to the nearest 0.1 cm)

Math@Work

9. Using Sketchpad, construct a quadrilateral *PQRS* in which *PQ* = 4.5 cm, *QR* = 5 cm, *RS* = 7 cm, *m∠PQR* = 95°, and *m∠QRS* = 70°.

(a) Measure ∠*SPQ* and give your answer correct to the nearest degree.

(b) Draw the perpendicular bisector of *PR*.

(c) Draw the angle bisector of ∠*PSR* and let it cut the perpendicular bisector of *PR* at *T*.

(d) Measure the length of *RT* and give your answer correct to the nearest 0.1 cm.

(e) Which other line has the same length as *RT*? Explain briefly.

Solutions

(a) $m\angle SPQ = 120°$

(b) & (c)

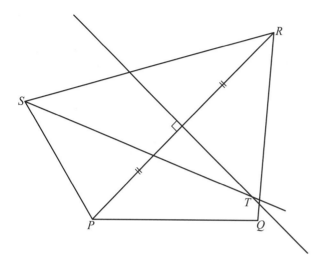

(d) $RT = 4.3$ cm (correct to the nearest 0.1 cm)

(e) PT has the same length as RT. This is because T is a point on the perpendicular bisector of PR, so T is equidistant to P and R.

10. A playground is in the shape of a quadrilateral $PQRS$ where $m\angle Q = 75°$, $m\angle R = 98°$, $PQ = QR = 400$ m, and $RS = 650$ m.

(a) Using a scale of 1 cm to represent 100 m, construct a plan of the playground.

(b) Quinn and Sam are playing with their friends at the corners Q and S of the playground respectively. How far apart are they? Give your answer correct to the nearest meter.

Solution

(a)

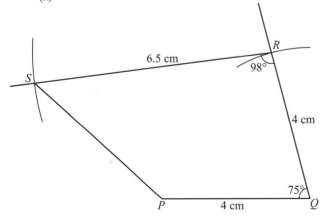

Construction Steps:

1. Draw a line segment PQ 4 cm long
2. Using a protractor, draw a ray with end point Q making an angle of 75° with PQ.
3. Mark a point R on the ray such that $QR = 4$ cm.
4. Using a protractor, draw a ray with end point R making an angle of 98° with QR.
5. Mark a point S on the ray such that $RS = 6.5$ cm.
6. Draw the line segment PS. $PQRS$ is the required quadrilateral.

(b) $QS = 8$ cm.
∴ Quinn and Sam are 800 m apart.

11. (a) Sketch two different quadrilaterals $ABCD$ in which $AB = CD = 3$ cm and $AD = BC = 2$ cm.

(b) What types of quadrilaterals can $ABCD$ be?

Solution

(a)

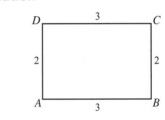

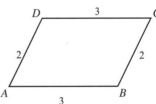

(b) $ABCD$ can be a rectangle or a parallelogram.

Revision Exercise 8

1. (a) Given that the angles $5p°$ and $(3p - 20)°$ are supplementary, find the value of p.

(b) Given that the angles $(33 - q)°$ and $(3q + 5)°$ are complementary, find the value of q.

Solution

(a) $5p + (3p - 20) = 180$
$$5p + 3p = 180 + 20$$
$$8p = 200$$
$$p = 25$$

(b) $(33 - q) + (3q + 5) = 90$
$$33 + 5 - q + 3q = 90$$
$$2q = 90 - 38$$
$$q = 26$$

2. In each of the following diagrams, *AB* and *XY* are straight lines. Find the measures of the angles marked *x* and *y* in each diagram.

(a)

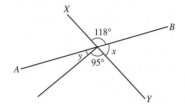

(b)

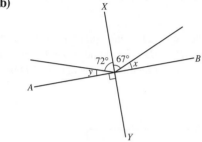

Solution

(a) $x + 118° = 180°$ (adj. ∠s on a st. line)
$$x = 62°$$
$$x + 95° + y = 180°$$ (adj. ∠s on a st. line)
$$62° + 95° + y = 180°$$
$$y = 23°$$

(b) $x + 67° = 90°$ (vert. opp. ∠)
$$x = 23°$$
$$y + 72° = 90°$$
$$y = 18°$$

3. In each of the following diagrams, *ABC* is a straight line. Find the value of *x* in each diagram.

(a)

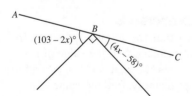

(b)

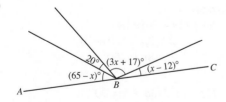

Solution

(a) $(103 - 2x)° + 90° + (4x - 58)° = 180°$
$$103 - 58 - 2x + 4x = 90$$
$$2x = 45$$
$$x = 22.5$$

(b) $(65 - x)° + 20° + (3x + 17)° + (x - 12)° = 180°$
$$65 + 17 - 12 - x + 3x + x = 160$$
$$3x = 90$$
$$x = 30$$

4. Find the value of *x* in each of the following diagram.

(a)   Straight lines *PQ*, *RS*, and *TU* intersect at *O*.

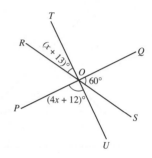

(b)

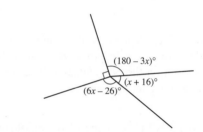

Solution

(a) $(4x + 12)° + (x + 13)° + 60°$
$$= 180°$$ (vert. opp. ∠, *PQ* is a straight line)
$$4x + x + 12 + 13 + 60 = 180$$
$$5x = 95$$
$$x = 19$$

(b) $(6x - 26)° + (x + 16)° + (180 - 3x)° = 360° - 90°$
$$6x + x - 3x - 26 + 16 + 180 = 270$$
$$4x = 100$$
$$x = 25$$

5. Find the values of *a* and *b* in each of the following diagrams.

(a)   *ABCD* is a rectangle.

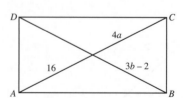

(b) *PQRS* is a rhombus.

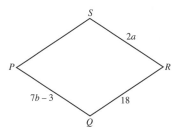

(c) *WXYZ* is a parallelogram.

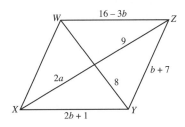

Solution

(a) $4a = 16$
$a = 4$
$3b - 2 = 16$
$3b = 18$
$b = 6$

(b) $2a = 18$
$a = 9$
$7b - 3 = 18$
$7b = 21$
$b = 3$

(c) $2a = 9$
$a = 4.5$
$2b + 1 = 16 - 3b$
$2b + 3b = 16 - 1$
$5b = 15$
$b = 3$

6. It is given that $m\angle A = 50°$, $m\angle B = 50°$, $m\angle C = 80°$, $PQ = 6.5$ cm, $QR = 6$ cm, and $PR = 2.5$ cm.

(a) Determine which triangle, $\triangle ABC$ or $\triangle PQR$, can be constructed.

(b) Construct the triangle.

(c) Classify the triangle by its sides and angles. State the measurement of any relevant sides or angles to support your answer.

Solution

(a) $\triangle ABC$ cannot be constructed, $\triangle PQR$ can be constructed.

(b)

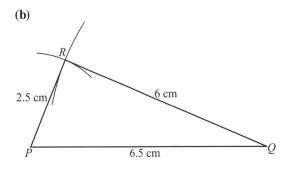

Construction Steps:

1. Draw the line segment PQ 6.5 cm long.
2. With P as center and 2.5 cm radius, draw an arc.
3. With Q as centre and 6 cm radius, draw an arc to cut the previous arc at R.
4. Draw the line segments PR and QR. Then PQR is the required triangle.

(c) Scalene (because no two sides are equal), right-angled ($m\angle PRQ = 90°$) triangle.

7. (a) Using a ruler and compasses, construct
(i) $\triangle ABC$ with $AB = 3$ cm, $BC = 3.5$ cm, and $AC = 5$ cm,
(ii) the perpendicular bisectors of the three sides of $\triangle ABC$, and labeling the point where the bisectors meet with the letter E.

(b) What can you say about the lengths AE, BE, and CE?

(c) Draw a circle, with center E, which passes through the vertices of $\triangle ABC$.

Solution

(a)

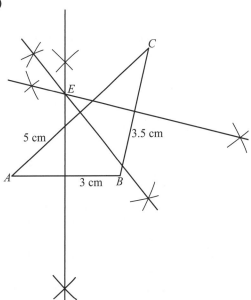

(i) Steps for constructing △*ABC*:
1. Draw the line segment *AB* with length 3 cm.
2. With *A* as center, draw an arc of radius 5 cm.
3. With *B* as center, draw an arc of radius 3.5 cm to cut the previous arc at *C*.
4. Join *A* and *C*. Join *B* and *C*. Then △*ABC* is the required triangle.

(ii) The perpendicular bisectors of the sides of △*ABC* are drawn as shown in the diagram.

(b) The perpendicular bisectors meet at a point *E* outside △*ABC*.
A circle with center *E* and radius *EA* will pass through the points *B* and *C*.

(c)

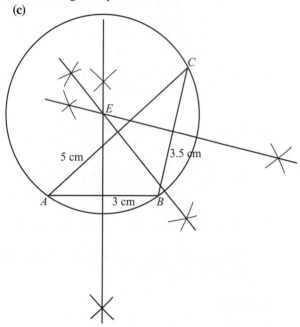

8. In the diagram, *AOB* and *COD* are straight lines such that $m\angle BOD = 50°$.

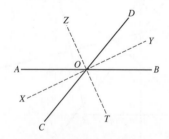

(a) Using a ruler and compasses, construct
  (i) the line *XOY* such that the ray *OY* is the angle bisector of $\angle BOD$,
  (ii) the line *TOZ* such that the ray *OT* is the angle bisector of $\angle BOC$.
(b) Is *OX* the angle bisector of $\angle AOC$? Why?
(c) Find $m\angle XOT$.

Solution

(a) (i) & (ii)
OY is the bisector of $\angle BOD$.
OT is the bisector of $\angle BOC$.

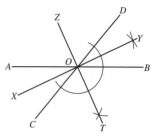

(b) $m\angle AOX = m\angle BOY$ (vert. opp. ∠s)
$m\angle COX = m\angle DOY$ (vert. opp. ∠s)
By construction, $m\angle BOY = m\angle DOY$.
Hence, $m\angle AOX = m\angle COX$.
OX is the angle bisector of $\angle AOC$.

(c)
$$m\angle COX = \frac{1}{2}m\angle AOC$$
$$m\angle COT = \frac{1}{2}m\angle BOC$$
$$m\angle COX + m\angle COT = \frac{1}{2}m\angle AOC + \frac{1}{2}m\angle BOC$$
$$m\angle XOT = \frac{1}{2}(m\angle AOC + m\angle BOC)$$
$$= \frac{1}{2} \times 180° \text{ (adj. ∠s on a st. line)}$$
$$m\angle XOT = 90°$$

9. Construct a rhombus *ABCD* in which *AC* = 5 cm and *BD* = 6 cm. Measure and write down
(a) the length of *CD*,
(b) the size of one of its acute angle.

Solution

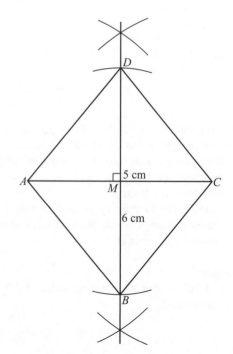

Construction Steps:

1. Draw a line segment *AC* 5 cm long and mark its midpoint *M*, where *AM* = *CM* = 2.5 cm.
2. Draw a line segment *BMD* perpendicular to *AC* such that *BM* = *DM* = 3 cm.
3. Draw the line segments *AB*, *BC*, *CD*, and *AD*. Then, *ABCD* is the required rhombus.

(a) *CD* = 3.9 cm

(b) *m*∠*B* = *m*∠*D* = 80°

10. Construct a trapezoid *PQRS* in which *PS* is parallel to *QR*, *PQ* = 3.5 cm, *QR* = 5 cm, *m*∠*PQR* = 60°, and *m*∠*QRS* = 80°.
    (a) Construct the perpendicular bisector of *PS*.
    (b) If the perpendicular bisector of *PS* meets *QR* at *T*, measure *TQ* and give your answer correct to the nearest 0.1 cm.

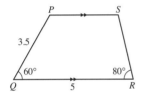

Solution

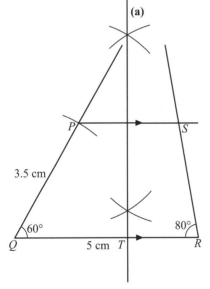

(a)

Construction Steps:

1. Draw a line segment *QR* 5 cm long.
2. Using a protractor, draw a ray with end point *Q* making an angle of 60° with *QR*.
3. Mark a point *P* on the ray such that *PQ* = 3.5 cm.
4. Using a protractor, draw a ray with end point *R* making an angle of 80° with *QR* and on the same side of *QR* as the *PQ*.
5. Using a ruler and a set square, draw a ray with end point *P* that is parallel to *QR*, to cut the previous ray at *S*. Then, *PQRS* is the required trapezoid.

(b) *TQ* = 3.1 cm (correct to the nearest 0.1 cm)

11. Construct a quadrilateral *PQRS* in which *PQ* = 5.5 cm, *PS* = 4 cm, *RS* = 2.5 cm, *m*∠*SPQ* = 105°, and *m*∠*PSR* = 90°.
    (a) Construct the angle bisector of ∠*PQR*.
    (b) Construct the perpendicular bisector of *QR*.
    (c) If the bisectors from **(a)** and **(b)** intersect at *W*, measure *WS* and give your answer correct to the nearest 0.1 cm.

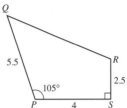

Solution

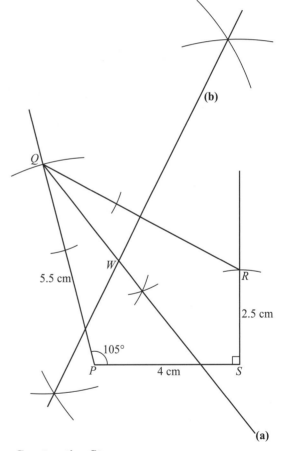

Construction Steps:

1. Draw a line segment *PS* 4 cm long.
2. Using a protractor, draw a ray with end point *P* making an angle of 105° with *PS*.
3. Mark a point *Q* on the ray such that *PQ* = 5.5 cm.
4. Using a protractor, draw a ray with end point *S* making an angle of 90° with *PS*.
5. Mark a point *R* on the ray such that *RS* = 2.5 cm.
6. Draw the line segment *QR*. *PQRS* is the required quadrilateral.

(a) **Construction Steps:**

1. With Q as center, and a fixed radius, draw an arc that cuts QR and PQ.
2. With the point of intersection of the arc on QR as center, and the same radius as in step 1, draw an arc between the lines PQ and QR.
3. With the point of intersection of the arc on PQ as center, and the same radius as in step 1, draw an arc between the lines PQ and QR to cut the previous arc.
4. Draw a ray with end point Q passing through the point of intersection of the arcs made in step 2 and step 3. Then, this ray is the required angle bisector.

(b) **Construction Steps:**

1. With Q as center and radius $> \frac{1}{2} QR$, draw an arc on each side of QR.
2. With R as center and same radius as in step 1, draw two arcs to cut the previous arcs.
3. Draw a line segment through both the points where the two sets of arcs cut each other. The line segment is the required perpendicular bisector.

(c) $WS = 4.3$ cm (correct to the nearest 0.1 cm)